# SOLUTIONS MANUAL

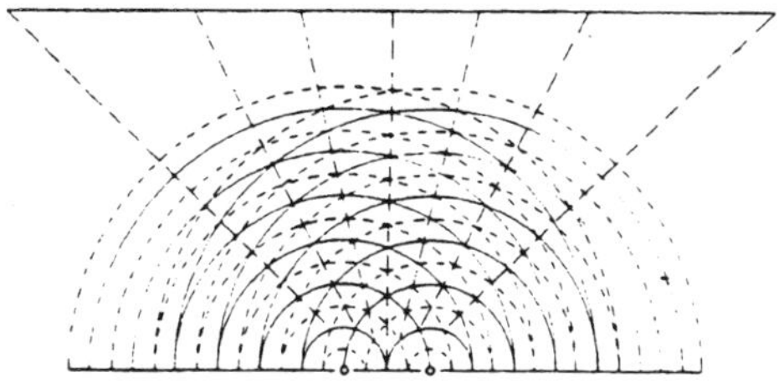

Second Edition

# *Introduction to Optics*

**FRANK L. PEDROTTI, S.J.**
*Marquette University*
*Milwaukee, Wisconsin*
*Vatican Radio,*
*Rome*

**LENO S. PEDROTTI**
*Center for Occupational*
*Research and Development*
*Waco, Texas*
*Emeritus Professor of Physics*
*Air Force Institute of Technology*
*Dayton, Ohio*

Prentice Hall, Englewood Cliffs, New Jersey 07632

A Simon & Schuster Company
Englewood Cliffs, N.J. 07632



10 9 8 7 6 5 4

**ISBN 0-13-502550-8**
Printed in the United States of America

CONTENTS

## Chapter 1 - Nature of Light

1-1. (a) $\lambda = \frac{h}{p} = \frac{h}{mv} = \frac{h}{(0.05\ Kg)(20\ m/s)} = 6.63 \times 10^{-34}\ m$

(b) $\lambda = \frac{h}{p} = \frac{h}{\sqrt{2mE}} = \frac{h}{[(1.602 \times 10^{-18} J)(2m)]^{1/2}} = 3.88 \times 10^{-10}\ m$

$= 3.88\ \text{Å}$

where $E = 10\,eV \times 1.602 \times 10^{-19}\ J/eV$

1-2. $P = \frac{E}{t} = \frac{n(h\nu)}{t} = \frac{n\,hc}{t\lambda} = \frac{100\,hc}{(1s)(550 \times 10^{-9}m)} = 3.61 \times 10^{-17}\ W$

1-3. $E = h\nu = hc/\lambda$

At $\lambda = 400\ nm$, $E = \frac{hc}{400 \times 10^{-9} m} = 4.966 \times 10^{-19}\ J = 3.10\,eV$

At $\lambda = 700\ nm$, $E = \frac{4}{7}(3.10\,eV) = 1.77\,eV$

1-4. $p = \frac{E}{c} = \frac{mc^2}{c} = mc = 2.73 \times 10^{-22}\ Kg\text{-}m/s$

$\lambda = \frac{h}{p} = \frac{hc}{E} = \frac{hc}{mc^2} = \frac{h}{mc} = 2.43 \times 10^{-12}\ m = 0.024\ \text{Å}$

1-5. $E_{v=0} = mc^2 = (9.109 \times 10^{-31} kg)(2.998 \times 10^{8}\ m/s)^2 = 8.187 \times 10^{-14}\ J$

$= 0.511\ MeV$

1-6. $cp = \sqrt{E^2 - m^2c^4}$, where $E = E_K + mc^2 = (1 + 0.511)\ MeV$

$cp = \sqrt{1.511^2 - 0.511^2} = 1.422\ MeV$

$p = 1.422\ MeV/c$

1-7. $\lambda = \frac{hc}{E} = \frac{(6.626 \times 10^{-34})(2.998 \times 10^{8})(J\,s)(m/s)}{E(eV)}$

$\lambda = \frac{1.9865 \times 10^{-25}}{E(eV)}\ J\,m = \frac{1.9865 \times 10^{-25}}{E}\left(\frac{J}{1.602 \times 10^{-19} J}\right)(10^{10}\ \text{Å})$

$\lambda = \frac{12400}{E(eV)}$, in Angstroms

1-8. $E_K = mc^2\left(\frac{1}{\sqrt{1-v^2/c^2}} - 1\right)$

For $v \ll c$, $v^2/c^2 \ll 1$, and $\frac{1}{\sqrt{1-v^2/c^2}} = (1-v^2/c^2)^{-1/2} \cong 1 + \frac{v^2}{2c^2}$

Then $E_K \cong mc^2\left(1 + \frac{v^2}{2c^2} - 1\right) = \frac{1}{2}mv^2$

1-9. $E = E_K + m_pc^2 = (2\times10^9 eV)(1.602\times10^{-19}\frac{J}{eV}) + (1.6725\times10^{-27} Kg)c^2$

$E = 4.707\times10^{-10} J$

(a) $p = \frac{\sqrt{E^2 - m_p^2c^4}}{c} = [(4.707\times10^{-10})^2 - (1.6725\times10^{-27})^2c^4]^{1/2}$

$p = 1.49\times10^{-18}$ Kg-m/s

(b) $\lambda = h/p = h/(1.49\times10^{-18}$ Kg-m/s$) = 4.45\times10^{-16}$ m

(c) $\lambda = h/p = hc/E = hc/(4.707\times10^{-10} J) = 4.22\times10^{-16}$ m

1-10.

$n = \frac{E_e}{h\nu} = \frac{E_e\lambda}{hc} = \frac{(1353\ W/m^2)(550\times10^{-9} m)}{hc} = \frac{3.746\times10^{21}}{m^2\text{-}s}$

$n = 3.746\times10^{17}/\ cm^2\text{-}s$

1-11. $\frac{n_1}{n_2} = \frac{(E_e\lambda/hc)_1}{(E_e\lambda/hc)_2} = \frac{\lambda_1}{\lambda_2}$

# Chapter 2 - Production + Measurement of Light

2-1. Visible spectrum : 380-770 nm

$$\nu_1 = \frac{c}{\lambda_1} = \frac{c}{380 \times 10^{-9} m} = 7.89 \times 10^{14} Hz$$

$$\nu_2 = \left(\frac{\lambda_1}{\lambda_2}\right) c = \frac{38}{77} (7.89 \times 10^{14}) = 3.89 \times 10^{14} Hz$$

2-2. $\Phi_e = 500 W$ , $\Phi_e (vis.) = (0.02)(500W) = 10W$

(a) $\Phi_v = K(\lambda) \Phi_e (vis) = 685 V(\lambda) \Phi_e (vis)$

$\Phi_v = 685 (0.3)(10) = 2055 \, lm$ (using Fig. 2-7)

(b) $I_e = \frac{\Phi_e}{\Omega} = \frac{500 W}{4\pi \, sr} = 39.8 \, W/sr$

$I_v = 685 \, V(\lambda) \, I_e (vis) = 685 (0.3)(0.02)(39.8) = 164 \, cd$

(c) $M_e = \frac{\Phi_e}{A} = \frac{500 W}{50 \times 10^{-4} m^2} = 10^5 W/m^2$

$M_v = \frac{\Phi_v (vis)}{A} = \frac{2055 \, lm}{50 \times 10^{-4} m^2} = 4.11 \times 10^5 \, lm/m^2$

(d) $E_e = \frac{\Phi_e}{A} = \frac{\Phi_e}{4\pi r^2} = \frac{500 W}{4\pi (2m)^2} = 9.947 \, W/m^2$

$E_v = \frac{\Phi_v}{A} = \frac{2055}{4\pi r^2} = \frac{2055 \, lm}{4\pi (2)^2 m^2} = 40.88 \, lm/m^2$

(e) $\Phi_e = E_e A = 9.947 \, W/m^2 (\pi)(0.025)^2 = 0.0195 \, W$

$\Phi_v = E_v A = 40.88 \, lm/m^2 (\pi)(0.025)^2 = 0.0803 \, lm$

2-3. (a) $\Phi_v = K(\lambda) \Phi_e = 685 \, V(\lambda) \Phi_e$

$$\frac{\Phi_v (He\text{-}Cd)}{\Phi_v (He\text{-}Ne)} = \frac{685 (0.02)(0.050)}{685 (0.2)(0.004)} = 1.25$$ (estimates from Fig. 2-7)

(b) $\Phi_v (Ar) = \Phi_v (He Ne)$

$685 \, V(\lambda_{AR}) \, \Phi_e (AR) = 685 \, V(\lambda_{He\text{-}Ne}) \, \Phi_e (He Ne)$

$(0.2) \phi_e = (0.95)(0.5 mW)$

$\Phi_e (Ar) = 2.4 \, mW$

2-4. (a) Inverse square law : $E_v = I_v / r^2$

$I_v = E_v r^2 = 100 (lm/m^2)(3m)^2 = 900\ lm/sr = 900\ cd$

(b) Cosine law : $I_v(\theta) = I_v(0) \cos\theta$

With inverse square law,

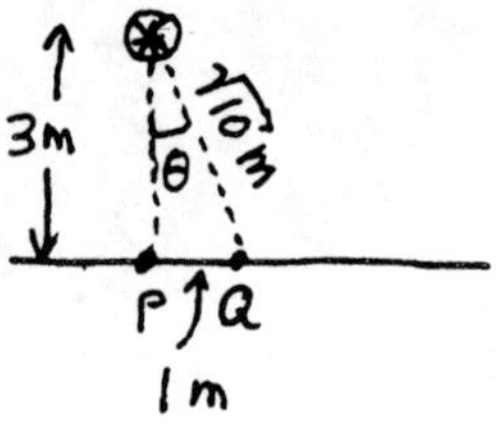


At Q, $E_v(r) = \dfrac{I_v(0)\cos\theta}{r^2} = \dfrac{(900\ lm)(3/\sqrt{10})}{(\sqrt{10}\ m)^2}$

$E_v(r) = 85.4\ lx$

2-5.

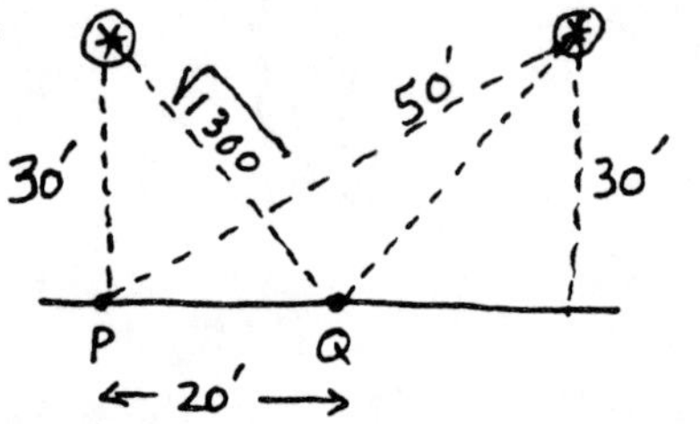


$E_v(P) = \dfrac{I_v(0)\cos(0)}{30^2} + \dfrac{I_v(0)\ (3/5)}{50^2}$

$E_v(P) = 1.351 \times 10^{-3}\ I_v(0)$

$E_v(Q) = 2\left[\dfrac{I_v(0)\ (30/\sqrt{1300})}{(\sqrt{1300})^2}\right]$

$E_v(Q) = 1.280 \times 10^{-3}\ I_v(0)$

$\dfrac{E_v(P)}{E_v(Q)} = 1.055$

2-6.

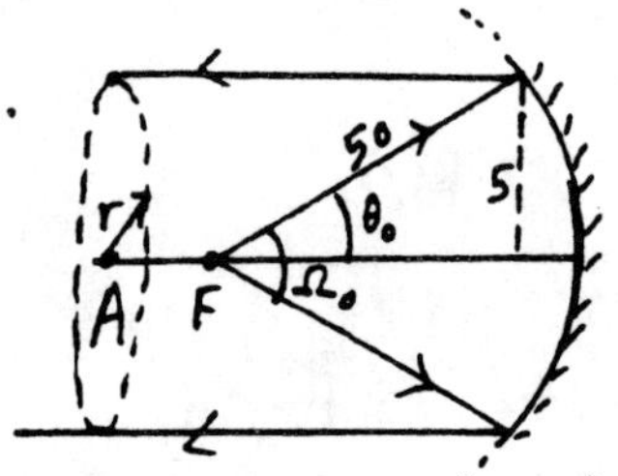


$\cos\theta_0 = \cos(\sin^{-1}\frac{5}{50})$

$= 0.9950$

$I_v = 100\ cd = 100\ lm/sr$

$\Phi_v$ (incident on mirror) $= I_v \Omega_0$

where $\Omega_0 = 2\pi(1-\cos\theta_0)$ sr

$\therefore \Phi_v(\text{incid}) = 2\pi(1-\cos\theta_0) I_v = 2\pi(1-.995)(100)$

$= \pi\ lm$

$\Phi_v(\text{ref}) = 0.80\ \Phi_v(\text{incid}) = 0.8\pi\ lm$

$E_v = \dfrac{\Phi_v(\text{ref})}{A} = \dfrac{0.8\pi\ lm}{\pi(0.05)^2} = 320\ lx$

2-7. (a)

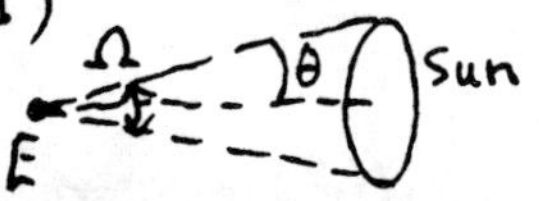


$\Omega = 2\pi(1-\cos\theta)$

$\Omega = 2\pi(1-\cos(0.25°))$

$\Omega = 5.98 \times 10^{-5}\ sr$

$E_v = 10^5\ lx = 10^5\ lm/m^2$

$L_v = \dfrac{E_v}{\Omega} = \dfrac{10^5\ lm/m^2}{5.98 \times 10^{-5}\ sr} = 1.67 \times 10^9\ cd/m^2$

(b) $E_v = L_v \Omega = L\left(\dfrac{lm}{m^2\text{-}sr}\right) \times 2\pi\,(sr) = 2\pi L\ lm/m^2$

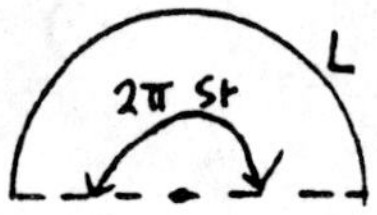

2-8.

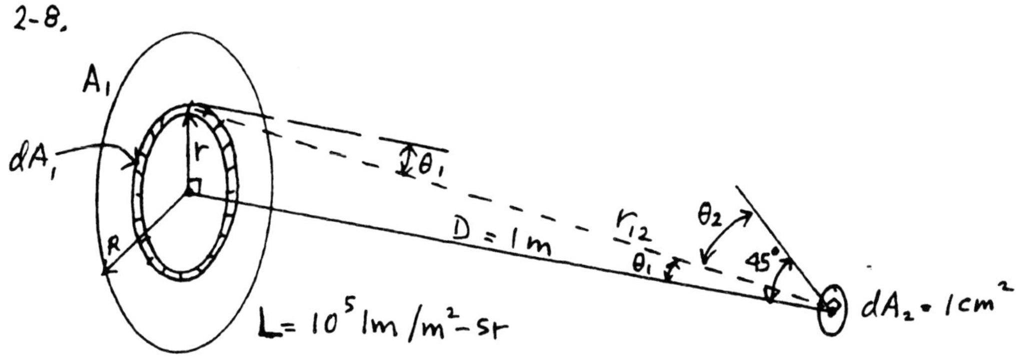


$$\phi_{12} = \int_{A_1}\int_{A_2} \frac{L\cos\theta_1 \cos\theta_2}{r_{12}^2} dA_1 dA_2 = L\,dA_2 \int_{A_1} \frac{\cos\theta_1 \cos\theta_2}{r_{12}^2} dA_1$$

Consider first illumination of $dA_2$ by annular ring of $A_1$, with radius $r$, as shown. Then

$dA_1 = 2\pi r\,dr$ $\qquad \cos\theta_1 = D/\sqrt{r^2+D^2}$

$r_{12}^2 = r^2 + D^2$ $\qquad \cos\theta_2 = \cos(45-\theta_1) = \cos 45 \cos\theta_1 + \sin 45 \sin\theta_1$

$$\cos\theta_2 = \frac{\sqrt{2}}{2}\left[\frac{D}{\sqrt{r^2+D^2}} + \frac{r}{\sqrt{r^2+D^2}}\right]$$

For the ring, integrating over the disc,

$$d\phi_{12} = L\,dA_2 \int_0^R \frac{\cos\theta_1 \cos(45-\theta_1)}{r^2+D^2}\, 2\pi r\,dr$$

$$d\phi_{12} = L\,dA_2 \int_0^R \frac{D}{\sqrt{r^2+D^2}} \frac{\sqrt{2}}{2}\left(\frac{D}{\sqrt{r^2+D^2}} + \frac{r}{\sqrt{r^2+D^2}}\right) 2\pi r\,dr$$

$$d\phi_{12} = \sqrt{2}\pi L D\,dA_2 \left\{ D\int_0^R \frac{r\,dr}{(r^2+D^2)^2} + \int_0^R \frac{r^2\,dr}{(r^2+D^2)^2} \right\}$$

$$d\phi_{12} = \sqrt{2}\pi L D\,dA_2 \left\{ D\left[\frac{-1}{2(r^2+D^2)}\right]_0^R + \left[\frac{-r}{2(r^2+D^2)} + \frac{1}{2D}\tan^{-1}\left(\frac{r}{D}\right)\right]_0^R \right\}$$

$$d\phi_{12} = \sqrt{2}\pi L D\,dA_2 \left\{ \frac{1}{2D}\tan^{-1}\left(\frac{R}{D}\right) + \frac{1}{2D} - \frac{(D+R)}{2(R^2+D^2)} \right\}$$

With $L = 10^5$ lm/sr-m², $D = 1$ m, $R = 0.2$ m, $dA_2 = 10^{-4}$ m²,

$d\phi_{12} = 0.97$ lm

**2-9.** $M_\lambda = \dfrac{2\pi hc^2}{\lambda^5}\left(\dfrac{1}{e^{hc/\lambda KT}-1}\right)$  To find the maximum $\lambda$ points of the curves in Fig. 2-8, we take $dM_\lambda/d\lambda = 0$. To shorten the work, it is sufficient to maximize the denominator:

$$\frac{d}{d\lambda}\left[\lambda^5\left(e^{hc/\lambda KT}-1\right)\right]=0$$

$$\lambda^5\left[e^{hc/\lambda KT}\frac{hc}{KT}\left(-\frac{1}{\lambda^2}\right)\right]+\left(e^{hc/\lambda KT}-1\right)5\lambda^4=0$$

Let $x \equiv hc/\lambda KT$:  $\lambda^5\left[xe^x\left(-1/\lambda\right)\right]+\left(e^x-1\right)5\lambda^4=0$

$xe^x = (e^x-1)5$  This is a transcendental eq. in $x$. With a calculator, one finds a best fit for $x = 4.9651$. Then

$$\frac{xe^x}{e^x-1}=4.999986$$

Thus,  $x=\dfrac{hc}{K(\lambda T)}$ or $\lambda_{max}T=\dfrac{hc}{Kx}=\dfrac{hc}{4.9651K}=2.898\times10^{-3}\,m\text{-}K$

or  $\lambda_{max}T = 2.898\times10^{+3}\,\mu m\text{-}K$

Note that Eq. (2-13) is not as accurate, using $x=5$.

**2-10.** $M_\lambda = \dfrac{2\pi hc^2}{\lambda^5}\left(\dfrac{1}{e^x-1}\right)$,  with $x \equiv hc/\lambda KT$

We need to calculate $M = \displaystyle\int_0^\infty M_\lambda\,d\lambda$.  At $x=0,\ \lambda\rightarrow\infty$
$\phantom{We need to calculate}$ $x\Rightarrow\infty,\ \lambda=0$

$dx = \dfrac{hc}{KT}\left(-\dfrac{d\lambda}{\lambda^2}\right)$ or $d\lambda = -\dfrac{\lambda^2 kT}{hc}\,dx$

Thus $M = 2\pi hc^2\displaystyle\int_\infty^0\frac{1}{\lambda^5}\left(\frac{1}{e^x-1}\right)\left(-\frac{\lambda^2 kT}{hc}\right)dx = -2\pi ckT\int_\infty^0\frac{1}{\lambda^3}\frac{dx}{e^x-1}$

But $\lambda^3 = \left(\dfrac{hc}{xkT}\right)^3$, so $M = 2\pi ckT\displaystyle\int_0^\infty\left(\frac{xkT}{hc}\right)^3\frac{dx}{e^x-1}$

$M = \dfrac{2\pi(kT)^4}{h^3c^2}\displaystyle\int_0^\infty\frac{x^3}{e^x-1}\,dx$.  Integral tables give

$$\int_0^\infty\frac{x^3}{e^x-1}\,dx = \frac{\pi^4}{15}$$

Thus $M = \left(\dfrac{2\pi k^4\pi^4}{15\,h^3c^2}\right)T^4$

or  $M = \sigma T^4$, where $\sigma = \dfrac{2k^4\pi^5}{15\,h^3c^2} = 5.668\times10^{-8}\,\dfrac{W}{m^2\text{-}K^4}$

2-11. $\lambda_{max} T = 2.88 \times 10^3\ \mu m\text{-}K$ or $T = \dfrac{2880}{\lambda_{max}}$

$\lambda_{max} = 500\,nm = 0.5\,\mu m$

$$T = \frac{2880}{0.5} \frac{\mu m\text{-}K}{\mu m} = 5760\,K$$

2-12. (a) $\lambda_{max} T = 2.898 \times 10^3\ \mu m\text{-}K$ : Wien's law

$$\lambda_{max} = \frac{2.898 \times 10^3\ \mu m\text{-}K}{6000\,K} = 0.4830\,\mu m$$

(b) $M_\lambda = \dfrac{3.745 \times 10^8}{\lambda^5} \left[\dfrac{1}{e^{14388/\lambda T} - 1}\right] \dfrac{W}{m^2\text{-}\mu m}$

With $\lambda = \lambda_{av} = 0.5505\,\mu m$ and $T = 6000\,K$,

$M_\lambda = 9.6265 \times 10^7\ W/m^2\text{-}\mu m$

$$\begin{Bmatrix}\text{Total power radiated} \\ \text{from hole}\end{Bmatrix} = 9.6265 \times 10^7 \frac{W}{m^2\text{-}\mu m} (0.551 - 0.550)\,\mu m \times A$$

where $A = \dfrac{\pi (10^{-3})^2}{4}\ m^2$

thus $P = 0.0756\,W$

2-13. $M = \sigma T^4$ At $\lambda_{max} = 0.550\,\mu m$, $T_1 = \dfrac{2898\ \mu m\text{-}K}{0.55\,\mu m} = 5269\,K$

For $M$ to double, $\sigma (T_2)^4 = 2 \times \sigma (T_1)^4$

or $T_2^4 = 2(5269)^4$ and $T_2 = 6266\,K$.

Then $\lambda_{max} = \dfrac{2898\ \mu m\text{-}K}{6266\,K} = 0.4625\,\mu m = 462.5\,nm$

2-14. The gray body at $T_2$ must match the blackbody at the lower temperature, $T_1$.

$$M_{GB}(T_2) = M_{BB}(T_1)$$

$$(\epsilon M_{BB})_{T_2} = (M_{BB})_{T_1}$$

$$\epsilon \sigma T_2^4 = \sigma T_1^4$$

$$T_2^4 = \frac{T_1^4}{\epsilon} = \frac{(5000)^4}{0.45}$$

$$T_2 = 6105\,K$$

# Chapter 3 - Geometrical Optics

3-1. $t = \dfrac{\sum d_{op}}{c} = \dfrac{\sum_i n_i x_i}{c}$

3-2. $n_o(x^2+y^2)^{1/2} + n_i\left[y^2+(s_o+s_i-x)^2\right]^{1/2} = n_o s_o + n_i s_i$

where quantities are defined in Fig. 3-12.

$$(1)\ (x^2+y^2)^{1/2} + 1.5\left[y^2+(30-x)^2\right]^{1/2} = 20 + 1.5(10) = 35$$

$$2.25\left[y^2+(30-x)^2\right] = \left[35-(x^2+y^2)^{1/2}\right]^2$$

$$2.25(y^2+900-60x+x^2) = 35^2 + (x^2+y^2) - 70(x^2+y^2)^{1/2}$$

$$1.25(x^2+y^2) + 70(x^2+y^2)^{1/2} - 135x + 800 = 0$$

At $y=0$, $x=20$, as it should. With a calculator one can determine values of $x$ that satisfy the equation for different choices of $y$:

| x | 20 | 20.2 | 22.0 | 26.5 | 26.5 | 20.8 | 24.6 |
|---|---|---|---|---|---|---|---|
| y | 0 | ±1 | ±3 | ±5 | ±7 | ±2 | ±4 |

This may be a good place to do a little programming that searches for a value of $x$ that best satisfies the equation to a specified accuracy. An example of such a program in "Basic" is:

```
5  M=100 : N=0
10 INPUT "Y= ?" ; Y
15 FOR X=20 TO 30 STEP .1
20 P= X^2 + Y^2
25 V= 1.25*P + 70*SQR(P) - 135*X + 800
30 N= N+1
40 IF ABS(V) > M THEN 50
45 M= V : S= N-1
50 NEXT X
55 X= 20 + S*.1
60 PRINT X
65 PRINT S
70 PRINT V
75 END
```

3-3.

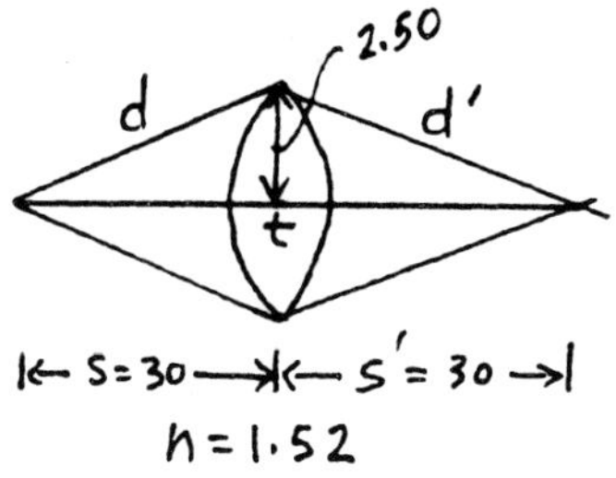


$$d = d' = \sqrt{30^2 + 2.5^2} = 30.104 \text{ cm.}$$

Fermat: $d + d' = s + s' - t + nt$

$$d + d' = s + s' + t(n-1)$$

$$2(30.10399) = 60 + t(1.52 - 1)$$

$$t = 4 \text{ mm}$$

3-4.

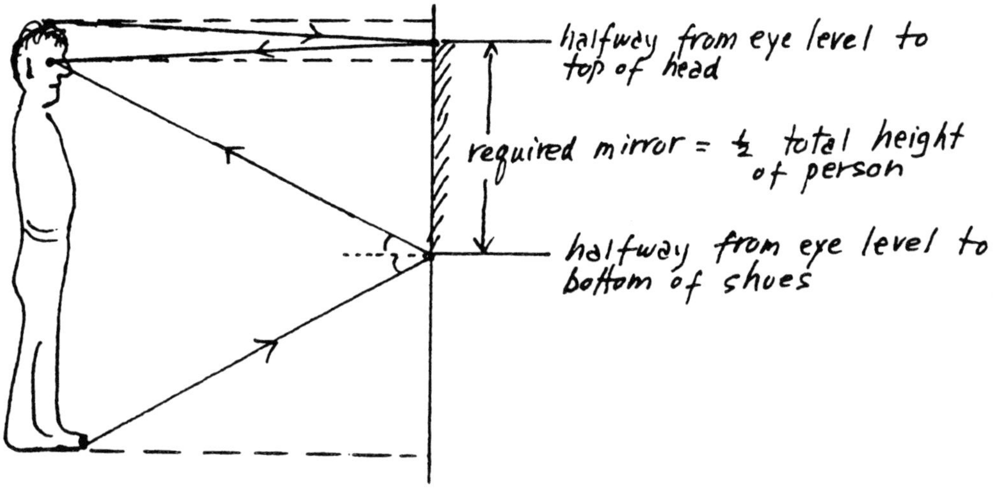


3-5.

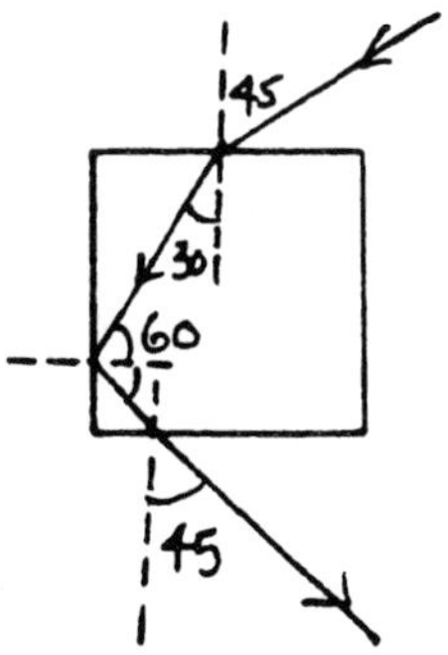


At top: $(1)\sin 45 = \sqrt{2}\,\sin\theta'$

$$\theta' = 30°$$

At side: $\sqrt{2}\,\sin 60 = (1)\sin\theta'$

$$\sin\theta' = \sqrt{1.5} > 1$$

Thus total internal reflection occurs

At bottom: reverse of top: $\theta' = 45°$

3-6.

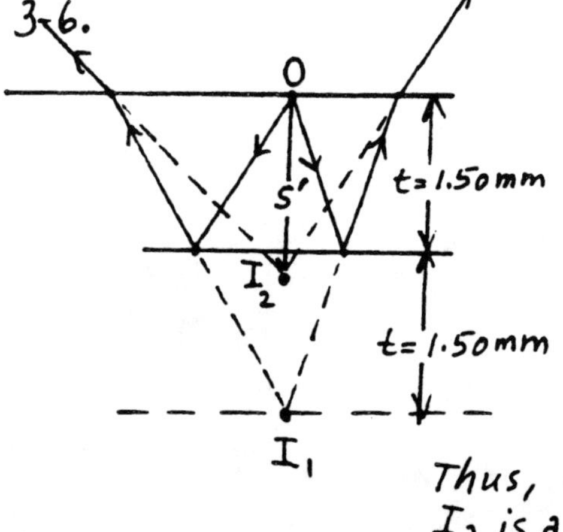


The microscope first focuses on scratch O using direct rays. Then it focuses on the image $I_2$ formed in a two-step process:

(1) reflection from bottom to produce intermediate image $I_1$

(2) refraction through top surface to produce image $I_2$.

Thus, $I_1$ is at $2t$ from top surface, and $I_2$ is at the apparent depth for $I_1$, serving as object: $s' = \frac{2t}{n}$ or $n = \frac{2t}{s'} = \frac{3}{1.87} = 1.60$

3-7.

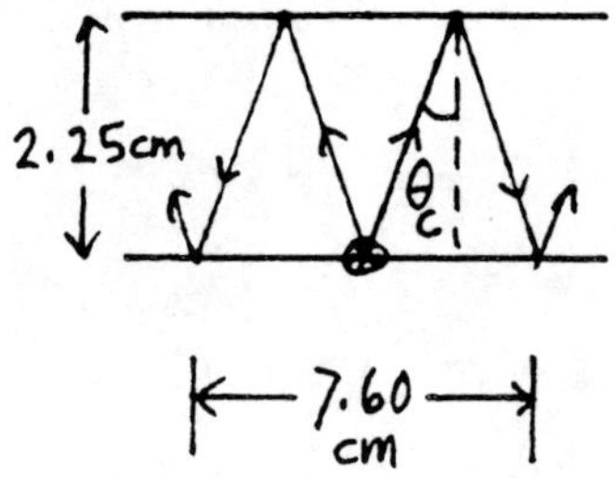


By geometry, $\tan\theta_c = \dfrac{7.60/4}{2.25}$

$\theta_c = 40.18^\circ$

Snell's law: $n \sin\theta_c = (1)\sin 90^\circ$

$n = \dfrac{1}{\sin 40.18^\circ} = 1.55$

3-8.

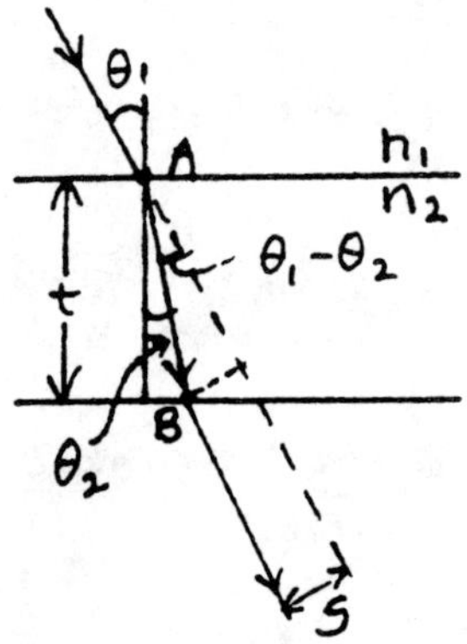


$S = AB \sin(\theta_1 - \theta_2)$ and $AB = \dfrac{t}{\cos\theta_2}$

$\therefore S = \dfrac{t \sin(\theta_1 - \theta_2)}{\cos\theta_2}$

For $t = 3\,cm$, $n_2 = 1.50$, $\theta_1 = 50^\circ$

Snell's law: $\sin\theta_2 = \dfrac{n_1}{n_2}\sin\theta_1 = \dfrac{1}{1.5}\sin 50$

$\theta_2 = 30.71^\circ$

$S = \dfrac{3\sin(50 - 30.71)}{\cos 30.71} = 1.153\ cm$

3-9. Image of near end, $s = 60\,cm$

$\dfrac{1}{60} + \dfrac{1}{s'} = \dfrac{1}{-40}$

$s' = -24\,cm$

Image of far end, $s = 60 + 100\ cm$

$\dfrac{1}{160} + \dfrac{1}{s'} = \dfrac{1}{-40}$

$s' = -32\,cm$.

$L' = \Delta s' = -24 - (-32) = 8\,cm$

3-10.

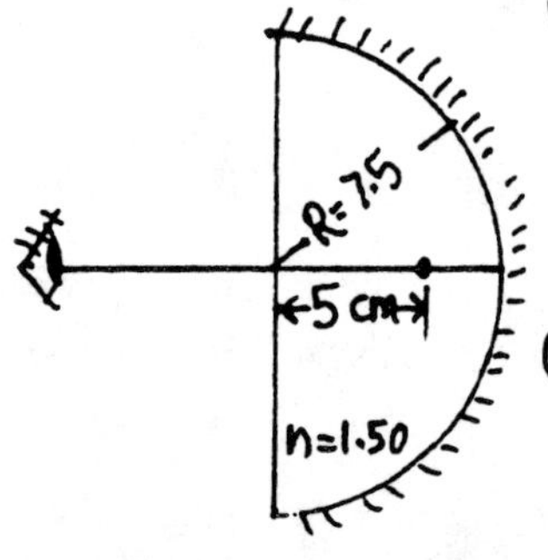


(a) Image due to rays directly from bubble through plane interface:

$\dfrac{n_1}{s} + \dfrac{n_2}{s'} = 0$ OR $\dfrac{1.5}{5} + \dfrac{1}{s'} = 0$

$s' = -3.33\,cm$

(b) Image due to rays first reflected in spherical mirror, then refracted through plane interface

reflection: $\dfrac{1}{s} + \dfrac{1}{s_1'} = -\dfrac{2}{R}$ OR $\dfrac{1}{2.5} + \dfrac{1}{s_1'} = -\dfrac{2}{-7.5}$

$s_1' = -7.5\,cm$

refraction: $\dfrac{n_1}{s} + \dfrac{n_2}{s_2'} = 0$ OR $\dfrac{1.5}{15} + \dfrac{1}{s'} = 0$

$s_2' = -10\,cm$

Thus the images are at 3.33 cm and 10 cm behind interface.

3-11. There are 5 unknowns: $s_1$ and $s_1'$ in position (1), $s_2$ and $s_2'$ in position (2), and the focal length $f$ of the mirror. The five equations that, solved simultaneously, yield the results are

(1) linear magnification: $s_1'/s_1 = 2$

(2) linear magnification: $s_2'/s_2 = 3$

(3) focal length from mirror equation: $f = \dfrac{s_1 s_1'}{s_1 + s_1'}$

(4) " " " " " $f = \dfrac{s_2 s_2'}{s_2 + s_2'}$

(5) image distance relation: $s_2' = s_1' + 75$

One finds $s_1 = 112.5$ cm, $s_2 = 100$ cm, $s_1' = 225$ cm, $s_2' = 300$ cm, $f = 75$ cm

3-12.

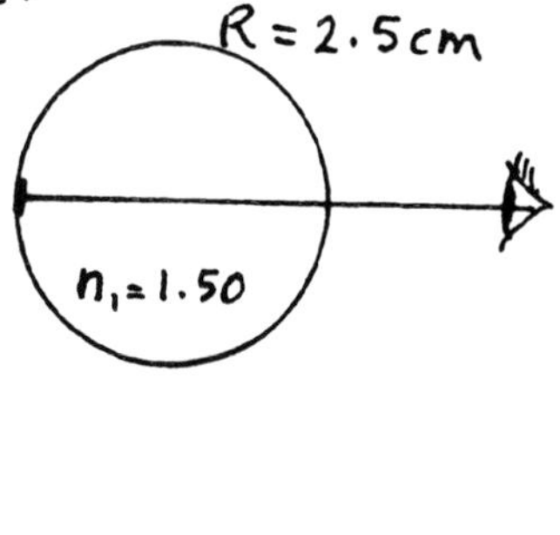


$$\frac{n_1}{s} + \frac{n_2}{s'} = \frac{n_2 - n_1}{R}$$

$$\frac{1.5}{5} + \frac{1}{s'} = \frac{1 - 1.5}{-2.5}$$

$s' = -10$ cm (behind front surface)

$$m = -\frac{n_1 s'}{n_2 s} = -\frac{(1.5)(-10)}{(1)(5)} = +3$$

3-13.

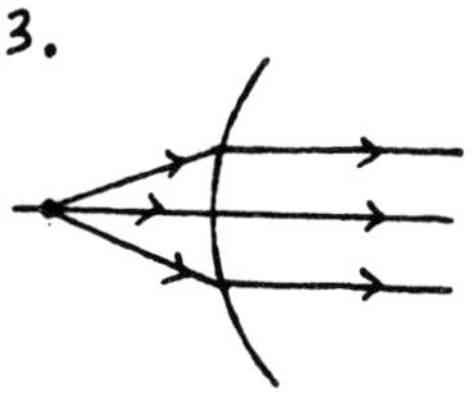

$$\frac{n_1}{s} + \frac{n_2}{s'} = \frac{n_2 - n_1}{R}$$

(a) $\dfrac{n_1}{f} + \dfrac{n_2}{\infty} = \dfrac{n_2 - n_1}{R}$ OR $f = \dfrac{n_1 R}{n_2 - n_1}$

(b) $n_2 > n_1$ : then $R > 0$ (convex)

$n_2 < n_1$ : then $R < 0$ (concave)

3-14.

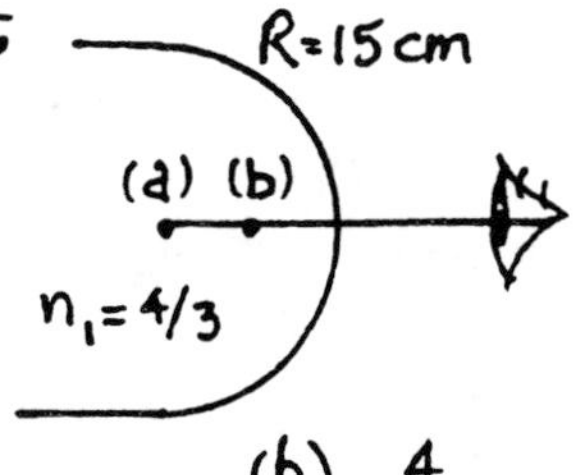


(a) $\dfrac{n_1}{s} + \dfrac{n_2}{s'} = \dfrac{n_2 - n_1}{R}$, $m = -\dfrac{n_1 s'}{n_2 s}$

$$\frac{4}{3(15)} + \frac{1}{s'} = \frac{1 - 4/3}{-15} \qquad m = -\frac{(4/3)(-15)}{(1)(15)}$$

$s' = -15$ cm (center) $\qquad m = 4/3$

(b) $\dfrac{4}{3(15/2)} + \dfrac{1}{s'} = \dfrac{1 - 4/3}{-15} \qquad m = -\dfrac{(4/3)(-45/7)}{(1)(15/2)}$

$s' = -6.4$ cm $\qquad m = 8/7$

**3-15.**

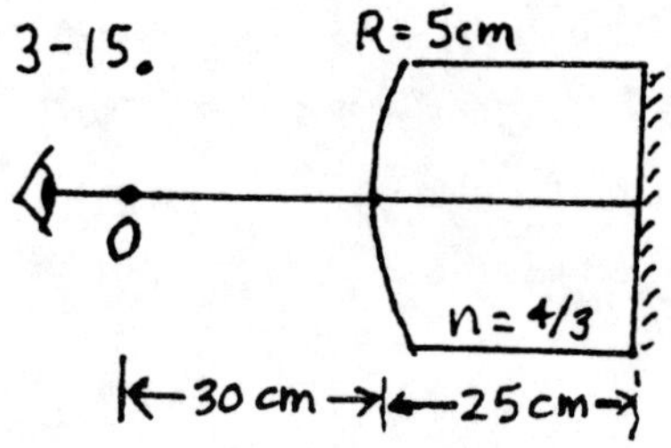


Rays from the object are
(a) refracted thru spherical window,
(b) then reflected from back plane mirror,
(c) then refracted out again thru spherical window.

(a) $\frac{n_1}{s} + \frac{n_2}{s'} = \frac{n_2 - n_1}{R}$

$\frac{1}{30} + \frac{4}{3s'} = \frac{4/3 - 1}{5}$

$s' = 40$ cm

$m = -\frac{n_1 s'}{n_2 s} = -\frac{(1)(40)}{(4/3)(30)}$

$m = -1$

(b) $s = 25 - 40 = -15$ cm (virtual object)

$s' = -s = +15$ cm

$m = +1$

(c) $\frac{4/3}{10} + \frac{1}{s'} = \frac{1 - 4/3}{-5}$ or $s' = -15$ cm

$m = \frac{-(4/3)(-15)}{(1)(10)} = +2$

Overall magnification $m = (-1)(+1)(+2) = -2$
Thus a virtual, inverted, double-sized image appears 15 cm behind (right) the spherical window.

**3-16.**

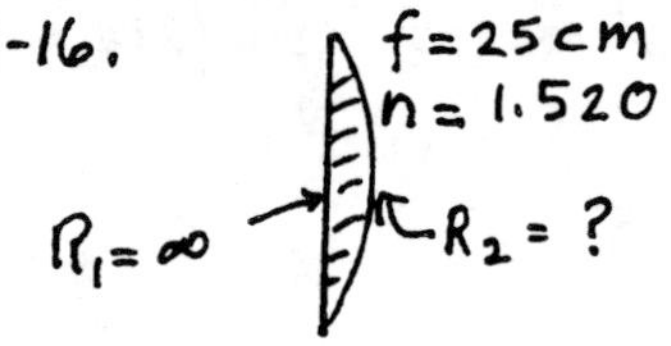


$\frac{1}{f} = \frac{n_2 - n_1}{n_1}\left(\frac{1}{R_1} - \frac{1}{R_2}\right)$ : Lensmaker's Eq.

$\frac{1}{25} = \frac{1.52 - 1}{1}\left(\frac{1}{\infty} - \frac{1}{R_2}\right)$ or $R_2 = -13$ cm

**3-17.**

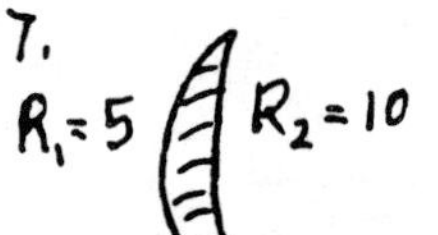


$\frac{1}{f} = \frac{n_2 - n_1}{n_1}\left(\frac{1}{R_1} - \frac{1}{R_2}\right)$

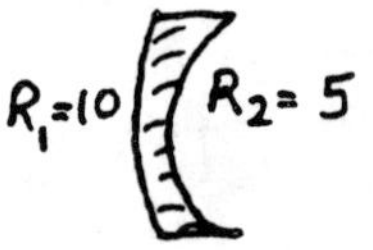


$\frac{1}{f} = \frac{1.50 - 1}{1}\left(\frac{1}{5} - \frac{1}{10}\right)$

$f = +20$ cm

$\frac{1}{f} = \frac{1.50 - 1}{1}\left(\frac{1}{10} - \frac{1}{5}\right)$

$f = -20$ cm

**3-18.** The thin lens equation assumes identical, refractive indices on both sides. In this case we can modify the procedure, beginning with Eq. (3-23), to allow for three distinct media:

$\frac{n_1}{s_1} + \frac{n_2}{s_1'} = \frac{n_2 - n_1}{R_1}$, left lens surface

$\frac{n_2}{s_2} + \frac{n_3}{s_2'} = \frac{n_3 - n_2}{R_2}$, right lens surface

3-18. (cont'd.)

For a thin lens, $s_2 \cong -s_1'$. Adding the equations,

$$\frac{n_1}{s_1} + \frac{n_3}{s_2'} = \frac{n_2 - n_1}{R_1} + \frac{n_3 - n_2}{R_2}$$

or, simply, $$\frac{n_1}{s} + \frac{n_3}{s'} = \frac{n_2 - n_1}{R_1} + \frac{n_3 - n_2}{R_2}$$

$$\frac{4}{3(20)} + \frac{1}{s'} = \frac{3/2 - 4/3}{30} + \frac{1 - 3/2}{-30}, \quad \text{or } s' = -22.5\text{cm}$$

Total magnification $m_T = m_1 m_2 = \left(-\frac{n_1 s_1'}{n_2 s}\right)\left(-\frac{n_2 s_2'}{n_3 s_2}\right)$

where $s_2 = -s_1'$: $\quad m_T = -\frac{n_1 s'}{n_3 s} = -\frac{(4/3)(-22.5)}{(1)(20)} = 1.50$

3-19. (a) Using $\frac{1}{f_{eq}} = \frac{1}{f_1} + \frac{1}{f_2}$, as in Eq. 3-33

$$\frac{1}{f_{eq}} = \frac{1}{-5} + \frac{1}{20} \quad \text{or } f_{eq} = -6.67 \text{ cm}$$

(b)

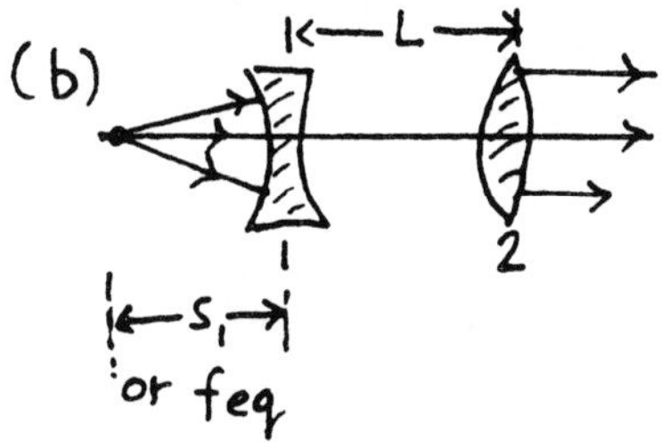


If the final image is at infinity, then $s_1$ is the equivalent $f$ of the pair. Working backwards,

Lens 2: $\frac{1}{s_2} + \frac{1}{\infty} = \frac{1}{f_2}$ or $s_2 = f_2$

But $s_2 = L - s_1'$ or $s_1' = L - f_2$

Lens 1: $\frac{1}{f_{eq}} + \frac{1}{L - f_2} = \frac{1}{f_1}$ or $f_{eq} = \frac{f_1(L - f_2)}{L - (f_1 + f_2)}$

$$f_{eq} = \frac{(-5)(10-20)}{10-(-5+20)} = -10 \text{ cm}$$

If the lenses are reversed, so $f_1 = 20$cm and $f_2 = -5$cm,

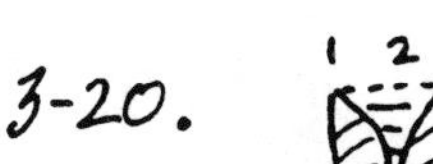

$$f_{eq} = \frac{20(10+5)}{10-(-5+20)} = -60 \text{ cm}$$

3-20.

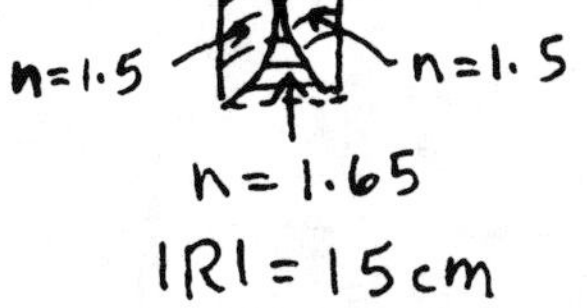


|R| = 15cm

Consider the three media as a sequence of three thin lenses. Each has a focal length given by the lensmaker's equation, and the equivalent focal length is given — Eq. 3-33 — by

$$\frac{1}{f_{eq}} = \frac{1}{f_1} + \frac{1}{f_2} + \frac{1}{f_3}$$

3-20. (cont'd.)

$$\frac{1}{f_1} = (1.5-1)\left(\frac{1}{\infty} - \frac{1}{-15}\right) \text{ or } f_1 = 30 \text{ cm}$$

$$\frac{1}{f_2} = (1.65-1)\left(\frac{1}{-15} - \frac{1}{15}\right) \text{ or } f_2 = -\frac{150}{13} \text{ cm}$$

$$\frac{1}{f_3} = \text{ same as for } f_1 \text{ : } f_3 = 30 \text{ cm}.$$

Then $\frac{1}{f_{eq}} = \frac{1}{30} + \frac{-13}{150} + \frac{1}{30}$ and $f_{eq} = -50\text{cm}$

3-21. One can use the formula derived in Problem 3-19.b, or do the calculation at first hand:

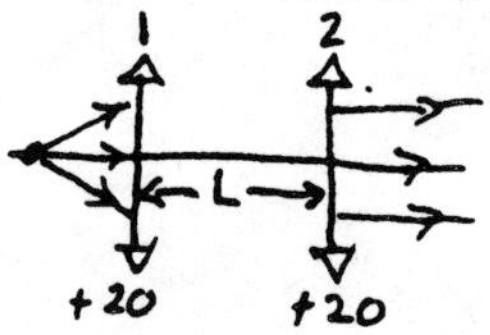


Second lens: $\frac{1}{s_2} + \frac{1}{\infty} = \frac{1}{20}$ or $s_2 = 20\text{ cm}$

$s_1' = 16 - 20 = -4\text{cm}$

First lens: $\frac{1}{s_1} + \frac{1}{-4} = \frac{1}{20}$ or $s_1 = 3.33\text{ cm}$

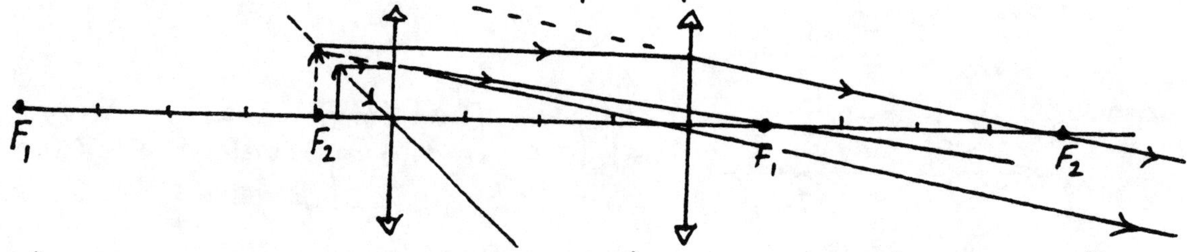


the image appears erect and magnified. Since it appears "at infinity," it is described by an angular magnification.

3-22.

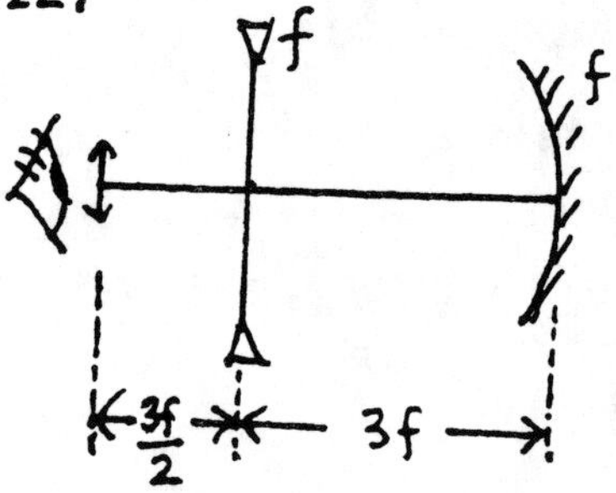


(b) Lens: $\frac{1}{3f/2} + \frac{1}{s'} = \frac{1}{-f}$ or $s' = -3f/5$
$\rightarrow$

$m_1 = -\frac{s'}{s} = -\left(\frac{3f}{5}\right)/\left(\frac{3f}{2}\right) = \frac{2}{5}$

Mirror: $s = 3f + 3f/5 = 18f/5$

$\frac{5}{18f} + \frac{1}{s'} = \frac{1}{f}$ or $s' = 18f/13$

$m_2 = -\frac{s'}{s} = -(18f/13)/(18f/5)$

$= -5/13$

Lens: $s = 3f = 18f/13 = 21f/13$
$\leftarrow$

$\frac{13}{21f} + \frac{1}{s'} = \frac{1}{-f}$ or $s' = -21f/34$

$m_3 = -s'/s = -(-21f/34)/(21f/13) = \frac{13}{34}$ $\quad m_T = \left(\frac{2}{5}\right)\left(-\frac{5}{13}\right)\left(\frac{13}{34}\right) = -\frac{1}{17}$

Image is inverted, (21/34)f behind (right of) lens, inverted, and 1/17 original size.

3-23.

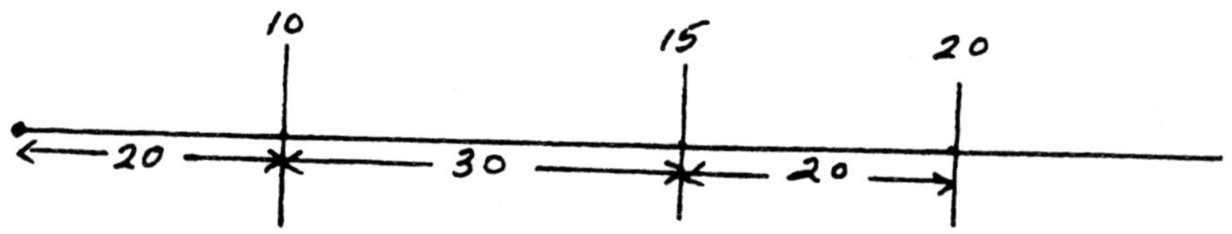


(a) $f_1 = +10\text{ cm}$, $f_2 = +15\text{ cm}$, $f_3 = +20\text{ cm}$

1st Lens : $\frac{1}{20} + \frac{1}{s'} = \frac{1}{10}$ $\quad s' = 20 \quad m_1 = -20/20 = -1$

2nd Lens : $\frac{1}{10} + \frac{1}{s'} = \frac{1}{15}$ $\quad s' = -30 \quad m_2 = -(-30)/10 = +3$

3rd Lens : $\frac{1}{50} + \frac{1}{s'} = \frac{1}{20}$ $\quad s' = 100/3 \quad m_3 = -100/3(50) = -2/3$

$m_T = m_1 m_2 m_3 = +2$

(b) $f_1 = +10\text{ cm}$, $f_2 = -15\text{ cm}$, $f_3 = +20\text{ cm}$

1ST Lens : $\frac{1}{20} + \frac{1}{s'} = \frac{1}{10}$ $\quad s' = 20 \quad m_1 = -20/20 = -1$

2nd Lens : $\frac{1}{10} + \frac{1}{s'} = \frac{1}{-15}$ $\quad s' = -6 \quad m_2 = -(-6)/10 = +0.6$

3rd Lens : $\frac{1}{26} + \frac{1}{s'} = \frac{1}{20}$ $\quad s' = 520/6 \quad m_3 = -520/(6\times 26) = -\frac{10}{3}$

$m_T = m_1 m_2 m_3 = +2$

(c) $f_1 = -10\text{ cm}$, $f_2 = +15\text{ cm}$, $f_3 = -20\text{ cm}$

1ST Lens : $\frac{1}{20} + \frac{1}{s'} = \frac{1}{-10}$ $\quad s' = -20/3 \quad m_1 = -(-20)/3(20) = \frac{1}{3}$

2nd Lens : $\frac{3}{110} + \frac{1}{s'} = \frac{1}{15}$ $\quad s' = 330/13 \quad m_2 = -\frac{(330)(3)}{(13)(110)} = -\frac{9}{13}$

3rd Lens : $-\frac{13}{70} + \frac{1}{s'} = \frac{1}{-20}$ $\quad s' = 140/19 \quad m_3 = -\frac{(140)(13)}{(19)(-70)} = \frac{26}{19}$

$m_T = m_1 m_2 m_3 = -6/19$

3-24. $\frac{1}{f} = \frac{n_2 - n_1}{n_1}\left(\frac{1}{R_1} - \frac{1}{R_2}\right)$

Air: $\frac{1}{30} = \frac{1.50-1}{1}\left(\frac{1}{R_1} - \frac{1}{R_2}\right)$ $\qquad$ Liquid: $-\frac{1}{188} = \frac{1.50 - n_L}{n_L}\left(\frac{1}{R_1} - \frac{1}{R_2}\right)$

Dividing equations, $-\frac{188}{30} = \frac{0.5\, n_L}{1.5 - n_L}$ or $n_L = 1.63$

3-25.

$R_1 = \infty$  $R_2 = 60$

$n = 1.50$

$\frac{1}{f} = \frac{n_2 - n_1}{n_1}\left(\frac{1}{R_1} - \frac{1}{R_2}\right) = \frac{1.5-1}{1}\left(0 + \frac{1}{60}\right)$

$f = 120\text{ cm}$

3-25. (cont'd.)

Newtonian equations: $m = -\frac{f}{x} = -\frac{x'}{f}$

For $m = -4$, $-4 = -\frac{f}{x} = -\frac{120}{x}$ or $x = 30$ cm

$-4 = -\frac{x'}{f} = -\frac{x'}{120}$ or $x' = 480$ cm.

Thus $s = x + f = 30 + 120 = 150$ cm

$s' = x' + f = 480 + 120 = 600$ cm

Check: $\frac{1}{s} + \frac{1}{s'} = \frac{1}{150} + \frac{1}{600} = \frac{1}{120} = \frac{1}{f}$

3-26. (a) $f_1 = 10$ cm  $f_2 = 20$ cm  $f_3 = -40$ cm

$P_1 = \frac{1}{0.1} = +10D$  $P_2 = \frac{1}{0.2} = +5D$  $P_3 = \frac{1}{-0.4} = -2.5D$

$P = P_1 + P_2 + P_3 = 10 + 5 - 2.5 = +12.5D$

(b) $\frac{1}{s} + \frac{1}{s'} = \frac{1}{f}$

$V + V' = P$, where $V = \frac{1}{s} = \frac{1}{0.12} = +8.33\ D$

$8.333 + V' = 12.5$

$V' = 4.167\ D$ or $s' = \frac{1}{V'} = \frac{1}{4.167} = 0.24\text{m} = 24\text{cm}$

3-27.

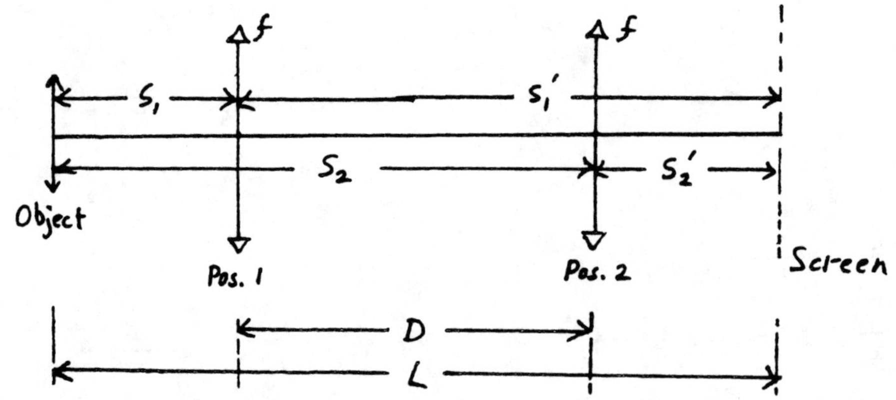


The applicable relations are:

Lens equations: $\frac{1}{s_1} + \frac{1}{s_1'} = \frac{1}{f}$ and $\frac{1}{s_2} + \frac{1}{s_2'} = \frac{1}{f}$

Geometrical: $L = s_1 + s_1' = s_2 + s_2'$

$D = s_2 - s_1 = s_1' - s_2'$

Thus $f = \frac{s_1 s_1'}{s_1 + s_1'} = \frac{s_1 s_1'}{L} = \frac{s_2 s_2'}{s_2 + s_2'} = \frac{s_2 s_2'}{L}$  (1)

3-27. (cont'd.)

Because the lens equation can be satisfied the second time by simply interchanging object and image distances,

$$s_2 = s_1' \text{ and } s_2' = s_1 \qquad (2)$$

Adding and subtracting the equations $L = s_1 + s_2$ and $D = -s_1 + s_2$, we get $L - D = 2s_1$ and $L + D = 2s_2$. Their product is

$$L^2 - D^2 = 4 s_1 s_2$$

$$\text{or } L^2 - D^2 = 4 s_1 s_1' \quad \text{by Eq (2)}$$

$$\text{or } L^2 - D^2 = 4fL \quad \text{by Eq (1)}$$

$$\text{thus} \quad \boxed{f = \frac{L^2 - D^2}{4L}}$$

3-28. Lens equations: $\frac{1}{s_1} + \frac{1}{s_1'} = \frac{1}{f}$ and $\frac{1}{s_2} + \frac{1}{s_2'} = \frac{1}{f}$

Calculate $\frac{1}{m_1} - \frac{1}{m_2} = -\frac{s_1}{s_1'} + \frac{s_2}{s_2'} = -\frac{s_1}{s_1 f/(s_1 - f)} + \frac{s_2}{s_2 f/(s_2 - f)}$

$$= \frac{s_2 - f}{f} - \frac{s_1 - f}{f} = \frac{s_2 - s_1}{f}$$

$$\text{OR} \quad \boxed{f = \frac{s_2 - s_1}{\frac{1}{m_1} - \frac{1}{m_2}}}$$

3-29.

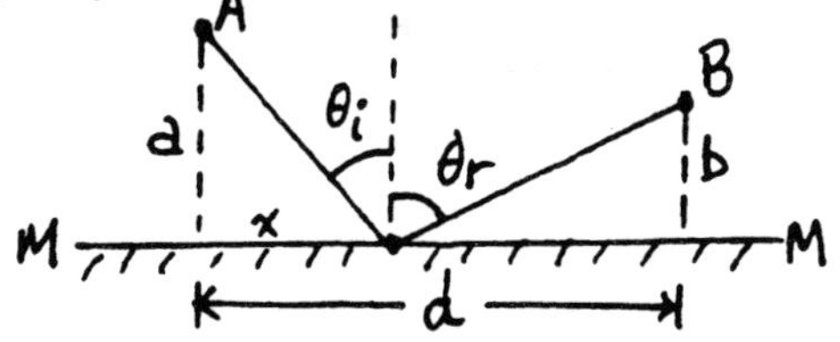


$$D = \sqrt{a^2 + x^2} + \sqrt{b^2 + (d - x)^2}$$

$$\frac{dD}{dx} = \frac{x}{\sqrt{a^2 + x^2}} + \frac{-(d - x)}{\sqrt{b^2 + (d - x)^2}} = 0$$

$$\sin \theta_i - \sin \theta_r = 0$$

$$\theta_i = \theta_r$$

3-30.

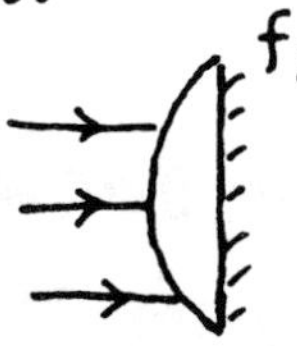


Refraction at curved side: $\frac{1}{\infty} + \frac{n}{s'} = \frac{n-1}{R}$; $s' = \frac{nR}{n-1}$

Reflection at plane side: $s' = -s = -\frac{nR}{n-1}$

Refraction at curved side: $\frac{n}{-nR/(n-1)} + \frac{1}{s'} = \frac{1-n}{-R}$

or $s' = R/2(n-1)$

3-30. (cont'd.)

Thus, $f_1 = \frac{R}{2(n-1)}$

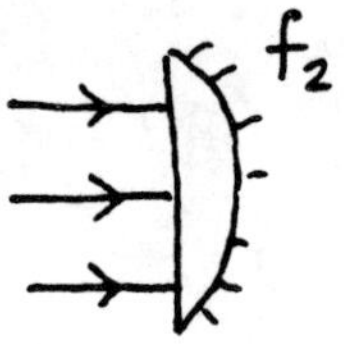


Reflection at curved face: $\frac{1}{\infty} + \frac{1}{s'} = -\frac{2}{R}$; $s' = -\frac{R}{2}$

Refraction at plane face: $\frac{n}{-R/2} + \frac{1}{s'} = 0$; $s' = \frac{R}{2n}$

Thus $f_2 = R/2n$

Ratio $\frac{f_1}{f_2} = \frac{R/2(n-1)}{R/2n} = \frac{n}{n-1}$

3-31. $D = s + s' = s + \frac{fs}{s-f}$

$$\frac{dD}{ds} = 1 + \frac{(s-f)f - fs}{(s-f)^2} = 0$$

$s(s-2f) = 0$

$s = 0,\ 2f$

$D = s + \frac{fs}{s-f}$

For $s = 2f$, $D = 4f$

This occurs when

$s = 2f$, $s' = 2f$

3-32.

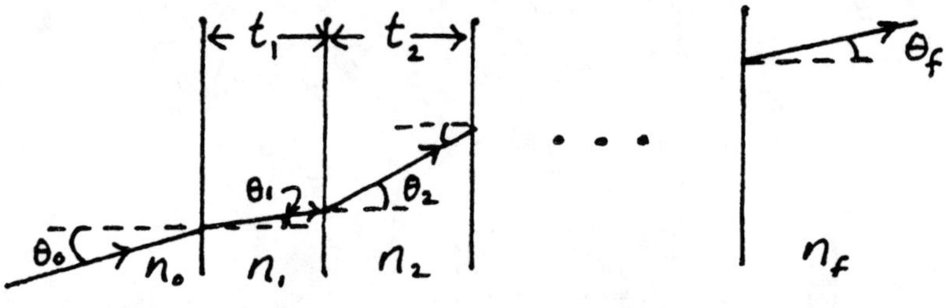


(a) $n_0 \sin\theta_0 = n_1 \sin\theta_1$

$n_1 \sin\theta_1 = n_2 \sin\theta_2$

- - - -

$n_{f-1} \sin\theta_{f-1} = n_f \sin\theta_f$

$n_0 \sin\theta_0 = n_f \sin\theta_f$

(b)

Lateral displacement =

$t_1 \tan\theta_1 + t_2 \tan\theta_2 + \ldots$

OR $\sum_i t_i \tan\theta_i$

3-33. 

$$\frac{n_1}{s_1} + \frac{n_2}{s_2} = \frac{n_2 - n_1}{R}$$

1st surface : no change

2nd surface : $\frac{1.5}{\infty} + \frac{1}{s_2} = \frac{1-1.5}{-4}$ OR $s_2 = 8$ cm.

1st surface : $\frac{1}{\infty} + \frac{1.5}{s_2} = \frac{1.5-1}{4}$ OR $s_2 = 12$ cm

2nd surface : Object distance $= 4 - 12 = -8$ cm (virtual)

$\frac{1.5}{-8} + \frac{1}{s_2} = \frac{1-1.5}{0}$ OR $s_2 = 5.33$ cm

3-34. 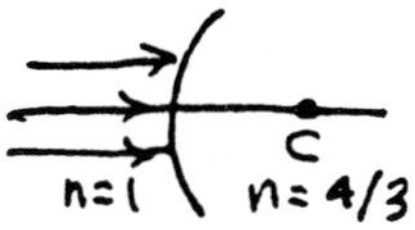


$\frac{1}{\infty} + \frac{4/3}{f} = \frac{4/3-1}{10}$ OR $f = +40$ cm

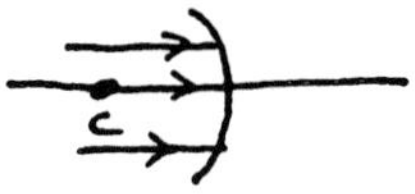


$\frac{4/3}{\infty} + \frac{1}{f} = \frac{1-4/3}{-10}$ OR $f = +30$ cm

Reversing indices of refraction,

$\frac{4/3}{\infty} + \frac{1}{f} = \frac{1-4/3}{10}$ OR $f = -30$ cm

$\frac{1}{\infty} + \frac{4/3}{f} = \frac{4/3-1}{-10}$ OR $f = -40$ cm

3-35. $|m| = \frac{s'}{s} = \frac{1}{50,000} = \frac{f}{s} = \frac{6''}{s}$ , since $s' = f$

$s = 50,000 \times 6'' = 25,000$ ft

4-1. $R_1 = +40$ $R_2 = -40$

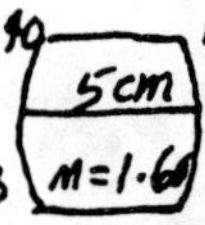


$n = 1.33$ $n = 1.6$ $n = 1.0$ Substituting into Eq. (4-1),

$$\frac{1}{f_1} = \frac{1.6-1}{1.33(-40)} - \frac{1.6-1.33}{1.33(40)} - \frac{(1.6-1.33)(1.6-1)}{1.33\ (1.6)}\ \frac{5}{40(-40)}, \text{ OR}$$

$$f_1 = -62.05 \text{ cm}$$

$$f_2 = -\frac{n'}{n} f_1 = -\left(\frac{1}{1.33}\right)(-62.05) = 46.66 \text{ cm}$$

$$r = \frac{n_L - n'}{n_L R_2} f_1 t = \frac{1.6-1}{1.6(-40)}(-62.05)(5) = 2.91 \text{ cm}$$

$$s = -\frac{n_L - n}{n_L R_1} f_2 t = -\frac{(1.6-1.33)}{(1.6)(+40)}(46.66)(5) = -0.98 \text{ cm}$$

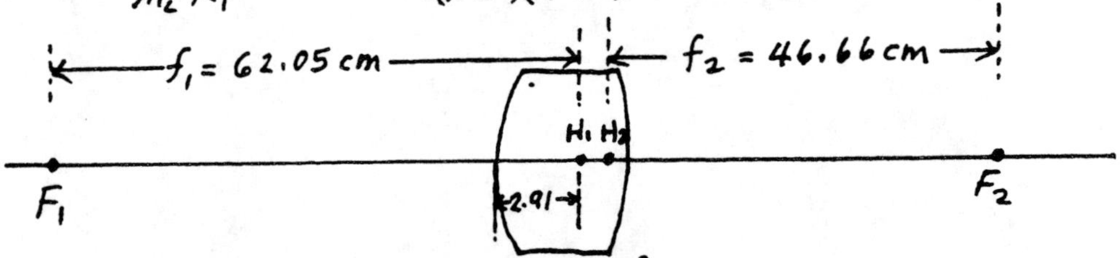


4-2. (a) $$\frac{1}{f_1} = \frac{1.53-1}{12.5} - \frac{1.53-1}{-20} - \frac{(1.53-1)^2}{1.53}\ \frac{3}{(-20)(12.5)}, \quad \text{Eq. (4-1)}$$

$$f_1 = 14.06 \text{ cm}$$

$$f_2 = -\frac{n'}{n} f_1 = -\frac{1}{1}(14.06) = -14.06 \text{ cm}$$

$$r = \frac{1.53-1}{1.53(12.5)}(14.06)(3) = +1.17 \text{ cm}$$

$$s = -\frac{1.53-1}{1.53(-20)}(-14.06)(3) = -0.73 \text{ cm}$$

} Eqs. (4-3)

(b) $s = 30$ cm from $V_1$ or 31.17 cm from H1

$$\frac{1}{s} + \frac{1}{s'} = \frac{1}{f}$$

$$\frac{1}{31.17} + \frac{1}{s'} = \frac{1}{-14.06} \quad \text{OR} \quad s' = -9.689 \text{ from } H_2$$

Since lens center is $1.50 - 0.73 = 0.77$ cm from $H_2$, image is $-9.689 + 0.77 = -8.92$ cm from lens center

(c) $$\frac{1}{f} = n-1\left(\frac{1}{R_1} - \frac{1}{R_2}\right) = (1.53-1)\left(\frac{1}{-20} - \frac{1}{12.5}\right) \text{ OR } f = -14.51 \text{ cm}$$

$$\frac{1}{s} + \frac{1}{s'} = \frac{1}{f}: \quad \frac{1}{30} + \frac{1}{s'} = \frac{1}{-14.51} \quad \text{OR} \quad s' = -9.780 \text{ cm from lens center}$$

$$\% \text{ error} = \frac{9.78 - 8.92}{8.92} = 9.6\%$$

4-3. Using Eq. (4-1),

$$\frac{1}{f_1} = \frac{1.5-1}{10} - \frac{1.5-1}{-20} - \frac{(1.5-1)^2}{1.5}\,\frac{5}{(-20)(10)} \quad \text{OR} \quad f_1 = +12.63 \text{ cm}$$

$$f_2 = -\frac{n'}{n} f_1 = -f_1 = -12.63 \text{ cm}$$

$$r = \frac{1.5-1}{1.5(10)}(12.63)(5) = +2.105 \text{ cm}$$

$$s = \frac{1.5-1}{1.5(-20)}(-12.63)(5) = -1.0525 \text{ cm}$$

} Eqs. (4-3)

Using $-\frac{f_1}{s_o} + \frac{f_2}{s_i} = 1$, with $s_o = 8 + r = 10.105$ cm,

$$-\frac{12.63}{10.105} + \frac{(-12.63)}{s_i} = 1 \quad \text{or} \quad s_i = -5.614 \text{ cm (left of } H_2)$$

$$s_i = -5.614 + s = -6.67 \text{ cm}$$

left of $V_2$

$$m = -\frac{(1)(-5.614)}{(1)(10.105)} = +0.556$$

or $h_i = m h_o = (0.556)(1'') = 0.556$ in.

4-4. Using Eq. (4-1),

$$\frac{1}{f_1} = \frac{1.61-1.33}{1(-10)} - \frac{1.61-1}{1(10)} - \frac{(1.61-1.33)(1.61-1)(2)}{(1)(1.61)(10)(-10)}$$

or $f_1 = -11.51$ cm and $f_2 = -\frac{1.33}{1}(-11.51) = 15.31$ cm

$$r = \frac{1.61-1.33}{1.61(-10)}(-11.51)(2) = 0.400 \text{ cm}$$

$$s = -\frac{1.61-1}{1.61(10)}(15.31)(2) = -1.16 \text{ cm}$$

} Eqs. (4-3)

$$v = \left[1 - \frac{1.33}{1} + \frac{1.61-1.33}{1.61(-10)}(2)\right](-11.51) = 4.20 \text{ cm}$$

$$w = \left[1 - \frac{1.33}{1} - \frac{1.61-1}{1.61(10)}(2)\right](15.31) = 2.64 \text{ cm}$$

} Eqs (4-4)

In the image equation $-\frac{f_1}{s_o} + \frac{f_2}{s_i} = 1$, $s_o = 60 + r = 60.4$ cm

$$-\frac{-11.51}{60.4} + \frac{15.31}{s_i} = 1 \quad \text{or} \quad s_i = 18.9 \text{ cm from } H_2$$

$$m = -\frac{(1)(18.914)}{(1.33)(60.4)} = -0.235$$

$$h_i = m h_o = (-0.235)(5 \text{ cm}) = -1.18 \text{ cm}$$

4-5. (a) Using Eq. 4-1,

$$\frac{1}{f_1} = \frac{1.33-1}{1(-10)} - \frac{1.33-1}{1(10)} - \frac{(1.33-1)^2}{1(1.33)}\frac{20}{(10)(-10)} \quad \text{OR} \quad f_1 = -20.15\text{ cm}$$

$$f_2 = -f_1 = +20.15\text{ cm}$$

$$r = \frac{1.33-1}{1.33(-10)}(-20.15)(20) = 10\text{ cm}$$

$$s = -\frac{1.33-1}{1.33(10)}(20.15)(20) = -10\text{ cm}$$

Since $n = n' = 1$, $v = r = +10\text{ cm}$ and $w = s = -10\text{ cm}$

(b) $s_o = 20 + 10 = 30\text{ cm}$ from $H_1$

$$-\frac{f_1}{s_o} + \frac{f_2}{s_i} = 1 \; ; \; -\frac{-20.15}{30} + \frac{20.15}{s_i} = 1 \quad \text{OR} \quad s_i = 61.38\text{ cm from center}$$

$$m = -\frac{s'}{s} = -\frac{61.38}{30} = -2.05$$

Image is inverted, real, approx. twice in size.

(c)

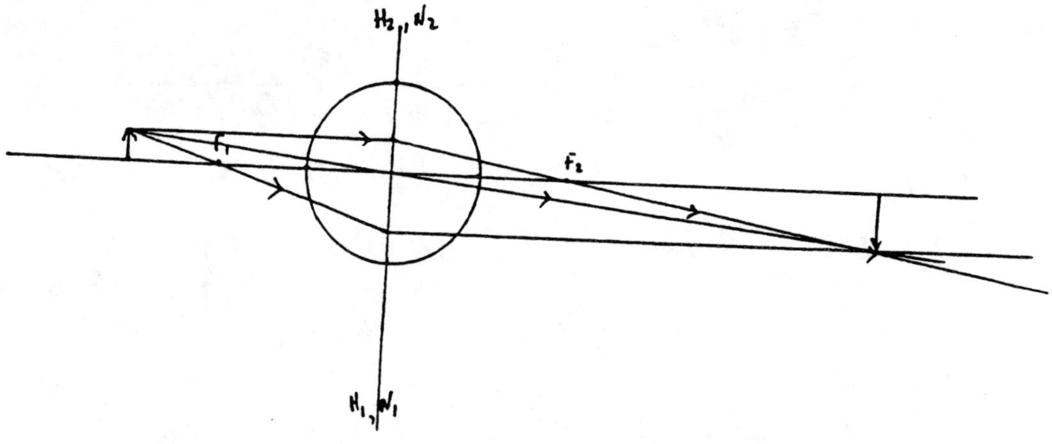


4-6. (a) $\mathcal{M} = \mathcal{R}(\text{sph})\,\mathcal{T}\,\mathcal{R}(\text{plane})$

$$\mathcal{M} = \begin{pmatrix} 1 & 0 \\ -1/10 & 3/2 \end{pmatrix}\begin{pmatrix} 1 & 5 \\ 0 & 1 \end{pmatrix}\begin{pmatrix} 1 & 0 \\ 0 & 2/3 \end{pmatrix} = \begin{pmatrix} 1 & 10/3 \\ -1/10 & 2/3 \end{pmatrix}$$

$$y = Ay_o + B\alpha_o = y_o + \tfrac{10}{3}\alpha_o$$
$$\alpha = Cy_o + D\alpha_o = -\tfrac{1}{10}y_o + \tfrac{2}{3}\alpha_o$$

For $y_o = 1$, $\alpha_o = 0$: $y = 1$, $\alpha = -\frac{1}{10}\text{ rad} = -5.73°$

(b) Add Translation matrix:

$$\mathcal{T} = \begin{pmatrix} 1 & x \\ 0 & 1 \end{pmatrix}$$

4-6. (cont'd.)

$$\mathcal{M}' = \mathcal{T}\mathcal{M} = \begin{pmatrix} 1 & x \\ 0 & 1 \end{pmatrix}\begin{pmatrix} 1 & 10/3 \\ -1/10 & 2/3 \end{pmatrix} = \begin{pmatrix} 1-x/10 & 10/3 + \frac{2x}{3} \\ -1/10 & 2/3 \end{pmatrix}$$

$$\left\{ \begin{array}{l} y = (1-x/10)\, y_0 + (10/3 + 2x/3)\, \alpha_0 \\ \alpha = -(1/10)\, y_0 + 2/3\, \alpha_0 \end{array} \right\}$$

(c) Ray crosses axis when $y = 0$. For $y_0 = 1$, $\alpha_0 = 0$

$(1 - x/10) = 0$ and $x = 10\text{ cm}$

4-7. $\left\{ \begin{array}{l} y_f = A y_0 + B\alpha_0 \\ \alpha_f = C y_0 + D\alpha_0 \end{array} \right\}$ From Fig. 4-12(b), $\alpha_0 = 0$, $y_0 = y_0$, $y_f = y_f$

Thus $\left\{ \begin{array}{l} y_f = A y_0 \\ \alpha_f = C y_0 \end{array} \right\}$

$$q \cong \frac{y_f}{-\alpha_f} = \frac{A y_0}{-C y_0} = -\frac{A}{C} \;; \qquad f_2 \cong \frac{y_0}{-\alpha_f} = \frac{y_0}{-C y_0} = -\frac{1}{C}$$

$$-s \cong \frac{y_0 - y_f}{-\alpha_f} = \frac{y_0 - A y_0}{-C y_0} = \frac{1-A}{-C} \quad \text{or} \quad s = \frac{1-A}{C}$$

(alternatively, $s = q - f_2 = -\frac{A}{C} + \frac{1}{C} = \frac{1-A}{C}$ )

From Fig. 4-12(c), $\alpha_0 = \alpha_f = \alpha$

thus $\left. \begin{array}{l} y_f = A y_0 + B\alpha \\ \alpha = C y_0 + D\alpha \end{array} \right\} \alpha = \frac{C y_0}{1-D}$

$$-w \cong \frac{y_f}{\alpha} = \frac{A y_0 + B\alpha}{\alpha} = A\frac{y_0}{\alpha} + B = A\frac{y_0}{C y_0/(1-D)} + B$$

$$-w \cong \frac{A - AD + BC}{C} = \frac{A - \text{Det}\,\mathcal{M}}{C} = \frac{A - n_0/n_f}{C}$$

$$w \cong \frac{n_0/n_f - A}{C}$$

4-8.

$$\mathcal{M} = \underbrace{\begin{pmatrix} 1 & 0 \\ \frac{1.6-1.3}{1.3(1.5)} & \frac{1.6}{1.3} \end{pmatrix}}_{\text{Refraction Surface 2}} \underbrace{\begin{pmatrix} 1 & 2 \\ 0 & 1 \end{pmatrix}}_{\text{Translation}} \underbrace{\begin{pmatrix} 1 & 0 \\ \frac{1-1.6}{(1.6)(1.5)} & \frac{1}{1.6} \end{pmatrix}}_{\text{Refraction Surface 1}} = \begin{pmatrix} 1/2 & 5/4 \\ -3/13 & 25/26 \end{pmatrix} \begin{matrix} A \;\; B \\ C \;\; D \end{matrix}$$

Check: $AD - BC = \frac{1}{1.3} = \text{Det}\,\mathcal{M}$

$p = D/C = -25/6 = -4.17\text{ cm}$

$q = -A/C = 13/6 = +2.17\text{ cm}$

$r = \frac{D - 1/1.3}{C} = -0.83\text{ cm}$

$s = (1-A)/C = -2.17\text{ cm}$

$f_1 = \frac{n_0/n_f}{C} = -3.33\text{ cm}$

$f_2 = -1/C = +4.33\text{ cm}$

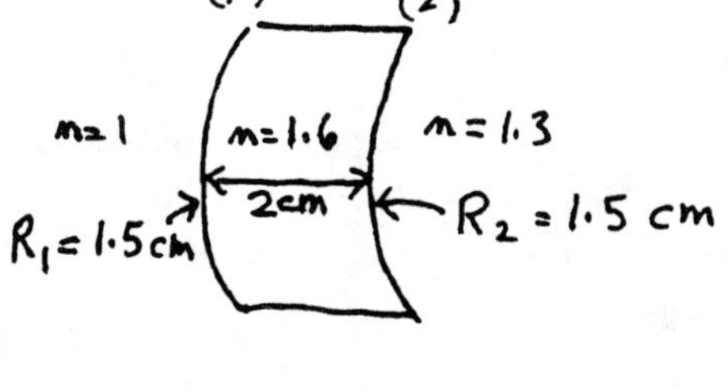

4-9.

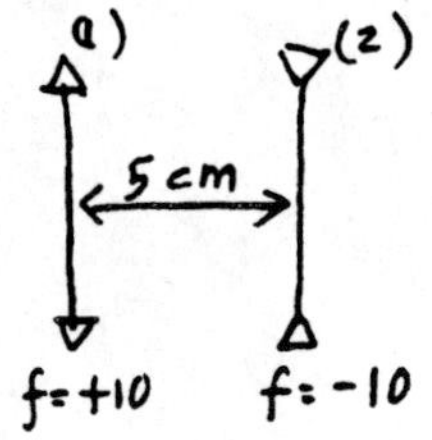


$$\mathcal{M} = \underbrace{\begin{pmatrix} 1 & 0 \\ \frac{1}{10} & 1 \end{pmatrix}}_{\text{Thin Lens 2 Matrix}} \underbrace{\begin{pmatrix} 1 & 5 \\ 0 & 1 \end{pmatrix}}_{\text{Translation}} \underbrace{\begin{pmatrix} 1 & 0 \\ -\frac{1}{10} & 1 \end{pmatrix}}_{\text{Thin Lens 1 Matrix}} = \begin{pmatrix} \frac{1}{2} & 5 \\ -\frac{1}{20} & \frac{3}{2} \end{pmatrix} \quad \begin{matrix} A & B \\ C & D \end{matrix}$$

Check: $AD - BC = 1 = \frac{n_1}{n_3}$

$f_1 = \frac{1}{C} = -20\text{ cm}$

$f_2 = -\frac{1}{C} = +20\text{ cm}$ $\quad r = \frac{D-1}{C} = -10\text{ cm}$

$q = -\frac{A}{C} = +10\text{ cm}$ $\quad s = \frac{1-A}{C} = -10\text{ cm}$.

$p = D/C = -30\text{ cm}$

4-10.

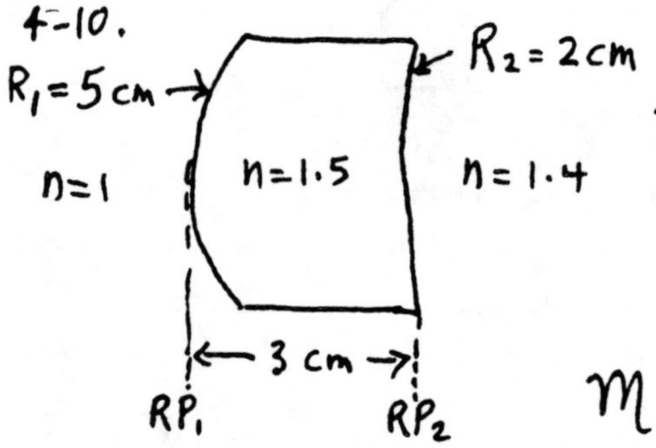


$$\mathcal{M} = \underbrace{\begin{pmatrix} 1 & 0 \\ \frac{.1}{1.4(2)} & \frac{1.5}{1.4} \end{pmatrix}}_{\text{Refraction at } R_2} \underbrace{\begin{pmatrix} 1 & 3 \\ 0 & 1 \end{pmatrix}}_{\text{Translation}} \underbrace{\begin{pmatrix} 1 & 0 \\ \frac{-.5}{1.5(5)} & \frac{1}{1.5} \end{pmatrix}}_{\text{Refraction at } R_1}$$

$$\mathcal{M} = \begin{pmatrix} 4/5 & 2 \\ -3/70 & 11/14 \end{pmatrix} \quad \text{Check: Det } \mathcal{M} = \frac{5}{7} = \frac{1}{1.4}$$

$A = 4/5$
$B = 2$
$C = -3/70$
$D = 11/14$

$f_1 = \frac{n_0/n_f}{C} = \frac{1/1.4}{C} = -16.67\text{ cm}$

$f_2 = -1/C = +23.33\text{ cm}$.

$p = D/C = -18.33\text{ cm}$, $\quad q = -A/C = +18.67\text{ cm}$

$r = \frac{D - n_0/n_f}{C} = -1.67\text{ cm}$, $\quad s = \frac{1-A}{C} = -4.67\text{ cm}$

4-11. (a)

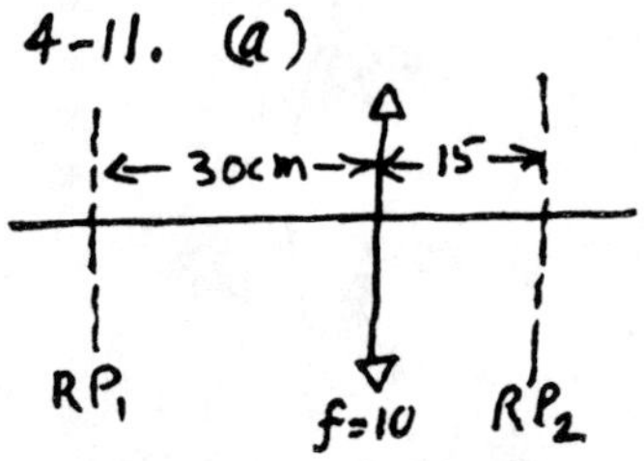


$$\mathcal{M} = \begin{pmatrix} 1 & 15 \\ 0 & 1 \end{pmatrix} \begin{pmatrix} 1 & 0 \\ -\frac{1}{10} & 1 \end{pmatrix} \begin{pmatrix} 1 & 30 \\ 0 & 1 \end{pmatrix} = \begin{pmatrix} -1/2 & 0 \\ -1/10 & -2 \end{pmatrix} \quad \begin{matrix} A & B \\ C & D \end{matrix}$$

$f_1 = \frac{1}{C} = -10\text{ cm}$ $\quad r = \frac{D-1}{C} = +30\text{ cm}$

$f_2 = -\frac{1}{C} = +10\text{ cm}$ $\quad s = \frac{1-A}{C} = -15\text{ cm}$

$p = D/C = +20\text{ cm}$ $\quad v = \frac{D-1}{C} = +30\text{ cm}$

$q = -A/C = -5\text{ cm}$ $\quad w = \frac{1-A}{C} = -15\text{ cm}$

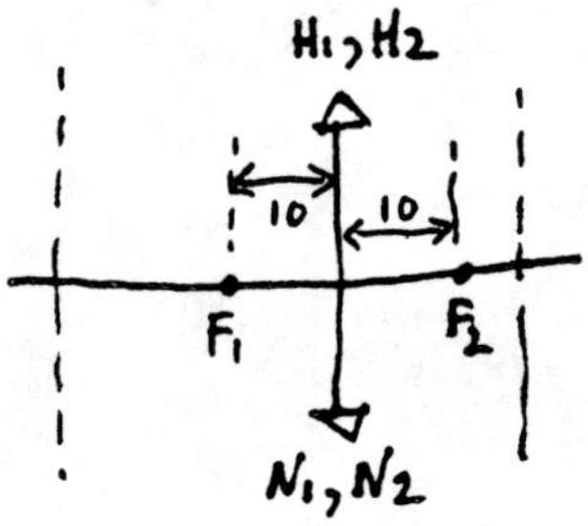


Principal and nodal points fall at lens center, focal points at 10 cm to each side.

4-11. (cont'd.)

(c) This is case (c), Fig. 4-9. $B=0$ signifies that reference planes are object-image, or conjugate, planes and $A$ represents the linear magnification.

Check by thin lens Eq: If an object is at the input plane,

$$\frac{1}{30}+\frac{1}{s'}=\frac{1}{10} \quad \text{OR} \quad s'=15\text{ cm, output plane.}$$

Then $m=-s'/s=-15/30=-1/2=A$.

4-12. (a)

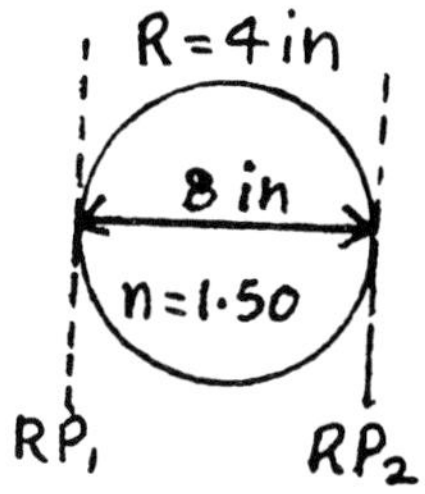


$$\mathcal{M}=\underbrace{\begin{pmatrix}1 & 0\\ \frac{.5}{-4} & \frac{3}{2}\end{pmatrix}}_{\text{Refract right}}\underbrace{\begin{pmatrix}1 & 8\\ 0 & 1\end{pmatrix}}_{\text{Trans}}\underbrace{\begin{pmatrix}1 & 0\\ \frac{-.5}{1.5(4)} & \frac{2}{3}\end{pmatrix}}_{\text{Refract left}}=\begin{pmatrix}\frac{1}{3} & \frac{16}{3}\\ -\frac{1}{6} & \frac{1}{3}\end{pmatrix}\begin{matrix}A & B\\ C & D\end{matrix}$$

Check: Det $\mathcal{M}=1$

$r=\frac{D-1}{C}=4$ in  $q=-A/C=+2$ in

$s=\frac{1-A}{C}=-4$ in  $f_1=1/C=-6$ in.

$p=D/C=-2$ in  $f_2=-1/C=+6$ in.

(b) Parallel light focuses at $F_2$, measured from output plane (or right surface) by $q=2$ in.

4-13.

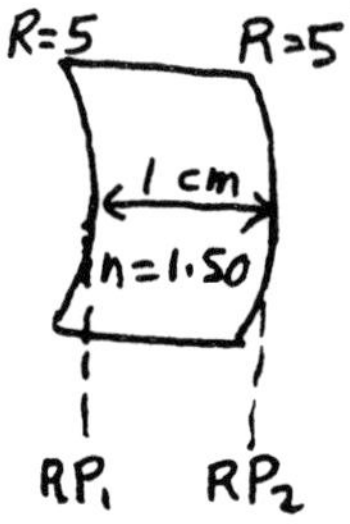


$$\mathcal{M}=\begin{pmatrix}1 & 0\\ \frac{.5}{(-5)} & \frac{3}{2}\end{pmatrix}\begin{pmatrix}1 & 1\\ 0 & 1\end{pmatrix}\begin{pmatrix}1 & 0\\ \frac{-.5}{1.5(-5)} & \frac{2}{3}\end{pmatrix}=\begin{pmatrix}16/15 & 2/3\\ -1/150 & 14/15\end{pmatrix}\begin{matrix}A & B\\ C & D\end{matrix}$$

Check: Det $=1$

$r=\frac{D-1}{C}=+10$ cm  $q=-A/C=+160$ cm

$s=\frac{1-A}{C}=+10$ cm  $f_1=1/C=-150$ cm

$p=D/C=-140$ cm  $f_2=-1/C=+150$ cm

4-14.

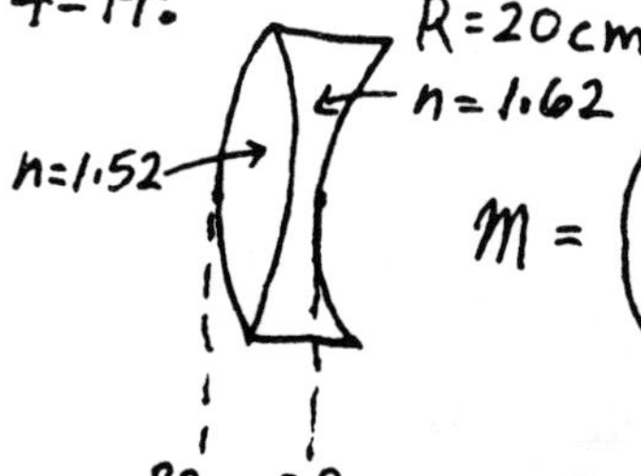


$t_1=1$ cm

$t_2=0.5$ cm

$$\mathcal{M}=\overset{\mathcal{R}}{\begin{pmatrix}1 & 0\\ \frac{.62}{20} & 1.62\end{pmatrix}}\overset{\mathcal{T}}{\begin{pmatrix}1 & 1/2\\ 0 & 1\end{pmatrix}}\overset{\mathcal{R}}{\begin{pmatrix}1 & 0\\ \frac{-.1}{-20(1.62)} & \frac{1.52}{1.62}\end{pmatrix}}\overset{\mathcal{T}}{\begin{pmatrix}1 & 1\\ 0 & 1\end{pmatrix}}\overset{\mathcal{R}}{\begin{pmatrix}1 & 0\\ \frac{-.52}{20(1.52)} & \frac{1}{1.52}\end{pmatrix}}$$

$$\mathcal{M}=\begin{pmatrix}0.9764 & 0.96755\\ 0.009182 & 1.0333\end{pmatrix}\begin{matrix}A & B\\ C & D\end{matrix}$$

check: Det $\mathcal{M}=1$

4-14. (cont'd.)

(b) $r = \frac{D-1}{C} = 3.62\text{ cm}$ $p = \frac{D}{C} = 112.53\text{ cm}$ $f_1 = \frac{1}{C} = 108.90\text{ cm}$

$s = \frac{1-A}{C} = 2.57\text{ cm}$ $q = -\frac{A}{C} = -106.33\text{ cm}$ $f_2 = \frac{-1}{C} = -108.90\text{ cm}$

(c) Consider each lens separately, in air: $\frac{1}{f} = \frac{n_2 - n_1}{n_1}\left(\frac{1}{R_1} - \frac{1}{R_2}\right)$

$$\frac{1}{f_1} = \frac{1.52-1}{1}\left(\frac{1}{20} - \frac{1}{-20}\right) = 0.052$$

$$\frac{1}{f_2} = \frac{1.62-1}{1}\left(\frac{1}{-20} - \frac{1}{20}\right) = -0.062$$

Equivalent focal length: $\frac{1}{f_{eq}} = \frac{1}{f_1} + \frac{1}{f_2} = 0.052 + 0.062$

$f_{eq} = -100\text{ cm}.$

4-15.

(a) $$M = \begin{pmatrix} 1 & s' \\ 0 & 1 \end{pmatrix}\underbrace{\begin{pmatrix} 2/3 & 2 \\ -1/6 & 1 \end{pmatrix}}_{\text{calculated in text}}\begin{pmatrix} 1 & s \\ 0 & 1 \end{pmatrix} = \begin{pmatrix} 2/3 - s'/6 & 2/3\, s + 2 - ss'/6 + s' \\ -1/6 & -s/6 + 1 \end{pmatrix}$$

(b) Input and output planes correspond to object and image planes when $B = 2/3\, s + 2 - ss'/6 + s' = 0$, OR $s' = \frac{4s+12}{s-6}$

When $B = 0$, $A = m = 2/3 - s'/6$

(c) For $s = 20\text{ cm}$, $s' = \frac{4(20)+12}{20-6} = 6\tfrac{4}{7}\text{ cm}$

$$m = 2/3 - \frac{6\tfrac{4}{7}}{6} = -0.429$$

(d) When $A = 2/3 - s'/6 = 0$, the output plane at $s' = 4\text{ cm}$ corresponds to the second focal plane.
when $D = -s/6 + 1 = 0$, the input plane at $s = 6\text{ cm}$ corresponds to the first focal plane.

4-16. Advisable to use a 2x2 matrix multiplication calculator or computer program. The sequence of matrices is

$$M = \begin{pmatrix} 1 & 0 \\ \frac{n_3-1}{6} & n_3 \end{pmatrix}\begin{pmatrix} 1 & t_3 \\ 0 & 1 \end{pmatrix}\begin{pmatrix} 1 & 0 \\ \frac{1-n_3}{n_3 r_5} & \frac{1}{n_3} \end{pmatrix}\begin{pmatrix} 1 & d_2 \\ 0 & 1 \end{pmatrix}\begin{pmatrix} 1 & 0 \\ \frac{n_2-1}{r_4} & n_2 \end{pmatrix}\begin{pmatrix} 1 & t_2 \\ 0 & 1 \end{pmatrix}\begin{pmatrix} 1 & 0 \\ \frac{1-n_2}{n_2 r_3} & \frac{1}{n_2} \end{pmatrix}$$

$$\begin{pmatrix} 1 & d_1 \\ 0 & 1 \end{pmatrix}\begin{pmatrix} 1 & 0 \\ \frac{n_1-1}{r_2} & n_1 \end{pmatrix}\begin{pmatrix} 1 & t_1 \\ 0 & 1 \end{pmatrix}\begin{pmatrix} 1 & 0 \\ \frac{1-n_1}{n_1 r_1} & \frac{1}{n_1} \end{pmatrix} = \begin{pmatrix} A & B \\ C & D \end{pmatrix}$$

$A = 0.93935$ $C = -0.009284$

$B = 22.2212$ $D = 0.8448$

4-16. (cont'd.) $p = D/C = -90.99$ mm $\qquad r = V = \frac{D-1}{C} = 16.72$ mm

$q = -A/C = 101.18$ mm $\qquad s = W = \frac{1-A}{C} = -6.53$ mm

$f_1 = \frac{1}{C} = -107.71$ mm $\qquad f_2 = -\frac{1}{C} = +107.71$ mm

Since $q$ is the distance of the focal point from the output plane, it is also the distance from the last surface to the film plane.

4-17. $$\mathcal{M} = \begin{pmatrix} 1 & 0 \\ \frac{n_L - n'}{n' R_2} & \frac{n_L}{n'} \end{pmatrix} \begin{pmatrix} 1 & t \\ 0 & 1 \end{pmatrix} \begin{pmatrix} 1 & 0 \\ \frac{n - n_L}{n_L R_1} & \frac{n}{n_L} \end{pmatrix} = \begin{pmatrix} A & B \\ C & D \end{pmatrix}$$

$$A = \frac{n - n_L}{n_L R_1} t + 1 \qquad B = \frac{n t}{n_L} \qquad D = \frac{n}{n'} + \left(\frac{n_L - n'}{n' R_2}\right)\frac{n t}{n_L}$$

$$C = \frac{n_L - n'}{n' R_2} - \frac{n_L - n}{n' R_1} - \frac{(n_L - n)(n_L - n')}{n' n_L} \frac{t}{R_1 R_2}$$

4-18. From Table 4-2, $f_1 = \frac{n}{n'}\left(\frac{1}{C}\right)$ or $\frac{1}{f_1} = \frac{n'}{n} C$. Substituting C from Problem 4-17,

$$\frac{1}{f_1} = \frac{n'}{n}\left[\frac{n_L - n'}{n' R_2} - \frac{n_L - n}{n' R_1} - \frac{(n_L - n)(n_L - n')}{n' n_L} \frac{t}{R_1 R_2}\right]$$

$$\frac{1}{f_1} = \frac{n_L - n'}{n R_2} - \frac{n_L - n}{n R_1} - \frac{(n_L - n)(n_L - n')}{n n_L} \frac{t}{R_1 R_2} \qquad \text{Q.E.D.}$$

Also, $f_2 = -\frac{1}{C}$, or $f_2 = -\frac{n'}{n} f_1$ Q.E.D.

4-19. From Table 4-2, and using results from Problem 4-17,

$$r = \frac{D - n/n'}{C} = \frac{\left[\frac{n}{n'} + \left(\frac{n_L - n'}{n' R_2}\right)\frac{n t}{n_L}\right] - \frac{n}{n'}}{C}. \text{ But } f_1 = \frac{n}{n'}\frac{1}{C}$$

$$r = \left(\frac{n_L - n'}{n' R_2}\right)\left(\frac{n t}{n_L}\right)\left(\frac{n'}{n} f_1\right) = \frac{n_L - n'}{n_L R_2} f_1 t \qquad \text{Q.E.D.}$$

$$s = \frac{1-A}{C} = \frac{1 - \left[\frac{n - n_L}{n_L R_1} t + 1\right]}{C} = \frac{n_L - n}{n_L R_1} \frac{1}{C}. \text{ But } \frac{1}{C} = -f_2$$

$$s = -\frac{n_L - n}{n_L R_1} t f_2 \qquad \text{Q.E.D.}$$

$$V = \frac{D-1}{C} = \left[\frac{n}{n'} + \left(\frac{n_L - n'}{n' R_2}\right)\frac{n t}{n_L} - 1\right]\left(\frac{n'}{n} f_1\right)$$

$$V = \left[1 - \frac{n'}{n} + \frac{n_L - n'}{n_L R_2} t\right] f_1 \qquad \text{Q.E.D.}$$

4-19. (cont'd.)

$$W = \frac{\frac{n}{n'} - A}{C} = \left[\frac{n}{n'} - \left(\frac{n - n_L}{n_L R_1} t + 1\right)\right](-f_2)$$

$$W = \left[1 - \frac{n}{n'} - \frac{n_L - n}{n_L R_1} t\right] f_2 \qquad \text{Q.E.D.}$$

4-20. A typical program in "Basic":

```
10 REM: MERIDIONAL RAY-TRACING. AFTER THE LAST SURFACE IS CALCULATED,
20 REM: ENTER ANY NEGATIVE NO. AS DISTANCE TO NEXT SURFACE TO TERMINATE.
30 INPUT "LEFT & RIGHT REF. INDICES: ",N1,N2
40 INPUT "RAY ANGLE (DEG) AND HEIGHT:", A,H
50 INPUT "DISTANCE FROM OBJ.PT. (IF INFINITY, ENTER ANYTHING):",D
60 REM: FOR RAY ENTERING PARALLEL TO AXIS, D IS NOT USED IN CALC.
70 P=3.1415926#: A=P*(A/180): REM ANGLE IS NOW IN RADIANS
80 IF A=0 THEN GOTO 110
90 S=D-H/TAN(A): Q=-S*SIN(A)
100 GOTO 140
110 Q=H
120 REM: FOR PLANE SURFACE, ENTER R>99990. THE ACTUAL VALUE IS NOT
130 REM: IMPORTANT, SINCE IT IS NOT USED IN THE CALCULATION.
140 INPUT "INPUT RAD OF CURV (99999 IF PLANE):",R
150 IF R>99990! THEN GOTO 210
160 B=Q/R+SIN(A): T=ATN(B/SQR(1-B*B)): REM  TAKING ARCSIN (B)
170 C=N1*SIN(T)/N2: T1=ATN(C/SQR(1-C*C)): REM TAKING ARCSIN (C)
180 A1=T1-T+A: A2=(A1/P)*180: REM  A2 CONVERTS A1 TO DEGREES AGAIN
190 Q1=(SIN(T1)-SIN(A1))*R: S1=-Q1/SIN(A1)
200 GOTO 240
210 X=N1*SIN(A)/N2: A1=ATN(X/SQR(1-X*X)): REM  TAKING ARCSIN (X)
220 Q1=Q*COS(A1)/COS(A)
230 S1=-Q1/SIN(A1): A2=(A1/P)*180: REM A2 IS A1 IN DEGREES
240 PRINT "RAY INTERSECTS AXIS AT ";S1;"FROM SURFACE."
250 PRINT "RAY ANGLE IN RADIANS IS ";A1
260 PRINT "RAY ANGLE IN DEGREES IS ";A2
270 PRINT "THE Q PARAMETER IS ";Q1
280 A=A1:N1=N2
290 INPUT "DISTANCE TO NEXT SURFACE: ",D1
300 IF D1<0 THEN 360
310 Q=Q1+D1*SIN(A1)
320 INPUT "NEW REFRACTIVE INDEX:",N2
330 INPUT "NEW RADIUS OF CURV (99999 IF PLANE):",R
340 IF R>99990! THEN GOTO 210
350 GOTO 160
360 END
```

4-21. Use the computer program (Problem 4-20) or Table 4-3 in a two-step process for each ray, yielding

$\alpha = 0°$ : $s' = 3.180$ cm and $\alpha' = -23.51°$

$\alpha = -20°$ ; $s' = 16.104$ cm and $\alpha' = 6.081°$

4-22. Use the computer program (Prob. 4-20), or Table 4-3, in a 3-step process, giving

$$s' = -49.525 \text{ cm} \quad \text{and} \quad \alpha' = 3.371°$$

4-23. Use the computer program (Prob. 4-20), or Table 4-3, in a 6-step process, to get

$$h = 1 : \quad s' = 98.20 \text{ mm}, \quad \alpha' = -0.567°$$

$$h = 5 ; \quad s' = 102.45 \text{ mm}, \quad \alpha' = -2.723°$$

# Chapter 5 Aberration Theory

5-1. $a(Q) = (n_1 l + n_2 l') - (n_1 s + n_2 s')$ Eq. 5-6

where $l = s\left\{1 + \frac{h^2(R+s)}{2Rs^2} - \frac{h^4(R+s)}{24R^3s^2} - \frac{h^4(R+s)^2}{8R^2s^4}\right\}$ Eq. 5-16

and $l'$ = ditto, with s replaced by $-s'$ inside brackets

When $l$ and $l'$ are substituted in Eq 5-6, the terms $n_1 s$ and $n_2 s'$ subtract out, leaving

$$a(Q) = \left\{\frac{n_1 h^2(R+s)}{2Rs} - \frac{n_1 h^4(R+s)}{24R^3 s} - \frac{n_1 h^4(R+s)^2}{8R^2s^3} + \frac{n_2 h^2(R-s')}{2Rs'} - \frac{n_2 h^4(R-s')}{24R^3s'} - \frac{n_2 h^4(R-s')^2}{8R^2s'^3}\right\}$$

Handling the $h^2$ terms first,

$$\frac{h^2}{2}\left\{\frac{n_1(R+s)}{Rs} + \frac{n_2(R-s')}{Rs'}\right\} = \frac{h^2}{2}\left\{\frac{n_1}{s} + \frac{n_1}{R} + \frac{n_2}{s'} - \frac{n_2}{R}\right\}$$

$$= \frac{h^2}{2}\left\{\frac{n_1}{s} + \frac{n_2}{s'} - \frac{(n_2-n_1)}{R}\right\}$$

This gives the first part of Eq. (5-18).

Next, the $h^4$ terms:

$$-\frac{h^4}{8}\left[\frac{n_1(R+s)}{3R^3s} + \frac{n_2(R-s')}{3R^3s'} + \frac{n_1(R+s)^2}{R^2s^3} + \frac{n_2(R-s')^2}{R^2s'^3}\right] =$$

$$-\frac{h^4}{8}\left[\frac{n_1}{s}\left(\frac{R+s}{3R^3} + \frac{(R+s)^2}{R^2s^2}\right) + \frac{n_2}{s'}\left(\frac{R-s'}{3R^3} + \frac{(R-s')^2}{R^2s'^2}\right)\right] =$$

$$-\frac{h^4}{8}\left\{\frac{n_1}{s}\left[\frac{R+s}{Rs}\left(\frac{s}{3R^2} + \frac{R+s}{Rs}\right)\right] + \frac{n_2}{s'}\left[\frac{R-s'}{Rs'}\left(\frac{s'}{3R^2} + \frac{R-s'}{Rs'}\right)\right]\right\} =$$

$$-\frac{h^4}{8}\left\{\frac{n_1}{s}\left(\frac{R+s}{Rs}\right)^2 + \frac{n_2}{s'}\left(\frac{R-s'}{Rs'}\right)^2 + \frac{n_1}{\cancel{s}}\frac{R+s}{Rs}\frac{\cancel{s}}{3R^2} + \frac{n_2}{\cancel{s'}}\frac{R-s'}{Rs'}\frac{\cancel{s'}}{3R^2}\right\} =$$

$$-\frac{h^4}{8}\left\{\frac{n_1}{s}\left(\frac{1}{s}+\frac{1}{R}\right)^2 + \frac{n_2}{s'}\left(\frac{1}{s'}-\frac{1}{R}\right)^2 + \frac{1}{3R^2}\underbrace{\left[\frac{n_1}{s} + \frac{n_2}{s'} - \frac{(n_2-n_1)}{R}\right]}_{0}\right\} =$$

$$-\frac{h^4}{8}\left[\frac{n_1}{s}\left(\frac{1}{s}+\frac{1}{R}\right)^2 + \frac{n_2}{s'}\left(\frac{1}{s}-\frac{1}{R}\right)^2\right]$$

This finishes Eq. (5-18).

5-2. (a) $\frac{n_1}{s} + \frac{n_2}{s'} = \frac{n_2 - n_1}{R}$ and $\frac{1}{s'} = \frac{1}{s} + \frac{1}{R}$

Substituting, $\frac{n_1}{s} + \frac{n_2}{s'} = n_2 - n_1 \left(\frac{1}{s'} - \frac{1}{s}\right) = \frac{n_2}{s'} - \frac{n_2}{s} - \frac{n_1}{s'} + \frac{n_1}{s}$

$n_2 s' = -n_1 s$ OR $s' = -(n_1/n_2)s$ Q.E.D.

(b) In $a(Q)$, the $h^2$ term is zero due to Gaussian imaging. For the remainder, we must show

$$\frac{n_1}{s}\left(\frac{1}{s} + \frac{1}{R}\right)^2 + \frac{n_2}{s'}\left(\frac{1}{s'} - \frac{1}{R}\right)^2 = 0$$

Substitute from $1/s' = 1/s + 1/R$ to give

$$\frac{n_1}{s}\left(\frac{1}{s'} - \frac{1}{R} + \frac{1}{R}\right)^2 + \frac{n_2}{s'}\left(\frac{1}{s} + \frac{1}{R} - \frac{1}{R}\right)^2 = \frac{n_1}{ss'^2} + \frac{n_2}{s's^2}$$

Using the result found in (a),

$$\frac{n_2^2}{n_1 s^3} - \frac{n_2^2}{n_1 s^3} = 0 \qquad \text{Q.E.D.}$$

(c) For $s' = R$, $s$ must be $-R$. These values make the parentheses $(1/s + 1/R)$ and $(1/s' - 1/R)$ vanish independently, so $a(Q) = 0$. Also, $a(Q) = 0$ when $h = 0$, for rays incident at the vertex ($s = s' = 0$).

(d) For $R = +8$ cm,

$$\frac{1}{s'} = \frac{1}{s} + \frac{1}{8} \quad \text{and} \quad s' = -\frac{1.36}{1.70}s = -0.8s$$

Solving simultaneously, $s = -18$ cm and $s' = 14.4$ cm. Thus the aplanatic images occur at $s' = 0$, $+8$ and $+14.4$ cm.

5-3. The paraxial image point is found from $\frac{n_1}{s} + \frac{n_2}{s'} = \frac{n_2 - n_1}{R}$

Since $s \to \infty$, $0 + \frac{1}{s'} = \frac{1 - 1.5}{-40} = \frac{1}{80}$ OR $s' = +80$ cm.

Then ray aberration

$$a(Q) = -\frac{h^4}{8}\left\{\frac{n_1}{s}\left(\frac{1}{s} + \frac{1}{R}\right)^2 + \frac{n_2}{s'}\left(\frac{1}{s'} - \frac{1}{R}\right)^2\right\}$$

For $s \to \infty$, $a(Q) = -\frac{h^4}{8}\frac{n_2}{s'}\left(\frac{1}{s'} - \frac{1}{R}\right)^2 = -\frac{(25)^4}{8}\frac{1}{80}\left(\frac{1}{80} - \frac{1}{40}\right)^2$

$$a(Q) = +0.954 \text{ mm}$$

$$\frac{da}{dh} = -\frac{h^3}{2}\frac{n_2}{s'}\left(\frac{1}{s'} - \frac{1}{R}\right)^2 = -\frac{25^3}{2}\frac{1}{80}\left(\frac{1}{80} - \frac{1}{40}\right)^2 = +0.01526$$

Then $b_y = \frac{s'}{n_2}\frac{da}{dh} = \frac{80}{1}(.01526) = +1.22$ mm

$$b_z = \frac{s' b_y}{y} = \frac{80}{25}(1.22) = +3.91 \text{ mm}$$

5-4.

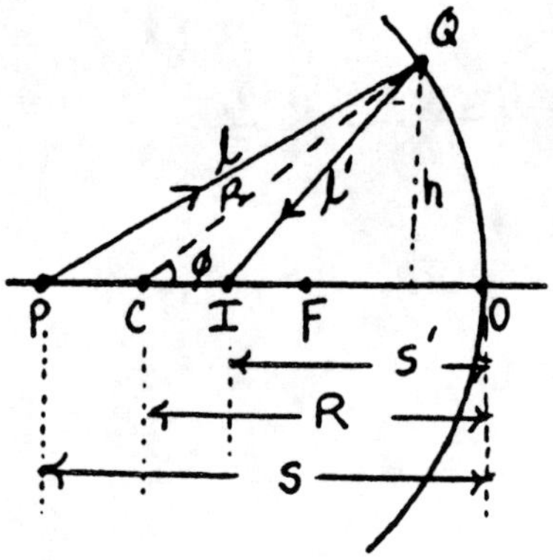


$$a(Q) = (PQI - POI)_{opd} = (\ell + \ell') - (s + s')$$

In $\Delta PQC$: $\ell^2 = R^2 + (s-R)^2 + 2R(s-R)\cos\phi$

In $\Delta CQI$: $\ell'^2 = R^2 + (R-s')^2 - 2R(R-s')\cos\phi$

$$\cos\phi \cong 1 - \frac{\phi^2}{2!} + \frac{\phi^4}{4!} \quad \text{and} \quad \phi \cong h/R$$

So $\cos\phi \cong 1 - \dfrac{h^2}{2R^2} + \dfrac{h^4}{24R^4}$

$$\ell^2 \cong R^2 + (s-R)^2 + 2R(s-R)\left(1 - \frac{h^2}{2R^2} + \frac{h^4}{24R^4}\right)$$

$$\ell'^2 \cong R^2 + (R-s')^2 - 2R(R-s')\left(1 - \frac{h^2}{2R^2} + \frac{h^4}{24R^4}\right)$$

Note that the equations are the same, except that $s \to s'$, since we can write equivalently,

$$\ell'^2 \cong R^2 + (s'-R)^2 + 2R(s'-R)\left(1 - \frac{h^2}{2R^2} + \frac{h^4}{24R^4}\right)$$

Hence we need to work only on one of them.

$$\ell^2 \cong R^2 + s^2 - 2sR + R^2 + (2Rs - 2R^2)\left(1 - \frac{h^2}{2R^2} + \frac{h^4}{24R^4}\right)$$

$$\ell^2 \cong R^2 + s^2 - 2sR + R^2 + 2Rs - 2R^2 + 2R(s-R)\left(-\frac{h^2}{2R^2} + \frac{h^4}{24R^4}\right)$$

$$\ell^2 \cong s^2 + R - s\left(\frac{h^2}{R} - \frac{h^4}{12R^3}\right) = s^2 + \frac{h^2(R-s)}{R} - \frac{h^4(R-s)}{12R^3}$$

$$\ell^2 \cong s^2\left\{1 + \frac{h^2(R-s)}{Rs^2} - \frac{h^4(R-s)}{12R^3s^2}\right\}$$

$$\ell \cong s\left\{1 + \underbrace{\frac{h^2(R-s)}{Rs^2} - \frac{h^4(R-s)}{12R^3s^2}}_{x}\right\}^{1/2}$$

$\ell \cong s(1+x)^{1/2} \cong s\left(1 + \dfrac{x}{2} - \dfrac{x^2}{8}\right)$ by the binomial expansion

$$\ell \cong s\left[1 + \frac{h^2(R-s)}{2Rs^2} - \frac{h^4(R-s)}{24R^3s^2} - \frac{h^4(R-s)^2}{8R^2s^4}\right],$$

where we have discarded terms in $h$ to powers higher than 4.

Then, similarly,

$$\ell' \cong s'\left[1 + \frac{h^2(R-s')}{2Rs'^2} - \frac{h^4(R-s')}{24R^3s'^2} - \frac{h^4(R-s')^2}{8R^2s'^4}\right]$$

5-4. (cont'd.)

Now return to $a = l + l' - s - s'$. We see that the terms s and s' cancel, and there remains

$$a(Q) = \frac{h^2(R-s)}{2Rs} - \frac{h^4(R-s)}{24R^3s} - \frac{h^4(R-s)^2}{8R^2s^3} + \frac{h^2(R-s')}{2Rs'} - \frac{h^4(R-s')}{24R^3s'} - \frac{h^4(R-s')^2}{8R^2s'^3}$$

$$a(Q) = \underbrace{\frac{h^2}{2}\left[\frac{R-s}{Rs} + \frac{R-s'}{Rs'}\right]}_{A} - \underbrace{\frac{h^4}{24R^2}\left[\frac{R-s}{Rs} + \frac{R-s'}{Rs'}\right]}_{B} - \underbrace{\frac{h^4}{8}\left[\frac{(R-s)^2}{R^2s^3} + \frac{(R-s')^2}{R^2s'^3}\right]}_{C}$$

Term A: $\frac{h^2}{2}\left[\left(\frac{1}{s} - \frac{1}{R}\right) + \left(\frac{1}{s'} - \frac{1}{R}\right)\right] = \frac{h^2}{2}\left[\frac{1}{s} + \frac{1}{s'} - \frac{2}{R}\right]$. But $\frac{1}{s} + \frac{1}{s'} = \frac{2}{R}$ to first order. This term then cancels.

Term B: $\frac{h^4}{24R^2}\left[\left(\frac{1}{s} - \frac{1}{R}\right) + \left(\frac{1}{s'} - \frac{1}{R}\right)\right] = \frac{h^4}{24R^2}\left[\frac{1}{s} + \frac{1}{s'} - \frac{2}{R}\right]$. Ditto

Term C: $\frac{h^4}{8}\left[\frac{1}{s}\left(\frac{R-s}{Rs}\right)^2 + \frac{1}{s'}\left(\frac{R-s'}{Rs'}\right)^2\right] = \frac{h^4}{8}\left[\frac{1}{s}\left(\frac{1}{s} - \frac{1}{R}\right)^2 + \frac{1}{s'}\left(\frac{1}{s'} - \frac{1}{R}\right)^2\right]$

By the Gaussian formula, $\frac{1}{s'} - \frac{1}{R} = \frac{1}{R} - \frac{1}{s}$

Thus $C = \frac{h^4}{8}\left[\frac{1}{s}\left(\frac{1}{s} - \frac{1}{R}\right)^2 + \frac{1}{s'}\left(\frac{1}{R} - \frac{1}{s}\right)^2\right]$

or $C = \frac{h^4}{8}\left[\frac{1}{s}\left(\frac{1}{s} - \frac{1}{R}\right)^2 + \frac{1}{s'}\left(\frac{1}{s} - \frac{1}{R}\right)^2\right]$

$C = \frac{h^4}{8}\left[\left(\frac{1}{s} - \frac{1}{R}\right)^2\left(\frac{1}{s} + \frac{1}{s'}\right)\right]$ But again, $\frac{1}{s} + \frac{1}{s'} = \frac{2}{R}$

$C = \frac{h^4}{8}\left[\left(\frac{1}{s} - \frac{1}{R}\right)^2 \frac{2}{R}\right] = \frac{h^4}{4R}\left(\frac{1}{s} - \frac{1}{R}\right)^2$

Thus $a(Q) \cong \frac{h^4}{4R}\left(\frac{1}{s} - \frac{1}{R}\right)^2$ Q.E.D.

5-5. $a = \frac{h^4}{4R}\left(\frac{1}{s} - \frac{1}{R}\right)^2 \xrightarrow{s\to\infty} \frac{h^4}{4R^3}$ ; $a = \frac{(25)^4}{4(400)^3} = 0.0153$ mm

$\frac{da}{dh} = \frac{h^3}{R}\left(\frac{1}{s} - \frac{1}{R}\right)^2 \xrightarrow{s\to\infty} \frac{h^3}{R^3}$ ; $\frac{da}{dh} = \frac{(25)^3}{(400)^3} = 2.441 \times 10^{-4}$

$b_y = \frac{s'}{n_2}\frac{da}{dy} = f\frac{da}{dy} = 200(2.441\times 10^{-4}) = 0.488$ mm

$b_z = \frac{s' b_y}{y} = \frac{f b_y}{h} = \frac{200(0.0488)}{25} = 3.91$ mm

5-6. As in Prob. 5-5, $\lim_{s\to\infty}(a) = \frac{h^4}{4R^3}$

(a) $a = \frac{h^4}{4R^3} = \frac{(40)^4}{4(600)^3} = 0.0296$ mm

(b) O.P.D. = 0.00296 cm = $n(\Delta t)$; $\Delta t = \frac{.00296}{1.40} = 0.021$mm

5-7. Given: $b_z = 1$ cm for a +4D, 6 cm lens ($h = 3$cm)

For $s = 50$ cm, $s' = \frac{sf}{s-f} = \frac{50(25)}{50-25} = 50$ cm

(a) $b_y = s'\frac{da}{dy} = \frac{h b_z}{s'} = \frac{(3)(1)}{50} = 0.6$ mm

(b) $d_{blur} = 2b_x = 2b_y = 2(0.6) = 1.2$mm

5-8. $\sigma = \frac{r_2 + r_1}{r_2 - r_1} = \frac{-10+10}{-10-10} = 0$ $\qquad \frac{1}{f} = (1.5-1)\left(\frac{1}{10} - \frac{1}{-10}\right)$ OR $f = 10$cm

For parallel rays, $s_p' = f = +10$cm

$p = \frac{s'-s}{s'+s} = \frac{s'/s - 1}{s'/s + 1} \to -1$ as $s \to \infty$

$\frac{1}{s_h'} - \frac{1}{10} = \frac{1}{8(10^3)}\frac{1}{(1.5)(.5)}\left[0 + 0 + \{3(1.5)+2\}\{1.5-1\}\{-1\}^2 + \frac{1.5^3}{1.5-1}\right.$ (Eq. 5-28)

$\frac{1}{s_h'} = \frac{1}{10} + 0.0015$ OR $s_h' = 9.8522$

$b_z = s_p' - s_h' = 10 - 9.8522 = 0.1478$ cm $= 1.48$ mm

$b_x = \left(\frac{h}{s'}\right)b_z = \left(\frac{1}{10}\right)(0.1478) = 0.15$mm

5-9. $\frac{1}{f} = (1.6-1)\left(\frac{1}{36} - \frac{1}{-18}\right)$ or $f = +20$cm $= s_p'$

$p = \frac{s'-s}{s'+s} = \frac{s'/s - 1}{s'/s + 1} \to -1$ as $s\to\infty$; $\sigma = \frac{-18+36}{-18-36} = -\frac{1}{3}$

$\frac{1}{s_h'} - \frac{1}{20} = \frac{h^2}{8(20)^3}\frac{1}{1.6(.6)}\left[\frac{3.6}{.6}\left(\frac{-1}{3}\right)^2 + 4(2.6)\left(\frac{-1}{3}\right)(-1) + 6.8(.6)(-1)^2 + \frac{1.6^3}{.6}\right]$

5-9. (cont'd.) $\frac{1}{s_h'} = 0.05 + 0.00024479\, h^2$

For $h=1$ : $s_h' = 19.90256$; $b_z = 20 - 19.90256 = +0.0974\ \text{cm} = 0.974\ \text{mm}$

Similarly,

$h = 2,\ b_z = 3.84\ \text{mm}$

$h = 3,\ b_z = 8.44\ \text{mm}$

$h = 4,\ b_z = 14.53\ \text{mm}$

$h = 5,\ b_z = 21.81\ \text{mm}$

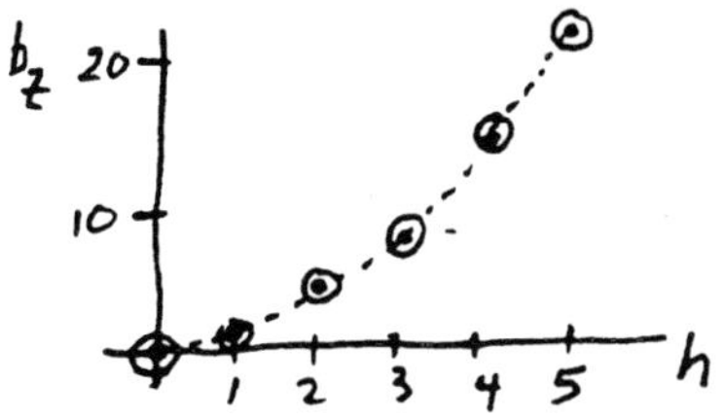


5-10. $\frac{1}{f} = (1.5-1)\left(\frac{1}{15} + \frac{1}{15}\right)$ OR $f = 15\ \text{cm}$; $\frac{1}{25} + \frac{1}{s'} = \frac{1}{15}$ OR $s_p' = 37.5\ \text{cm}$

$p = \frac{37.5 - 25}{37.5 + 25} = 0.2$ $\sigma = \frac{-15 + 15}{-15 - 15} = 0$

Eq. 5-28

$$\frac{1}{s_h'} - \frac{1}{37.5} = \frac{2^2}{8(15)^3}\,\frac{1}{1.5(0.5)}\left[0 + 0 + (6.5)(0.5)(0.2)^2 + \frac{(1.5)^3}{0.5}\right] = 0.001359$$

$s_h' = 35.6816$

$b_z = s_p' - s_h' = 37.50 - 35.68 = 1.82\ \text{cm}$

$b_y = \frac{h}{s'}\, b_z = \frac{2}{37.5}(1.82) = 0.970\ \text{mm}$

5-11. Since $L = \frac{s_p' - s_h'}{s_p' s_h'} = \frac{b_z}{s_p' s_h'}$, a minimum in $L$ gives a minimum in $b_z$. From Eq. (5-28),

$$\frac{dL}{d\sigma} = \frac{h^2}{8f^3}\,\frac{1}{n(n-1)}\left[\frac{2(n+2)}{n-1}\sigma + 4(n+1)p\right] = 0$$

$$\frac{2(n+2)\sigma}{n+1} = -4(n+1)p \quad \text{and} \quad \sigma = -\frac{2(n^2-1)}{n+2}p \qquad \text{Q.E.D.}$$

5-12. The equations

$$\sigma = \frac{r_2 + r_1}{r_2 - r_1} \quad \text{and} \quad \frac{1}{f} = (n-1)\left(\frac{1}{r_1} - \frac{1}{r_2}\right)$$

can be solved simultaneously for $r_1$ and $r_2$. The general result is

$$r_1 = \frac{2f(n-1)}{\sigma + 1} \quad \text{and} \quad r_2 = \frac{2f(n-1)}{\sigma - 1}$$

Thus, for $\sigma = 0.700$, $r_1 = \frac{2(30)(.5)}{1.7} = +17.65\ \text{cm}$

$r_2 = \frac{2(30)(.5)}{-.3} = -100\ \text{cm}$

For $\sigma = 3$, $r_1 = \frac{2(30)(.5)}{4} = 7.50\ \text{cm}$ and $r_2 = \frac{2(30)(.5)}{2} = 15.0\ \text{cm}$

5-13. $s' = \frac{sf}{s-f} = \frac{(30)(20)}{30-20} = +60 \text{ cm}$ : lens eq.

$$\sigma = -\frac{2(n^2-1)}{n+2}\,\frac{s'-s}{s'+s} = -\frac{2(1.6^2-1)}{1.6+2}\,\frac{30-60}{30+60} = 0.289$$

Then $r_1 = \frac{2f(n-1)}{\sigma+1} = \frac{2(20)(.6)}{1.289} = 18.62 \text{ cm}$

$r_2 = \frac{2f(n-1)}{\sigma-1} = \frac{2(20)(.6)}{-0.711} = -33.75 \text{ cm}$

5-14. In either case, the radius of curvature of the spherical side, found from the lensmaker's formula, is $\pm 50$ cm.

Ideal $\sigma = \frac{-2(n^2-1)}{n+2}\,\frac{s'-s}{s'+s} = -\frac{2(n^2-1)}{n+2}\,\frac{s'/s-1}{s'/s+1} = -\frac{2(1.6^2-1)}{1.6+2}\,\frac{0-1}{0+1} = +0.714$

$\sigma = \frac{r_2+r_1}{r_2-r_1} = \frac{r_2/r_1+1}{r_2/r_1-1} = -1$ as $r_1 \to \infty$

$\sigma = \frac{r_2+r_1}{r_2-r_1} = \frac{1+r_1/r_2}{1-r_1/r_2} = +1$ as $r_2 \to \infty$

Since $\sigma = +1$ is closer to $\sigma = +0.714$, the second orientation is better.

5-15. $\sigma = -\frac{2(n^2-1)}{n+2}\,\frac{s'-s}{s'+s}$

(a) $\lim_{s\to\infty} \sigma = \lim_{s\to\infty} -\frac{2(n^2-1)}{n+2}\,\frac{s'/s-1}{s'/s+1} = -\frac{2(1.5^2-1)}{1.5+2}(-1) = +0.714$

(b) To find $r_1, r_2$: solve two equations simultaneously:

$\frac{1}{f} = (n-1)\left(\frac{1}{r_1}-\frac{1}{r_2}\right)$ $\qquad \sigma = \frac{r_1+r_2}{r_2-r_1}$

$\frac{1}{30} = (1.5-1)\left(\frac{1}{r_1}-\frac{1}{r_2}\right)$ $\qquad 0.714 = \frac{r_1+r_2}{r_2-r_1}$

$\frac{1}{r_1}-\frac{1}{r_2} = \frac{1}{15}$ $\qquad \frac{r_2}{r_1} = -6$

These yield $r_1 = 17.5$ cm, $r_2 = -105$ cm

(c) $\lim_{s'\to\infty} \sigma = \lim_{s'\to\infty} -\frac{2(n^2-1)}{n+2}\left(\frac{1-s/s'}{1+s/s'}\right) = -\frac{2(1.5^2-1)}{1.5+2}(+1) = -0.714$

5-16.
(a) $\sigma = \left(\frac{2n^2-n-1}{n+1}\right)\underbrace{\left(\frac{s-s'}{s+s'}\right)}_{\lim_{s\to\infty} = +1} = \frac{2(1.5)^2-1.5-1}{1.5+1} = 0.8$

As in Prob. 5-15, simultaneous solution of

$\frac{r_2}{r_1} = \frac{\sigma+1}{\sigma-1} = \frac{1.8}{-.2} = -9$ and $\frac{1}{15} = \frac{1}{r_1} - \frac{1}{r_2}$

give $r_1 = +16.67$ cm and $r_2 = -150$ cm

5-16. (cont'd.)

$$\sigma = \left(\frac{2n^2-n-1}{n+1}\right)\underbrace{\left(\frac{s-s'}{s+s'}\right)}_{\lim_{s'\to\infty} = -1} = \frac{2(1.5)^2-1.5-1}{1.5+1}(-1) = -0.8$$

5-17. With $s = s'$, $\sigma = \frac{2(n^2-1)}{n+2}\left(\frac{s'-s}{s'+s}\right) = 0$

For $\sigma = \frac{r_2+r_1}{r_2-r_1} = 0$, $r_1 = -r_2$

Then $\frac{1}{f} = (n-1)\left(\frac{1}{r_1} - \frac{1}{r_2}\right) = (1.5-1)\left(\frac{2}{r_1}\right) = \frac{1}{r_1}$

So $r_1 = f = 20\text{ cm}$ and $r_2 = -r_1 = -20\text{ cm}$.

5-18. $\sigma = \left(\frac{2n^2-n-1}{n+1}\right)\left(\frac{s-s'}{s+s'}\right) = 0$, as in Prob. 5-17. Thus answers are the same as in Prob. 5-17.

5-19. $\sum_i \frac{1}{n_i f_i} = \frac{1}{R_p}$ For a flat Petzval surface, $R_p \to \infty$

Then $n_1 f_1 + n_2 f_2 = 0$

$(1.523)(20) + (1.72) f_2 = 0$ OR $f_2 = -17.71\text{ cm}$.

5-20. (a) $\frac{1}{R} = \sum \frac{1}{n_i f_i} = \frac{1}{(1.5736)(3.543)} + \frac{1}{(1.6039)(-5.391)}$

$R = 15.7\text{ cm}$

(b) $\frac{1}{R} = 0 = \frac{1}{(1.5736)(3.543)} + \frac{1}{(1.6039) f_2}$

$f_2 = -3.476\text{ cm}$.

5-21. The calculations proceed stepwise, as follows, given the values of refractive index from Table 5-1, and the desired over-all focal length $f_D$ of the doublet.

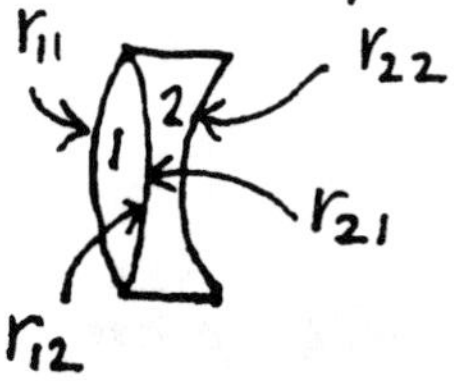


$P_D = \frac{1}{f_D}$ $V_1 = \frac{n_{1D}-1}{n_{1F}-n_{1C}}$ ; $V_2 = \frac{n_{2D}-1}{n_{2F}-n_{2C}}$

$P_{1D} = P_D\left(\frac{-V_1}{V_2-V_1}\right)$ $P_{2D} = P_D\left(\frac{V_2}{V_2-V_1}\right)$

$K_1 = \frac{P_{1D}}{n_{1D}-1}$ $K_2 = \frac{P_{2D}}{n_{2D}-1}$

$r_{11} = \frac{2}{K_1}$ ; $r_{12} = -r_{11}$ ; $r_{21} = r_{12}$ ; $r_{22} = \frac{r_{12}}{1-K_2 r_{12}}$

$f_{1D} = \frac{1}{K_1(n_{1D}-1)}$ ; $f_{2D} = \frac{1}{K_2(n_{2D}-1)}$ ; $f_D = \frac{f_{1D} f_{2D}}{f_{1D}+f_{2D}}$

5-21. (cont'd.)

The last line is repeated for fc and fD. A calculator or computer may be conveniently programmed with this scheme, as follows:

```
INPUT "N1C,N1D,N1F = ?" ; MC,MD,MF
INPUT "N2C,N2D,N2F = ?" ; NC,ND,NF
INPUT "DESIRED F = ?"; FD
P=1/FD
V1=(MD-1)/(MF-MC) : V2=(ND-1)/(NF-NC)
P1=P*-V1/(V2-V1) : P2=P*V2/(V2-V1)
K1=P1/(MD-1) : K2=P2/(ND-1)
R1=2/K1 : R2=-R1 : S1=R2 : S2=R2/(1-K2*R2)
D1=1/(K1*(MD-1)) : D2=1/(K2*(ND-1)) : D=D1*D2/(D1+D2)
C1=1/(K1*(MC-1)) : C2=1/(K2*(NC-1)) : C=C1*C2/(C1+C2)
F1=1/(K1*(MF-1)) : F2=1/(K2*(NF-1)) : F=F1*F2/(F1+F2)
PRINT R1;R2
PRINT S1;S2
PRINT D1;D2
PRINT D
PRINT C1;C2
PRINT C
PRINT F1;F2
PRINT F
END
```

For this case, the step-by-step calculations are as follows:

| | | $n_C$ | $n_D$ | $n_F$ |
|---|---|---|---|---|
| (1) | # 517/645 | 1.51461 | 1.51707 | 1.52262 |
| (2) | # 620/380 | 1.61564 | 1.62045 | 1.63198 |

$f_{eq} = 20\,cm$ $\qquad V_1 = \dfrac{n_{1D}-1}{n_{1F}-n_{1C}} = 64.5531$

$P_D = \frac{1}{.2} = +5D$

or $P_D = 0.05\,cm^{-1}$ $\qquad V_2 = \dfrac{n_{2D}-1}{n_{2F}-n_{2C}} = 37.9712$

$$P_{1D} = P_D \frac{-V_1}{V_2-V_1} = 0.121423\,cm^{-1} \qquad P_{2D} = P_D \frac{V_2}{V_2-V_1} = -0.071423\,cm^{-1}$$

$$K_1 = \frac{P_{1D}}{n_{1D}-1} = 0.234830\,cm^{-1} \qquad K_2 = \frac{P_{2D}}{n_{2D}-1} = -0.115115\,cm^{-1}$$

$$r_{11} = \frac{2}{K_1} = 8.5168\,cm \qquad r_{12} = -r_{11} = -8.5168\,cm = r_{21}$$

$$r_{22} = \frac{r_{12}}{(1-K_2 r_{12})} = -434.89\,cm$$

$$\lambda_D:\quad f_{1D} = \frac{1}{(n_{1D}-1)K_1} = 8.23565\,cm \qquad f_{2D} = \frac{1}{(n_{2D}-1)K_2} = -14.0010\,cm$$

$$f_D = \frac{f_{1D}\,f_{2D}}{f_{1D}+f_{2D}} = 20.0000\,cm$$

$$\lambda_C:\quad f_{1C} = \frac{1}{(n_{1C}-1)K_1} = 8.2750\,cm \qquad f_{2C} = \frac{1}{(n_{2C}-1)K_2} = -14.1104\,cm$$

5-21. (cont'd.)

$$f_C = \frac{f_{1C} f_{2C}}{f_{1C} + f_{2C}} = 20.0096 \text{ cm}$$

$\lambda_F$: $f_{1F} = \dfrac{1}{(n_{1F}-1)K_1} = 8.1482 \text{ cm}$ $\quad f_{2F} = \dfrac{1}{(n_{2F}-1)K_2} = -13.7456 \text{ cm}$

$$f_F = \frac{f_{1F} f_{2F}}{f_{1F} + f_{2F}} = 20.0096 \text{ cm}$$

Note: Even though results are given here rounded off at each step, calculations are carried out with the more exact, stored values by calculator or computer.

5-22. Calculations proceed as outlined in detail in Prob. 5-21. Data and results are listed:

| | | $n_C$ | $n_D$ | $n_F$ |
|---|---|---|---|---|
| $f_{eq} = 5$ cm | (1) #638/555 | 1.63461 | 1.63810 | 1.64611 |
| $P_D = 0.2$ cm$^{-1}$ | (2) #805/255 | 1.79608 | 1.80518 | 1.82771 |

(a) $r_{11} = 3.4535$ cm $\quad r_{12} = -r_{11} = -3.4535 \text{ cm} = r_{21}$

$r_{22} = -12.6576$ cm

(b)

| | $f_1$ | $f_2$ | $f_3$ |
|---|---|---|---|
| $\lambda_D$ | 2.7061 | -5.8985 | 5.0000 |
| $\lambda_C$ | 2.7210 | -5.9659 | 5.0026 |
| $\lambda_F$ | 2.6726 | -5.7380 | 5.0026 |

(c) $P_{1D} = 0.369534 = \dfrac{1}{f_{1D}}$ $\quad P_{2D} = -0.169534 = \dfrac{1}{f_{2D}}$

Dispersive Powers: $\Delta_1 = \dfrac{1}{V_1} = 0.018022$, $\Delta_2 = \dfrac{1}{V_2} = 0.039283$

(d) Check: $V_2 P_{1D} + V_1 P_{2D} = (25.4562)(.369534) + (55.48696)(-.169534)$
$= 0$

5-23. Calculations proceed as outlined in detail in Prob. 5-21. Data and results are listed:

| | | $n_C$ | $n_D$ | $n_F$ |
|---|---|---|---|---|
| $f_{eq} = -10$ cm | (1) #573/574 | 1.56956 | 1.57259 | 1.57953 |
| $P_D = -0.1$ cm$^{-1}$ | (2) #689/312 | 1.68250 | 1.68893 | 1.70462 |

(a) $r_{11} = -5.2415$ cm ; $r_{12} = -r_{11} = r_{21} = 5.2415$ cm ; $r_{22} = 53.1840$ cm

(b) and (c):

| | $f_1$ | $f_2$ | $f_3$ |
|---|---|---|---|
| $\lambda_D$ | -4.5770 | 8.4399 | -10.0000 |
| $\lambda_C$ | -4.6013 | 8.5194 | -10.0050 |
| $\lambda_F$ | -4.5222 | 8.2520 | -10.0050 |

# Chapter 6 - Optical Instrumentation

6-1.

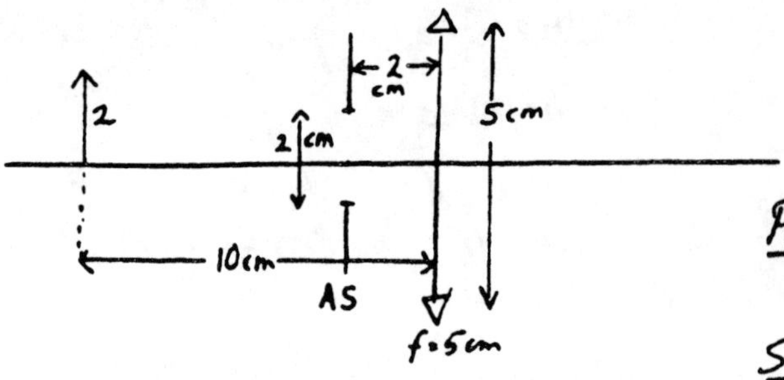


Entrance Pupil = Aperture Stop (no elements preceding)

Exit Pupil: Image of AS formed by lens

Position of $E_xP$: $\frac{1}{2} + \frac{1}{s'} = \frac{1}{5}$

$s' = -3.33$ cm

Size of $E_xP$: $m = -\frac{s'}{s} = -\frac{-3.33}{2} = \frac{5}{3}$

$\therefore$ Size $= \frac{5}{3} \times 2$cm $= 3.33$ cm

Image:

Position: $\frac{1}{10} + \frac{1}{s'} = \frac{1}{5}$ OR $s' = 10$cm

Size: $m = -s'/s = -10/10 = -1$

size $= 1 \times 2 = 2$cm, inverted.

6-2.

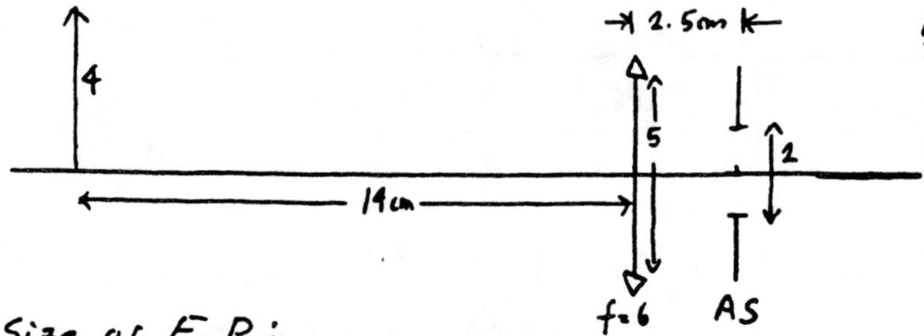


Exit Pupil = AS (no elements follow)

Entrance Pupil: Image of AS formed by lens

Position of $E_nP$

$\frac{1}{2.5} + \frac{1}{s'} = \frac{1}{6}$

or $s' = -4.29$ cm $= -30/7$ (right of lens)

Size of $E_nP$:

$m = -s'/s = -\frac{-30}{7} \cdot \frac{2}{5} = \frac{12}{7}$

Size $= \frac{12}{7} \times 2 = 3.43$cm

Image $\frac{1}{14} + \frac{1}{s'} = \frac{1}{6}$ or $s' = 10.5$ cm

$m = -s'/s = -10.5/14 = -0.75$; Size $= \frac{3}{4} \times 4 = 4$cm, inverted

6-3.

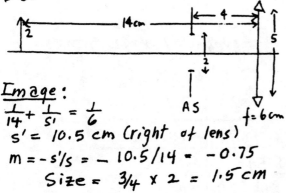

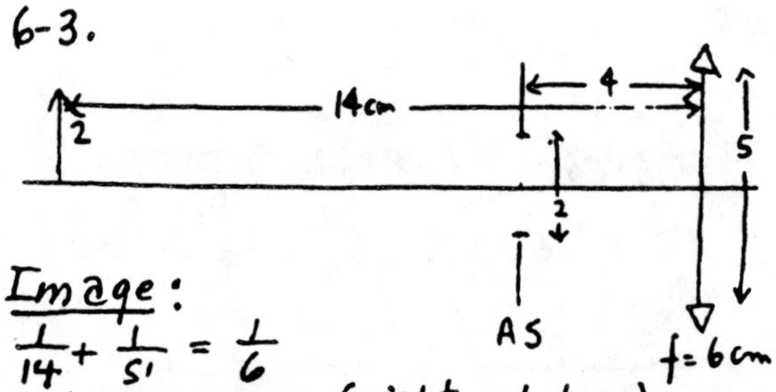


Entrance Pupil = AS (no preceding elements)

Exit Pupil: Image of AS thru lens.

$\frac{1}{4} + \frac{1}{s'} = \frac{1}{6}$ or $s' = -12$ cm

$m = -s'/s = -\frac{-12}{4} = +3$

SIZE $= 3 \times 2 = 6$ cm

Image:

$\frac{1}{14} + \frac{1}{s'} = \frac{1}{6}$

$s' = 10.5$ cm (right of lens)

$m = -s'/s = -10.5/14 = -0.75$

Size $= 3/4 \times 2 = 1.5$ cm

6-4.

(a)

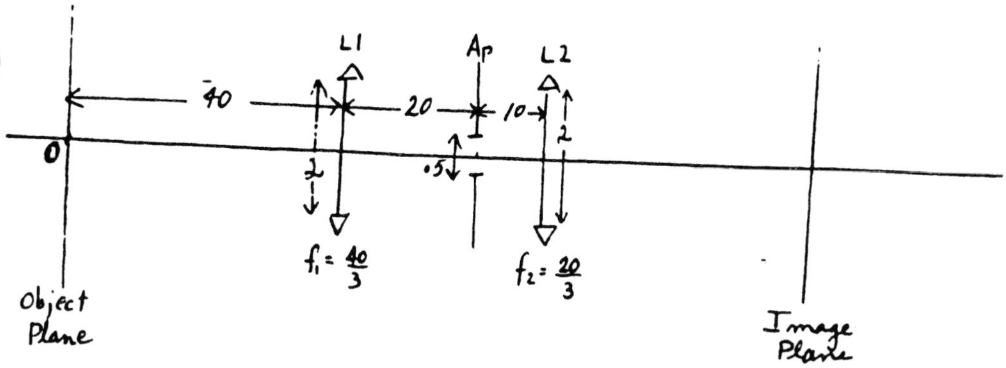


(b) Image Plane:

$$s_1' = \frac{f_1 s_1}{s_1 - f_1} = \frac{(40/3)(40)}{40 - 40/3} = 20\text{ cm (right of L1)}$$

$$s_2' = \frac{f_2 s_2}{s_2 - f_2} = \frac{(20/3)(10)}{10 - 20/3} = 20\text{ cm (right of L2)}$$

(c) Candidates as AS: Lens 1 or Ap or Lens 2

Lens subtends at an angle of $\theta_{L1} = \frac{2}{40} = 0.05$ rad

Ap image in L1: $s' = \frac{20(40/3)}{20 - 40/3} = 40$ cm, or at object plane

Then $\theta_{Ap} = 0°$

L2 image thru L1: $s' = \frac{30(40/3)}{30 - 40/3} = 24$ cm left of L1 or 16 cm right of O.

$m = -s'/s = -24/30 = -0.8$

so SIZE $= 0.8 \times 2 = 1.6$ cm

$\theta_{L2} = \frac{1.6}{16} = 0.1 > 0.05$

Thus L1 behaves as the AS. It is also the $E_nP$, being the first in line.

(d) Exit Pupil $E_xP$: Image of AS (i.e., L1) in L2

$$s' = \frac{sf_2}{s - f_2} = \frac{30(20/3)}{30 - 20/3} = 8.57\text{ cm, right of L2}$$

$$m = -\frac{s'}{s} = -\frac{8.57}{30} = 0.2857 = 2/7 \quad \text{so } D_{E_xP} = \frac{2}{7} \times 2 = \frac{4}{7}\text{ cm}$$

(e) Field Stop: Either Ap or L2, whichever subtends the smaller angle at center of $E_nP = L1$

$$\theta_{Ap} = \frac{0.5}{20} = 0.025 \; ; \; \theta_{L2} = \frac{2}{30} = 0.067$$

Thus the Aperture Stop behaves as the field stop (FS).

Entrance window: Image of FS formed by preceding elements – lens L1. As found in (c), image is in the object plane. There $m = -s'/s = -40/20 = -2$, so the diameter of the entrance window is $2 \times 0.5 = 1.0$ cm.

6-4. (cont'd.)

Exit Window : Image of FS in following elements — lens L2.

$$s' = \frac{(10)(20/3)}{10 - 20/3} = 20 \text{ cm}, \text{ right of L2 or in image plane.}$$

$$m = -s'/s = -20/10 = -2 \quad \text{so } D_{ExW} = 2 \times 0.5 = 1.0 \text{ cm}$$

(f) Angular field of view :

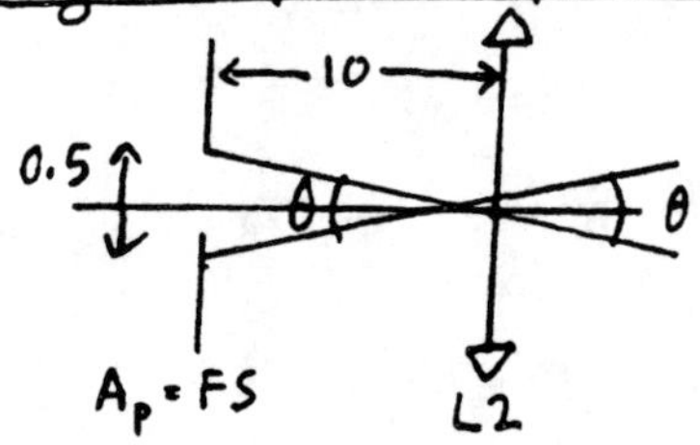


$$\theta = \frac{0.5}{10} = 0.05 \text{ rad} = 2.86°$$

6-5. Equations 6-7 to 6-11 can be programmed as in the following Basic program, where variables are, as given in Fig. 6-5: $\theta_1 \to T$ $\theta_1' \to Y$ $\theta_2 \to I$ $\theta_2' \to U$ $\delta \to D$

```
10 N=1.52
20 A=60
30 INPUT T
40 Y=ASN((SIN T)/N)
50 U=A-Y
60 I=ASN(N*SIN U)
70 D=T+I-Y-U
80 PRINT D
90 GOTO 30
```

One finds:

| $\theta_1$ | $\delta$ (deg) |
|---|---|
| 30 | 53.27 |
| 40 | 40.63 |
| 45 | 39.26 |
| 50 | 38.933 |
| 55 | 39.37 |
| 60 | 40.45 |
| 70 | 44.39 |
| 80 | 50.68 |
| 90 | 59.43 |

reveals a minimum around 50°

Closer inspection around $\theta_1 = 50°$ results in a minimum at $\theta_1 = 49.46°$

6-6.
$$n = \frac{\sin\left(\frac{A+\delta_m}{2}\right)}{\sin(A/2)} = \frac{\sin(30+\delta/2)}{1/2} \qquad n_R = 1.525 \quad n_B = 1.535$$

red: $\sin(30+\delta/2) = \frac{1}{2}(1.525)$ or $\delta_m = 39.37018°$

blue: $\sin(30+\delta/2) = \frac{1}{2}(1.535)$ or $\delta_m = 40.2598°$

$$\Delta\delta = 0.88966° = 53'$$

6-7. Data:

| | n (crown) | n (flint) |
|---|---|---|
| (1) F (486.1 nm) | 1.5286 | 1.7328 |
| (2) C (656.3 nm) | 1.5205 | 1.7076 |

(a) Cauchy relation for $\lambda_F$ and $\lambda_C$: $n_F = A + B/\lambda_F^2$

Solved simultaneously, $n_C = A + B/\lambda_C^2$

$$A = n_F - \frac{B}{\lambda_F^2} \quad \text{and} \quad B = \frac{n_F - n_C}{(1/\lambda_F^2 - 1/\lambda_C^2)}$$

For crown glass:

$$A = 1.5286 - \frac{4240}{466.1^2} = 1.511 \qquad B = \frac{1.5286 - 1.5205}{\frac{1}{(486.1)^2} - \frac{1}{(656.3)^2}} = 4240\ \text{nm}^2$$

For flint glass:

$$A = 1.7328 - \frac{1.319\times10^4}{486.1^2} = 1.677\ ; \quad B = \frac{1.7328 - 1.7076}{\frac{1}{(486.1)^2} - \frac{1}{(656.3)^2}} = 1.319\times10^4\ \text{nm}^2$$

Then for a third wavelength $\lambda_D = 589.2$ nm,

Crown: $n_D = A + \frac{B}{\lambda_D^2} = 1.511 + \frac{4240}{(589.2)^2} = 1.523$ (table: 1.5230).

Flint: $n_D = 1.677 + \frac{1.319\times10^4}{(589.2)^2} = 1.715$ (table: 1.7205)

(b) $\mathcal{D} = \frac{dn}{d\lambda} = -\frac{2B}{\lambda^3}$ $\qquad \mathcal{D}_{crown} = \frac{-2(4240\ \text{nm}^2)}{(589.2\ \text{nm})^3} = -4.146\times10^{-5}\ \text{nm}^{-1}$

$$\mathcal{D}_{Flint} = \frac{-2(13190\ \text{nm}^2)}{(589.2\ \text{nm})^3} = -1.290\times10^{-4}\ \text{nm}^{-1}$$

(c) $\mathcal{R}_C = b\,\mathcal{D}_C = (7.5\times10^7\ \text{nm})(4.146\times10^{-5}\ \text{nm}^{-1}) = 3110$

$\mathcal{R}_F = b\,\mathcal{D}_F = (7.5\times10^7\ \text{nm})(1.290\times10^{-4}\ \text{nm}^{-1}) = 9675$

crown: $(\Delta\lambda)_{min} = \lambda/\mathcal{R}_C = 5892\,\text{Å}/3110 = 1.9\,\text{Å}$

flint: $(\Delta\lambda)_{min} = \lambda/\mathcal{R}_F = 5892\,\text{Å}/9675 = 0.61\,\text{Å}$

6-8. (a) $1.6381 = \frac{\sin(30 + \delta/2)}{\sin 30}$ or $\delta = 50°$

(b) $\Delta = \frac{n_F - n_C}{n_D - 1} = \frac{1.63461 - 1.64611}{1.6381 - 1} = -\frac{1}{55.5}$

(c) $\mathcal{D} = -2B/\lambda^3$ where $B = \frac{n_1 - n_2}{\left(\frac{1}{\lambda_1^2} - \frac{1}{\lambda_2^2}\right)}$, as in Prob. 6-7a

For the long wavelength region, take $\lambda_1 = 587.6$ nm and $\lambda_2 = 656.3$ nm.

Then $B = \frac{1.63810 - 1.63461}{1/587.6^2 - 1/656.3^2} = 6073.7\ \text{nm}^2$

6-8. (cont'd.)

and $A = n_1 - \frac{B}{\lambda_1^2} = 1.63810 - \frac{6073.7}{587.6^2} = 1.6205$

Then $\mathcal{D}(\text{at } \lambda = 656.3\,\text{nm}) = \frac{-2\,(6073.7)}{656.3^3} = 4.297 \times 10^{-5}\ \text{nm}^{-1}$

(d) $\mathcal{R} = \frac{\lambda_{AV}}{\Delta\lambda} = b\,\mathcal{D}$ or $b = \frac{\lambda_{AV}}{\mathcal{D}\,\Delta\lambda} = \frac{656.28\,\text{nm}}{(4.297 \times 10^{-5}\,\text{nm}^{-1})(0.0136\,\text{nm})}$

$\Delta\lambda = 656.2852 - 656.2716$

$\Delta\lambda = 0.0136$ nm

$b = 1.12 \times 10^{9}\ \text{nm} = 1.12\ \text{m}!$

6-9. $n_C = \frac{\sin[(60 + 38°20')/2]}{\sin(60/2)} = 1.51323$

Similarly, $n_D = 1.51570$ and $n_F = 1.52308$

Then $\Delta = \frac{n_F - n_C}{n_D - 1} = 0.01909$

6-10.

Let flint prism be prism (1), crown be prism (2)

$\delta_{D1} = (1.635 - 1)(5°) = 3.175°$. This dispersion must be matched by the crown prism:

$\delta_{D2} = 3.175° = (1.53 - 1)\,A_2$, or $A_2 = 5.99°$

For the C & F rays, with this double prism,

$\delta_{F2} = (1.536 - 1)(5.99) = 3.211°$
$\delta_{F1} = (1.648 - 1)(5) = 3.240°$
} Net $\delta_{F12} = \delta_{F1} - \delta_{F2} = 0.029°$

$\delta_{C2} = (1.527 - 1)(5.99) = 3.157°$
$\delta_{C1} = (1.630 - 1)(5) = 3.150°$
} Net $\delta_{C12} = \delta_{C1} - \delta_{C2} = -0.007°$

Dispersion $= \delta_{F12} - \delta_{C12} = 0.029 - (-0.007) = 0.036° = 2.16'$

6-11. Let crown = Prism (1) and flint = Prism (2)

$\delta_{C1} = (n_{C1} - 1)\,A_1 = (1.5205 - 1)\,15 = 7.8075°$

$\delta_{F1} = (n_{F1} - 1)\,A_1 = (1.5286 - 1)\,15 = 7.929°$

Relative deviation $\delta_{F1} - \delta_{C1} = 0.1215°$. This must be reversed by the flint prism:

$\delta_{F2} - \delta_{C2} = 0.1215° = (n_{F2} - n_{C2})A_2 = (1.7328 - 1.7076)A_2$

$A_2 = 4.82°$

Deviation of D line is then

$\delta_{D1} - \delta_{D2} = (n_{D1} - 1)A_1 - (n_{D2} - 1)A_2 = (.523)(15) - (0.7205)(4.821)$

$\delta_{D1} - \delta_{D2} = 4.37°$

6-12. (a) $M_e = \frac{P}{A} = \frac{25\,W}{(0.05\,m)^2} = 1 \times 10^4\ W/m^2$

$I_e = \frac{P}{\Omega} = \frac{25\,W}{2\pi\ sr} = 3.98\ W/sr$

$L_e = \frac{P}{A\text{-}\Omega} = \frac{25\,W}{(0.05m)^2(2\pi\ sr)} = 1.59 \times 10^3\ W/m^2\text{-}sr$

(b) $\frac{f}{D} = 8 = \frac{4\ cm}{D}$ OR $D = 0.5cm$

Flux entering camera $= \Phi_F = \Phi_0 \left[\frac{\text{Area of lens}}{\text{Area of half-sphere at lens}}\right]$

$\Phi_F = \frac{\pi(0.25cm)^2}{2\pi(100\,cm)^2} \times 25W = 7.81 \times 10^{-5}\ W$

(c) $E_e = \frac{\Phi_F}{\text{Image Area}} = \frac{\Phi_F}{A'} = \frac{\Phi_F}{\ell'^2}$, where $\ell' = m\ell$

Image distance $= s' = \frac{sf}{s-f}$ and $|m| = \frac{s'}{s} = \frac{f}{s-f}$

$\ell' = \left(\frac{f}{s-f}\right)\ell = \left(\frac{4}{100-4}\right)5\,cm$ and $A' = \ell'^2 = \left(\frac{20}{96}\,cm\right)^2 = 4.34 \times 10^{-6}\ m^2$

$E_e = \frac{\Phi_F}{A'} = \frac{7.81 \times 10^{-5}\ W}{4.34 \times 10^{-6}\ m^2} = 18\ W/m^2$

6-13.

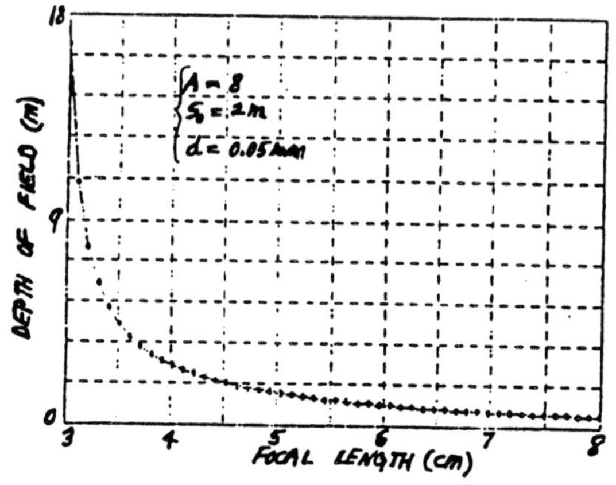


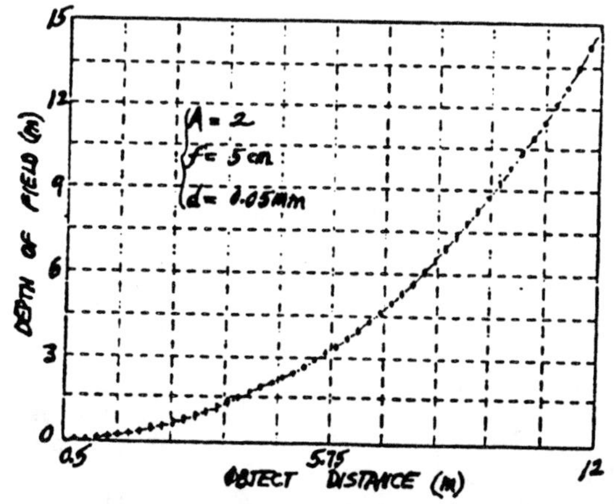


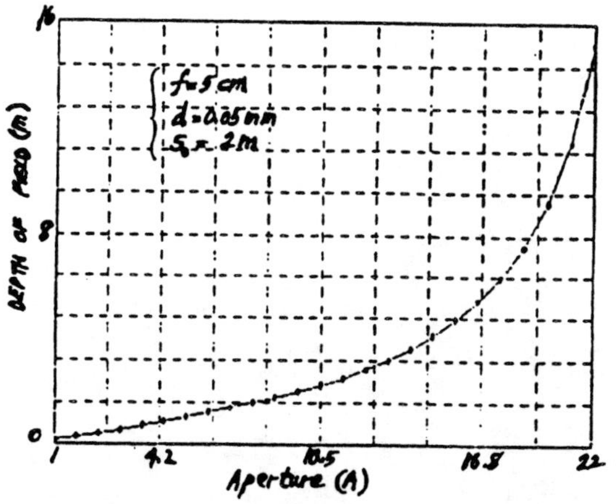

6-14. From Eqs. (6-30) and (6-31),

$$s_o - s_1 = \frac{A s_o d (s_o - f)}{f^2 + A s_o d} = \frac{(4)(6)(10^{-6})(6-0.05)}{(.05)^2 + (4)(6)(10^{-6})} = 0.057\,m = 5.7\,cm$$

$$s_2 - s_o = \frac{A s_o d (s_o - f)}{f^2 - A s_o d} \cong s_o - s_1 = 5.7\,cm$$

Thus, object points at 5.7 cm nearer or farther than the middle row create blur circles larger than the silver grain dimension. Under these demanding conditions, the picture could not be taken successfully.

6-15. (a)

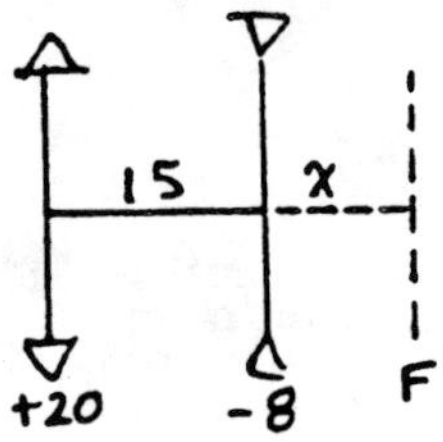


$$\frac{1}{f} = \frac{1}{f_1} + \frac{1}{f_2} - \frac{L}{f_1 f_2} = \frac{1}{20} + \frac{1}{-8} - \frac{15}{(20)(-8)}\ ; \quad f = 53.3\ cm$$

$x = s_2'$ where $s_2 = L - s_1' = 15 - 20 = -5\ cm$

$$\frac{1}{-5} + \frac{1}{s_2'} = \frac{1}{-8} \quad \text{or} \quad s_2' = 13.33\ cm = x$$

$$\tan 2^\circ = \frac{h'}{x} \quad \text{OR} \quad h' = 13.22 \tan 2^\circ = 1.86\ cm$$

(b)

$$M = \begin{pmatrix} 1 & 0 \\ 1/8 & 1 \end{pmatrix} \begin{pmatrix} 1 & 15 \\ 0 & 1 \end{pmatrix} \begin{pmatrix} 1 & 0 \\ -1/20 & 1 \end{pmatrix} = \begin{pmatrix} 1/4 & 15 \\ -3/160 & 23/8 \end{pmatrix}$$

$$f = \left|\frac{1}{C}\right| = \frac{160}{3} = 53.3\,cm$$

$$r = \frac{D-1}{C} = -\frac{160}{3}\left(\frac{23}{8} - 1\right) = -100\,cm$$

$$s = \frac{1-A}{C} = -\frac{160}{3}(1 - 1/4) = -40\,cm$$

$$x = f_2 + s = 53.33 - 40 = 13.33\,cm.$$

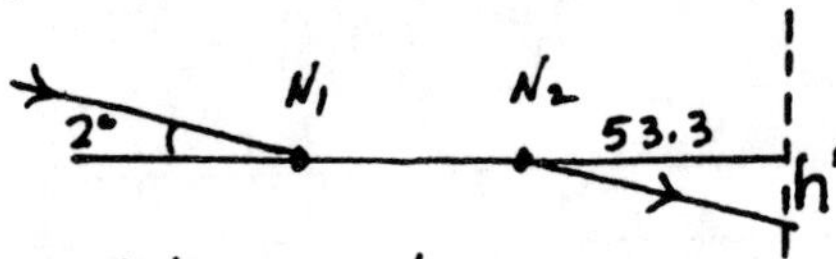


Nodal points = Principal points

$$\tan 2^\circ = \frac{h'}{53.3}$$

6-16. $f = 5\,cm = 0.1640\,ft$
$s_o = 6\,ft$
$d = 0.05\,mm = 1.640 \times 10^{-4}\,ft$
$A = f/4 = 4$

$$s_1 = \frac{s_o f (f + A d)}{f^2 + A d s_o} = 5.26\ ft$$

$$s_2 = \frac{s_o f (f - A d)}{f^2 - A d s_o} = 7.00\ ft.$$

6-17.

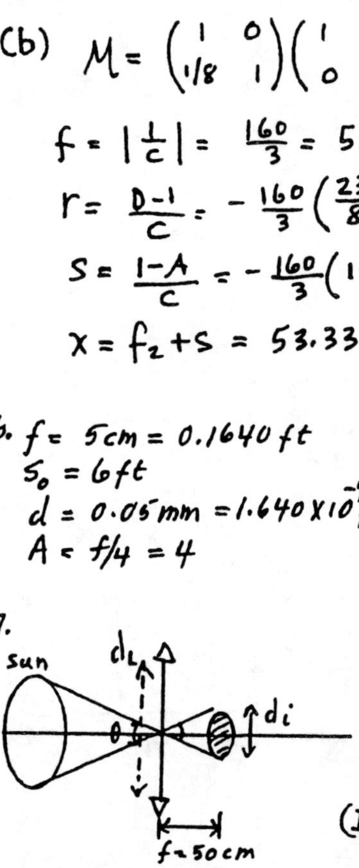


$\theta = 0.5° = 8.727 \times 10^{-3}\,rad$
$(I_v)_L = 10^5\ lx\ (lm/m^2)$
$d_L = 5\ cm$
$f_L = 50\ cm.$

Assuming no absorption, lumens on lens equals lumens on image.

$$(I_v)_L A_L = (I_v)_i A_i$$

$$(I_v)_L d_L^2 = (I_v)_i d_i^2$$

$$(I_v)_i = \left(\frac{d_L}{d_i}\right)^2 (I_v)_L = \left(\frac{d_L}{f\theta}\right)^2 (I_v)_L$$

$$(I_v)_i = \left[\frac{5}{(50)(8.727 \times 10^{-3})}\right]^2 (10^5) = 1.31 \times 10^7\ lx$$

6-18. (a) $f = 15\text{ cm}$
$s = 100\text{ ft} = 3048\text{ cm}$
$h_o = 6\text{ ft}$

$$m = -\frac{s'}{s} = -\frac{f}{s} = \frac{-15}{3048}$$

$$h_i = |m| h_o = \left(\frac{15}{3048}\right)6 = 0.0295\text{ ft}$$

$$h_i = 0.9\text{ cm}$$

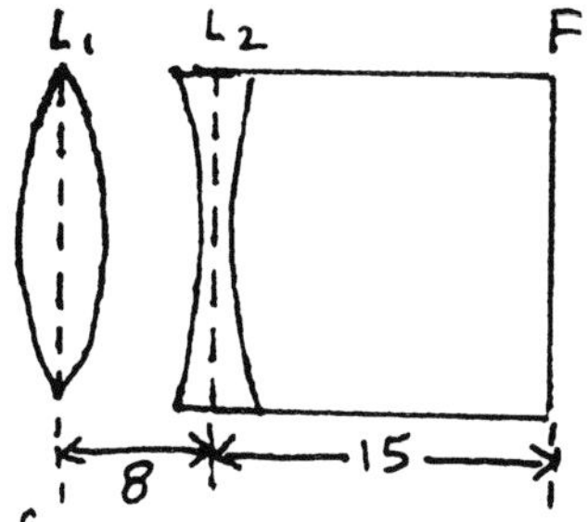

$f_1 = 12\text{cm}$

(b) Distant objects form an image by $L_1$ at $f_1 = 12$ cm. Thus, $s$ for $L2 = 8 - 12 = -4\text{cm}$. $s'$ for $L2 = 15$ cm, necessarily, and

$$f_2 = \frac{ss'}{s+s'} = \frac{(-4)(15)}{-4+15} = -5.45\text{ cm}$$

For the person at 100 ft,

$$m = m_1 m_2 = \left(-\frac{s_1'}{s_1}\right)\left(-\frac{s_2'}{s_2}\right) = \left(\frac{-12}{3048}\right)\left(\frac{-15}{-4}\right) = -0.0148$$

Ratio of magnifications: $\dfrac{|m|}{|m(\text{telephoto})|} = \dfrac{15/3048}{180/4(3048)} = \dfrac{1}{3}$

6-19. (a) $D = \dfrac{f}{1.8} = \dfrac{50\text{mm}}{1.8} = 27.8\text{ mm}$

(b) Factor of $\sqrt{3}$ : $f/1.8 \to f/3.1 \to f/5.4 \to f/9.4$

(c) $D = 50/3.1 = 16.0\text{mm}$ ; $D = 50/5.4 = 9.26\text{mm}$ ; $D = 50/9.4 = 5.35\text{mm}$

(d) $f/1.8$ at $\frac{1}{100}$ s is equivalent in exposure to $f/3.1$ at $3/100$ s , $f/5.4$ at $9/100$ s , $f/9.4$ at $27/100$ s

6-20. $M = \dfrac{25}{f_{eq}}$ where $\dfrac{1}{f_{eq}} = \dfrac{1}{f_1} + \dfrac{1}{f_2} - \dfrac{L}{f_1 f_2}$

and L is determined by the condition for elimination of chromatic aberration : $L = \frac{1}{2}(f_1 + f_2)$

Then $\dfrac{1}{f_{eq}} = \dfrac{1}{f_1} + \dfrac{1}{f_2} - \dfrac{f_1+f_2}{2f_1f_2} = \dfrac{1}{2}\left(\dfrac{1}{f_1} + \dfrac{1}{f_2}\right)$

and $M = \dfrac{25}{f_{eq}} = 12.5\left(\dfrac{1}{f_1} + \dfrac{1}{f_2}\right)$ Q.E.D.

6-21. $f_1 = f_2 = 3\text{ cm}$
$L = 2.8\text{ cm}$

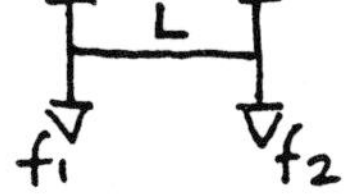


(a) $\dfrac{1}{f_{eq}} = \dfrac{1}{f_1} + \dfrac{1}{f_2} - \dfrac{L}{f_1 f_2} = \dfrac{1}{3} + \dfrac{1}{3} - \dfrac{2.8}{9}$

$f_{eq} = 2.8125\text{ cm}$

(b) $M = \dfrac{25}{f_{eq}} + 1 = \dfrac{25}{2.8125} + 1 = 9.9 \cong 10X$

6-22.

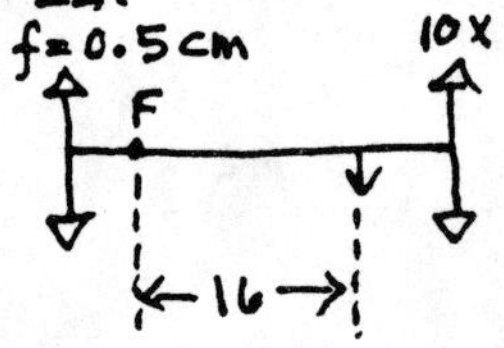


(a) $M = m_{obj} \times M_{oc} = \frac{s'}{s} \times 10$

where $s' = f + 16 = 16.5\,cm$

$$s = \frac{s'f}{s'-f} = \frac{(16.5)(0.5)}{16.5-0.5} = \frac{8.25}{16}$$

$$\text{IML} \; \frac{s'}{s} = \frac{(16.5)(16)}{8.25} = 32$$

$$M = (32)(10) = 320x$$

(b) $s = \frac{8.25}{16}$

$s = 0.516\,cm$

6-23. (a) $M = m_{obj} \times M_{oc} = \frac{s'_{obj}}{s_{obj}}\left(\frac{25}{f_{oc}} + 1\right)$

$$s'_{obj} = \frac{s_o f_{obj}}{s_o - f_{obj}} = \frac{(1.20)(1)}{1.20-1} = 6\,cm.$$

$$M = \left(\frac{6}{1.20}\right)\left(\frac{25}{3}+1\right) = 46.7X$$

(b) $L = s'_{obj} + s_{oc} = 6 + 2.68 = 8.68\,cm.$

where $s_{oc} = \frac{s'_{oc} f_{oc}}{s'_{oc} - f_{oc}} = \frac{(-25)(3)}{-25-3} = 2.68\,cm.$

6-24. $M = -\left(\frac{25}{f_e}\right)\left(\frac{L}{f_o}\right)$ and $L = d - f_o - f_e$

$$-20 = -\left(\frac{25}{4}\right)\left(\frac{25-4-f_o}{f_o}\right) \quad \text{OR} \quad f_o = 5\,cm.$$

6-25. $\frac{1}{30} + \frac{1}{s'} = \frac{1}{0.2}$ OR $s' = 0.2013\,m.$

$$m = \frac{s'}{s} = \frac{0.2013}{30} = 0.006711$$

$$h' = mh \quad \text{OR} \quad h = \frac{h'}{m} = \frac{0.001}{0.006711} = 0.149\,m = 14.9\,cm$$

6-26.

"7x35"

$M = 7x$

$D_{obj} = 35\,mm$

$f_{obj} = 14\,cm$; $D_f = 1.8\,cm.$

(a) $M = 7X$ (b) $M = \frac{f_{obj}}{f_{oc}}$ OR $f_{oc} = \frac{14}{7} = 2\,cm$

(c) $M = \frac{D_{obj}}{D_{ex}}$ OR $D_{ex} = \frac{35}{7} = 5\,mm$

(d) Eye relief: Exit pupil position is image of L1 in L2, or

$$s' = \frac{sf}{s-f} = \frac{L f_{oc}}{L - f_{oc}} = \frac{(14+2)(2)}{(14+2)-2} = \frac{16}{7} = 2.3\,cm$$

(e) Field of view

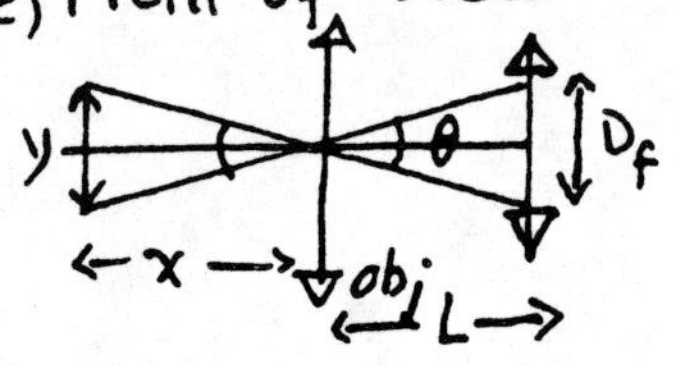


$$\theta = \frac{D_f}{L} = \frac{1.8}{14+2} = 0.1125\,rad.$$

$$\theta = \frac{y}{x} \quad \text{or} \quad y = x\theta = (3000\,ft)(0.1125)$$

$y = 337$ ft. at 1000 yd.

6-27.

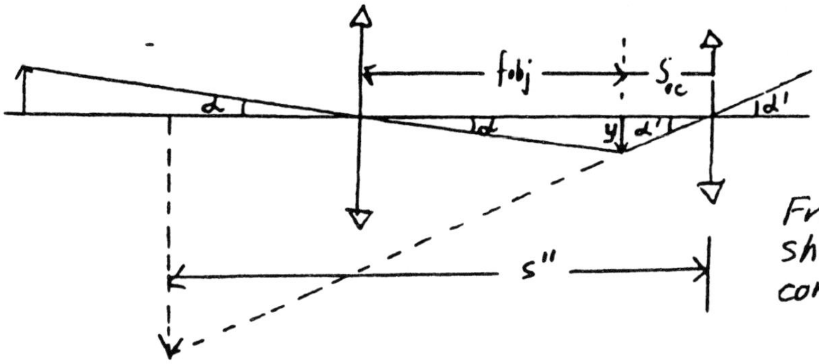


Compare with Fig. 6-27 for image at infinity.

From the right triangles sharing image $y$ as a common side,

$$M \equiv \frac{\alpha'}{\alpha} \cong \frac{\tan\alpha'}{\tan\alpha} = \frac{y/s_{oc}}{y/f_{obj}} = \frac{f_{obj}}{s_{oc}} .$$ But $m_{oc} = -\,s''/s_{oc}$

$$\therefore\ M = -\frac{f_{obj}\, m_{oc}}{s''}$$ Q.E.D.

(b) $f_{obj} = 30\text{ cm}$, $f_{oc} = 4\text{ cm}$

Viewed at infinity, $M = \frac{f_o}{f_e} = \frac{30}{4} = 7.5\text{X}$

Viewed at 25 cm, $s'' = -25\text{ cm}$ and

$$m_{oc} = -\frac{s''}{s_{oc}} = -\frac{s''}{(s''f_{oc}/(s''-f_{oc})} = -\frac{s''-f_{oc}}{f_{oc}}$$

$$m_{oc} = -\frac{(-25)-4}{4} = \frac{29}{4} = 7.25\text{X}$$

So that, by the formula in (a), $M = -\frac{(30)(7.25)}{(-25)} = 8.70\text{X}$

6-28.

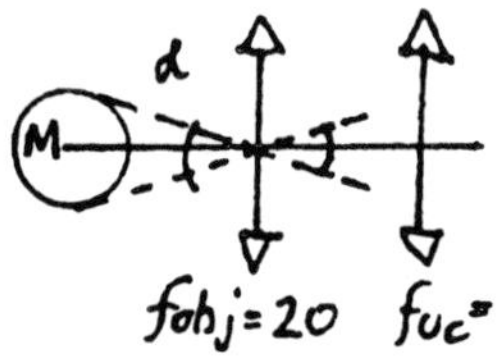


$\alpha = 0.5^\circ = \frac{\pi}{360}$ rad.

The image size of the moon is determined by $\alpha'$, where $M = \alpha'/\alpha$. $D_{MOON} = 25\alpha'$ (see Fig. in Prob 6-27a)

To find $\alpha'$, use $M = \frac{f_{obj}}{s_{oc}}$ (shown above, Prob. 6-27a)

Here, $s_{oc} = \frac{s''f_{oc}}{s''-f_{oc}} = \frac{(-25)(5)}{-25-5} = \frac{25}{6}$ so that $M = \frac{20}{25/6} = \frac{24}{5}\text{X}$

Then $\alpha' = M\alpha = \left(\frac{24}{5}\right)\left(\frac{\pi}{360}\right) = \frac{\pi}{75}$ and $D_{MOON} = s''\alpha' = (25)\left(\frac{\pi}{75}\right) = \frac{\pi}{3} = 1.05\text{ cm}$

6-29. (a) $L = f_{obj} + f_{oc} = 12 - 4 = 8\text{ cm}$ ; $M = \frac{f_{obj}}{f_{oc}} = \frac{12}{4} = 3\text{X}$

(b) Image at $s'' = 30\text{ cm}$: $s_{oc} = \frac{s''f_{oc}}{s''-f_{oc}} = \frac{(-30)(-4)}{-30+4} = -\frac{60}{13}\text{ cm}$

$$M = \frac{f_{obj}}{s_{oc}} = \frac{12}{60/13} = \frac{13}{5} = 2.6\text{X}$$

$$L = f_{obj} + s_{oc} = 12 - \frac{60}{13} = 7.38\text{ cm}$$

6-30.

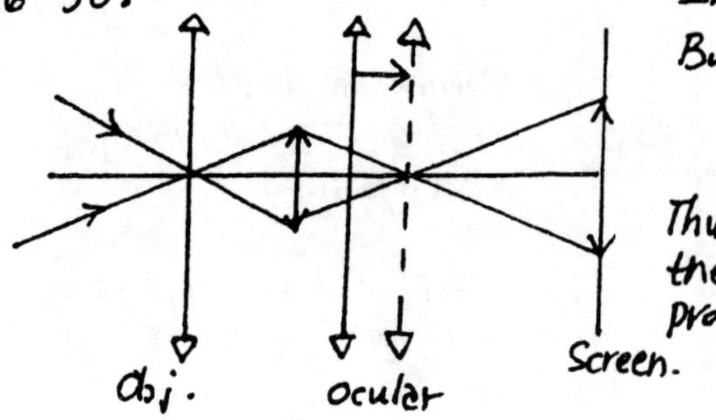


In normal position, $s_{oc} = f_{oc} = 5cm$
But when $s'' = +25$ cm,

$$s_{oc} = \frac{s'' f_{oc}}{s'' - f_{oc}} = \frac{25(5)}{25-5} = 6.25cm$$

Thus ocular must be moved farther from the objective by $6.25 - 5 = 1.25$ cm. to produce a real image on the screen 25cm away.

6-31. $f_1 = f_2 = 2cm$ ; $L = 2$ cm ; $\frac{1}{f_{eq}} = \frac{1}{f_1} + \frac{1}{f_2} - \frac{L}{f_1 f_2} = \frac{1}{2} + \frac{1}{2} - \frac{2}{4}$
or $f_{eq} = 2cm$

(a) $M_\infty = \frac{25}{f_{eq}} = \frac{25}{2} = 12.5X$ (b) $f_{obj} = 30cm$ $D_{obj} = 4.50cm$ $M_{tel} = \frac{f_{obj}}{f_{oc}} = \frac{30}{2} = 15X$

(c) Exit Pupil = Image of AS or objective lens, formed by ocular. Since ocular consists of 2 lenses, argue as follows: To produce parallel rays leaving ocular (image at ∞), the field lens must be at $F_{obj}$, 30 cm from objective, so that the image there is 2cm from eye lens $[\frac{1}{2} + \frac{1}{s'} = \frac{1}{2}$ and $s' \to \infty]$.

Given this separation, the image of the objective in the field lens is $s_1' = \frac{(30)(2)}{30-2} = \frac{15}{7}$ cm or $\frac{1}{7}$ cm beyond eye lens. The image formed by the eye lens is then at

$$s_2' = \frac{(-1/7)(2)}{-1/7 - 2} = 0.133 \text{ cm}.$$

Thus the exit pupil falls at 0.133cm from the eye lens. From $M = D_{obj} / D_{EP}$, we also have $D_{EP} = \frac{4.50}{15} = 3mm$.

(d) $\theta = \frac{D_{FL}}{L} = \frac{2}{30} = \frac{1}{15}$ rad or 3.8°

6-32.

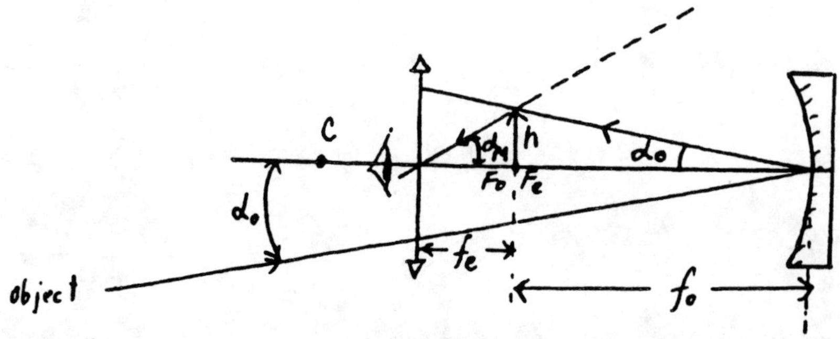


"Unfolding" the right angle in the optical axis of Fig. 6-30a, the equivalent optics is seen. From the diagram,

$$M \equiv \frac{\alpha_M}{\alpha_o} = \frac{h/f_e}{h/f_o} = \frac{f_o}{f_e} \qquad \text{Q.E.D.}$$

6-33.

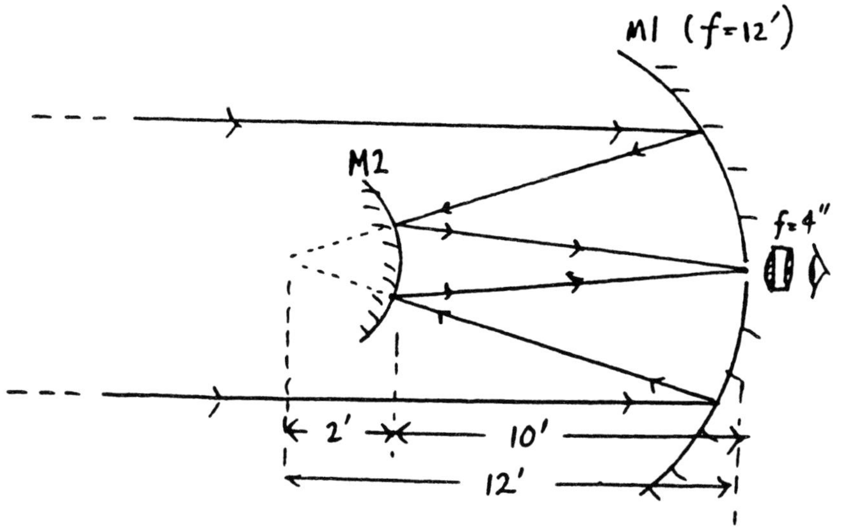


f for M2: $\frac{1}{s} + \frac{1}{s'} = \frac{1}{f}$ $\qquad f = \frac{ss'}{s+s'} = \frac{(-2)(10)}{-2+10} = -2.5\text{ ft.}$

Without the intermediate convex mirror, the optical system is the same as a Newtonian telescope, whose magnification is given (see Problem 6-32) by

$$M = -\frac{f_{obj}}{f_{oc}} = -\frac{12}{4/12} = -36\text{ X}$$

The magnification is increased by the convex mirror by a factor

$$m = -\frac{s'}{s} = -\frac{(10)}{(-2)} = +5$$

The overall magnification is then

$$m\,M = (+5)(-36) = -180\text{ X}$$

# Chapter 7 – Optics of the Eye

7-1. Power for a refracting surface is defined as $\frac{n_2 - n_1}{R}$

$\therefore P = \frac{n_{A.H} - 1}{R} = \frac{1.333 - 1}{8 \times 10^{-3}\,m} = 41.6\ m$, in agreement with Table 7-1.

7-2. (a) $n_{lens} = 1.45$ ; $R_1 = +10\,mm$ ; $R_2 = -6\,mm$

$$\frac{1}{f} = \frac{n_{lens} - 1}{1}\left(\frac{1}{R_1} - \frac{1}{R_2}\right) = \frac{1.45 - 1}{1}\left(\frac{1}{10} - \frac{1}{-6}\right) \quad \text{OR} \quad f = 8.33\,mm$$

$$P = \frac{1}{8.33 \times 10^{-3}\,m} = 120\ D$$

(b) $$\frac{1}{f} = \frac{n_{lens} - n_{AH}}{n_{AH}}\left(\frac{1}{R_1} - \frac{1}{R_2}\right) = \frac{1.45 - 1.33}{1.33}\left(\frac{1}{10} - \frac{1}{-6}\right) \quad \text{OR} \quad f = 41.7\,mm$$

$$P = \frac{1}{41.7 \times 10^{-3}} = 24.0\ D$$

(c) Thick lens : 2 successive refractions

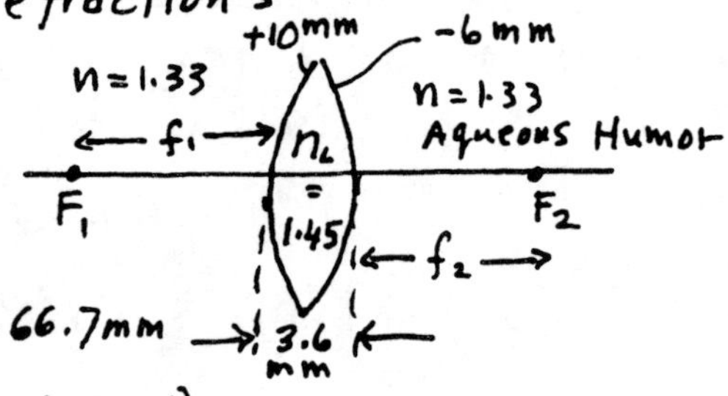


For $f_1$: $s_2' = \infty$, $s_1 = f_1$ (measured from first surface)

$$\frac{n_{lens}}{s_2} + \frac{n_{AH}}{\infty} = \frac{n_{AH} - n_{lens}}{R_2}$$

$$\frac{1}{s_2} = \frac{1.33 - 1.45}{(1.33(-6))} = 0.0150 \quad \text{OR} \quad s_2 = 66.7\,mm$$

$s_1' = -(66.7 - 3.6) = -63.1\,mm$ (virtual)

$$\frac{n_{AH}}{s_1 = f_1} + \frac{n_{lens}}{-63.1} = \frac{1.45 - 1.33}{+10} \quad \text{OR} \quad s_1 = f_1 = 38\,mm$$

For $f_2$: $s_1 = \infty$, $s_2' = f_2$ (measured from 2nd surface)

$$\frac{n_{AH}}{\infty} + \frac{n_{lens}}{s_1'} = \frac{1.45 - 1.33}{+10} \quad \text{OR} \quad s_1' = 120.8\,mm.$$

$s_2 = -(120.8 - 3.6) = -117.2\,mm$ (virtual)

$$\frac{n_{lens}}{-117.2} + \frac{n_{AH}}{s_2 = f_2} = \frac{1.33 - 1.45}{-6} \quad \text{OR} \quad s_2 = f_2 = 41.1\,mm$$

MATRIX METHOD:

$$\mathcal{M} = \underbrace{\begin{pmatrix} 1 & 0 \\ \frac{1.45 - 1.33}{1.33(-6)} & \frac{1.45}{1.33} \end{pmatrix}}_{\text{Surface } R_2} \underbrace{\begin{pmatrix} 1 & 3.6 \\ 0 & 1 \end{pmatrix}}_{\text{Trans.}} \underbrace{\begin{pmatrix} 1 & 0 \\ \frac{1.33 - 1.45}{1.45(10)} & \frac{1.33}{1.45} \end{pmatrix}}_{\text{Surface } R_1}$$

$$\mathcal{M} = \begin{pmatrix} A = 0.9702 & B = 3.3021 \\ C = -0.02361 & D = 0.9503 \end{pmatrix}$$

7.2 (cont'd.) $r = \frac{D-1}{C} = 2.105\,mm$ $\quad s = \frac{1-A}{C} = -1.262\,mm$

$p = D/C = -40.25\ mm \quad q = -\frac{A}{C} = 41.09\ mm$

$f_1 = \frac{1}{C} = -42.355\ mm \quad f_2 = -\frac{1}{C} = +42.355\ mm$

$$P = \frac{1}{f} = 23.6\,D$$

*Focal lengths here are measured relative to principal planes!*

7-3.

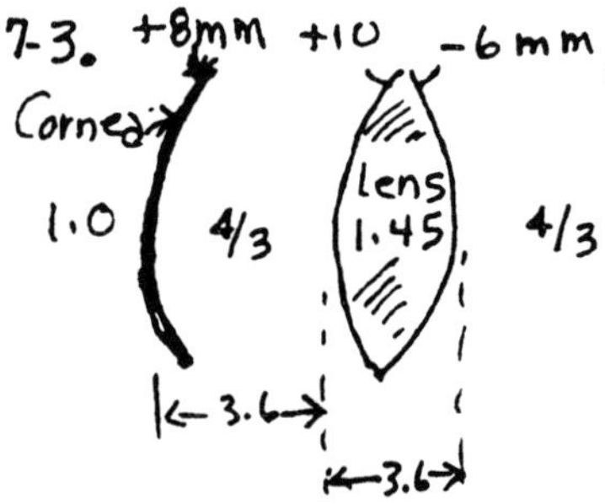


(Use 4/3 = 1.333)

(a) Object at ∞; unaccommodated eye

At cornea: $\frac{n_1}{s} + \frac{n_2}{s'} = \frac{n_2 - n_1}{R}$

$s \to \infty, \quad s' = \frac{n_2 R}{n_2 - n_1} = \frac{4/3\,(8)}{4/3 - 1} = 32\ mm$, right of cornea.

At front surface of lens: $s = 3.6 - 32$
$s = -28.4\ mm$

$$\frac{1.333}{-28.4} + \frac{1.45}{s'} = \frac{1.45 - 1.333}{+10}$$

$s' = 24.73\ mm$ (right of 1st lens surface)

At rear surface of lens:

$s = 3.6 - 24.73 = -21.13\ cm$

$\frac{1.45}{-21.13} + \frac{1.333}{s'} = \frac{1.333 - 1.45}{-6}$ OR $s' = 15.13\ mm$ (right of rear lens surface)

Object at infinity therefore focuses at $15.13 + 7.2 = 22.33\ mm$ from cornea — the back focal plane of the eye. Compare with Table 7-1.

(b) Object at 25 cm; accommodated eye

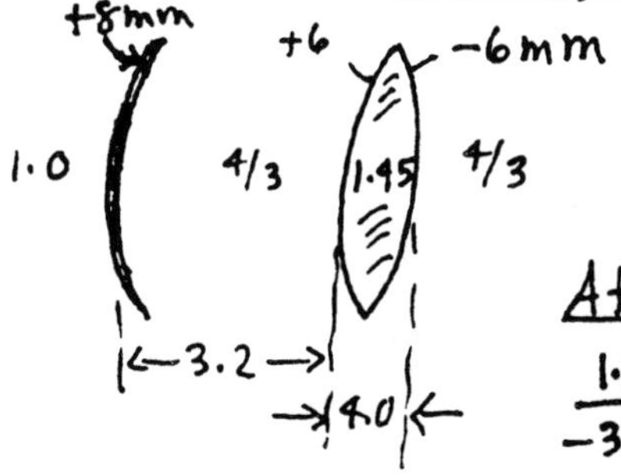


At cornea: $\frac{1.0}{250} + \frac{1.333}{s'} = \frac{1.333 - 1}{8}$

OR $s' = 35.43\,mm$ (right of cornea)

At front surface: $s = 3.2 - 35.43 = -32.23\,mm$

$$\frac{1.333}{-32.23} + \frac{1.45}{s'} = \frac{1.45 - 1.333}{6}$$

OR $s' = 23.83\ mm$ (right of front lens surface)

At rear lens surface: $s = 4 - 23.83 = -19.83$ (virtual object)

$\frac{1.45}{-19.83} + \frac{1.333}{s'} = \frac{1.333 - 1.45}{-6}$ OR $s' = 14.39\ mm$ (right of surface)

For an accommodated eye at the normal near point, the image is formed at $14.39 + 7.2\ mm = 21.59\ mm$ from cornea.

7.4

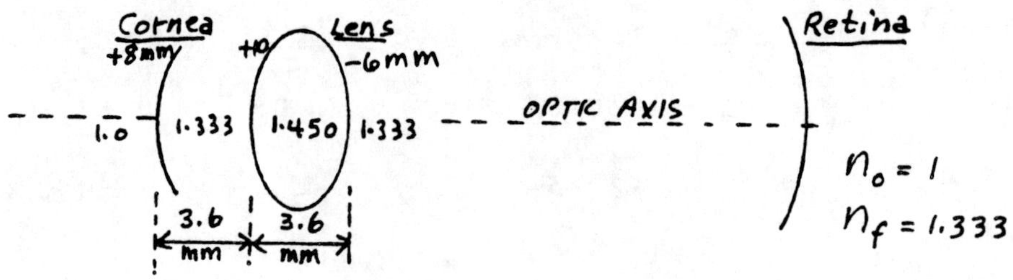


(a) Cornea to rear lens surface:

$$\mathcal{M} = \underbrace{\begin{pmatrix} 1 & 0 \\ \frac{1.45-1.333}{1.333(-6)} & \frac{1.45}{1.333} \end{pmatrix}}_{\text{Rear Lens Surface}} \underbrace{\begin{pmatrix} 1 & 3.6 \\ 0 & 1 \end{pmatrix}}_{Tr} \underbrace{\begin{pmatrix} 1 & 0 \\ \frac{1.333-1.45}{1.45(10)} & \frac{1.333}{1.45} \end{pmatrix}}_{\text{Front Lens Surface}} \underbrace{\begin{pmatrix} 1 & 3.6 \\ 0 & 1 \end{pmatrix}}_{Tr} \underbrace{\begin{pmatrix} 1 & 0 \\ \frac{1-1.333}{1.333(8)} & \frac{1}{1.333} \end{pmatrix}}_{\text{Cornea Refraction}}$$

Define elements as follows:

$$\mathcal{M} = \begin{pmatrix} 1 & 0 \\ T & V \end{pmatrix}\begin{pmatrix} 1 & 3.6 \\ 0 & 1 \end{pmatrix}\begin{pmatrix} 1 & 0 \\ U & J \end{pmatrix}\begin{pmatrix} 1 & 3.6 \\ 0 & 1 \end{pmatrix}\begin{pmatrix} 1 & 0 \\ I & G \end{pmatrix}$$

$T = -0.01463$
$V = +1.08777$
$U = -0.00807$
$J = +0.91931$
$I = -0.03123$
$G = +0.75019$

$$\mathcal{M} = \begin{pmatrix} 1 & 3.6 \\ T & 3.6T+V \end{pmatrix}\begin{pmatrix} 1 & 0 \\ U & J \end{pmatrix}\begin{pmatrix} 1+3.6I & 3.6G \\ I & G \end{pmatrix}$$

$$\mathcal{M} = \begin{pmatrix} 1+3.6U & 3.6J \\ T+U(3.6T+V) & J(3.6T+V) \end{pmatrix}\begin{pmatrix} 1+3.6I & 3.6G \\ I & G \end{pmatrix}$$

$$\mathcal{M} = \begin{pmatrix} A = 0.75846 & B = 5.1050 \\ C = -0.05012 & D = 0.65180 \end{pmatrix}$$

$r = \dfrac{D - n_0/n_f}{C} = -1.963$ mm

$s = \dfrac{1-A}{C} = -4.820$ mm

$p = \dfrac{D}{C} = -13.005$ mm

$q = -\dfrac{A}{C} = +15.133$ mm

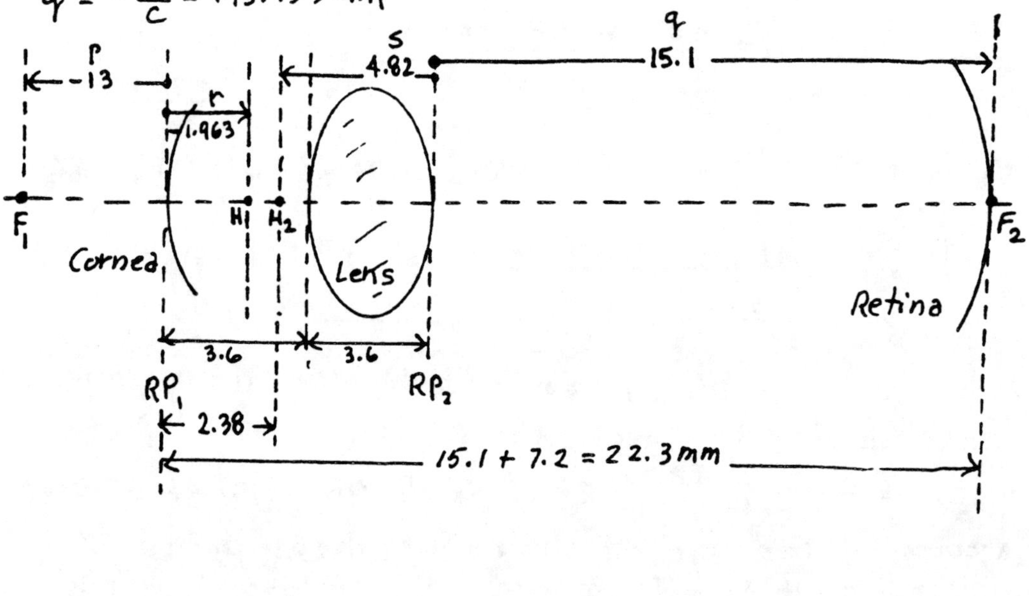

7-5.

$y \cong 5\theta$, where $\theta = 5'$ of arc for block letters
$\theta = 1'$ of arc for letter detail

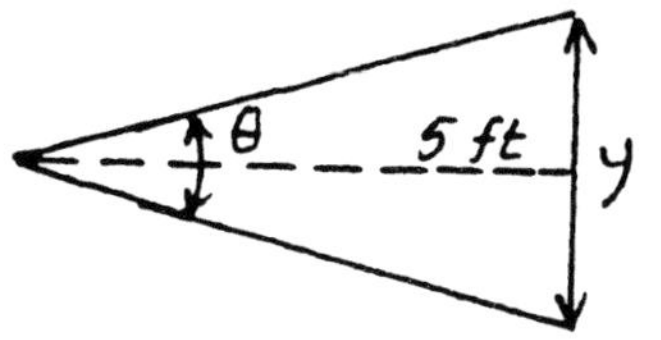


$5'$ of arc $= \frac{5}{60} = 0.08333° = 0.001454$ rad.

$1'$ of arc $= \frac{1}{60} = 0.01667 = 0.0002909$ rad.

20/20 line: $y = 5\theta_{5'} = 5(.001454)\text{ft} = 0.0872\text{ in.}$

$y_{detail} = \frac{0.0872}{5} = 0.0174\text{ in.}$

20/15 line: $y_{letter} = \frac{15}{20}\overbrace{(.0872)}^{y_{20/20}} = 0.00654\text{ in.}$

$y_{detail} = \frac{0.00654}{5} = 0.00131\text{ in.}$

20/300 line: $y_{letter} = \frac{300}{20} \times (.0872) = 1.308\text{ in.}$

$y_{detail} = \frac{1}{5} y_{letter} = 0.262\text{ in.}$

20/100 line: $y_{letter} = \frac{100}{20} \times (.0872) = 0.436\text{ in.}$

$y_{detail} = \frac{1}{5} y_{letter} = 0.0872\text{ in.}$

20/60 line: $y_{letter} = \frac{60}{20}(.0872) = 0.262\text{ in.}$

$y_{detail} = \frac{1}{5} y_{letter} = 0.0523\text{in.}$

7-6. (a) $\frac{1}{25} + \frac{1}{-125} = \frac{1}{f}$ OR $f = 31.25$ cm and $P = \frac{1}{f} = 3.2\text{ D}$

(b) Objects further from the eye than 25 cm will be incident on the cornea with smaller divergence angles. Hence the eye can accommodate and focus all such rays on the retina. The answer is YES.

7-7. (a) When $s' = 50$ cm, $s = \infty$ $\quad \frac{1}{\infty} + \frac{1}{-50} = \frac{1}{f}$ OR $f = -0.5$ m and $P = 1/f = -2.0\text{ D}$

(b) What is $s$ for $s' = -15$ cm?
$\frac{1}{s} + \frac{1}{-15} = \frac{1}{-50}$ OR $s = 21.4$ cm
The new near point is a little closer to the eye than the normal near point.

7-8. (a) either Argon ion or frequency-doubled Nd:YAG
(b) $CO_2$ (c) Nd:YAG

7-9. (a) −1.50 D to correct for myopia; −1.50 D to correct for astigmatism, cylinder axis horizontal.
(b) −2.00 D to correct for simple myopia
(c) +2.00 D " " " hyperopia
(d) +2.00 D for hyperopia; −1.50 D for astigmatism, axis horiz.

7-10. (a) $CO_2$ laser emits ir light at 10.6 μm. Such ir light is almost totally absorbed by glass, passed by germanium.

(b) $\theta_{out} = \frac{1}{5}\theta_{in} = \frac{2.2 \text{ mrad}}{5} = 0.44 \text{ mrad}.$

(c) $D \cong f\theta_{out} = 3.3 \text{ cm} \times 0.44 \times 10^{-3} \text{ rad} = 1.45 \times 10^{-3} \text{ cm} = 14.5 \mu m$

(d) $E_e = P/A = \frac{5W}{0.7854(1.45 \times 10^{-3} \text{cm})^2} = 3.02 \times 10^6 \text{ W/cm}^2$

7-11. (a) $P_{AV} = \frac{E}{t} = \frac{10 \times 10^{-3} J}{10 \times 10^{-9} s} = 10^6 \text{ J/s} = 1 \text{ MW}$

(b) $D \cong f\theta = \left(\frac{1}{D} m\right)(0.1 \times 10^{-3}) = \frac{0.1 \times 10^{-3}}{20 m^{-1}} = 5 \times 10^{-6} m = 5 \mu m$

(c) $E_e = \frac{P}{A} = \frac{10^6 W}{(0.7854)(5 \times 10^{-6})^2} = 5.1 \times 10^{16} \frac{W}{m^2} = 5.1 \times 10^{12} \frac{W}{cm^2}$

7-12. (a) $E_e$ at exit of laser: $P = 4 \times 10^{-3} W$; $r = \frac{0.7cm}{2} = 0.35 cm$

$E_e = \frac{4 \times 10^{-3} W}{\pi (0.35 cm)^2} = 1.04 \times 10^{-2} W/cm^2$

(b) $E_e$ at retinal surface: $P = 4 \times 10^{-3} W$; $f = 17 cm$;
$\theta = 1.5 \times 10^{-3}$ rad.

Spot diameter at retinal surface: $D \cong f\theta$

$D \cong f\theta = (1.7 cm)(1.5 \times 10^{-3} \text{rad}) = 2.55 \times 10^{-3} cm$

$E_e = \frac{4 \times 10^{-3} W}{\pi \left(\frac{2.55 \times 10^{-3} cm}{2}\right)^2} = 783 \text{ W/cm}^2$

(c) Multiplying factor $= \frac{783 \text{ W/cm}^2}{1.04 \times 10^{-2} \text{ W/cm}^2} = 75,288$

Thus, ocular focusing of beam increases the irradiance by a factor of about 75,000 times! One should never stare into the beam.

7-13. (a) radiant energy density $W_e$ = energy/pulse = $80 \times 10^{-3} J$
pulse diameter = 0.7cm

$E_p = W_e = \frac{80 \times 10^{-3} J}{\pi \left(\frac{0.7 cm}{2}\right)^2} = 0.21 \text{ J/cm}^2$

(b) optical density of required filter: (Note $W_e = E_p$)

$O.D. = \log_{10}(E_p/MPE)$; $MPE = 5.0 \times 10^{-6} \text{ J/cm}^2$

$O.D. = \log_{10}\left[\frac{0.21 \text{ J/cm}^2}{5 \times 10^{-6} \text{ J/cm}^2}\right] = 4.6$

A filter with O.D. = 4.6 that absorbs 1.06 μm radiation provides the necessary protection.

# Chapter 8 – Wave Equations

8-1.

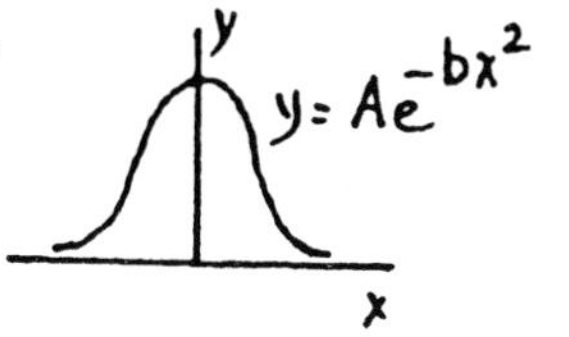


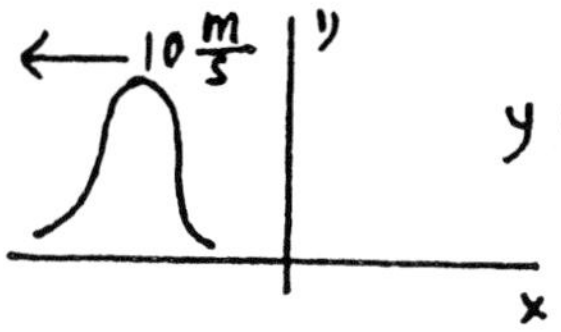


$y = Ae^{-b(x+10t)^2}$

8-2. (a) Replace $x$ by $x+vt$:

$$y = \frac{4}{(x+2.5t)^2+2}$$

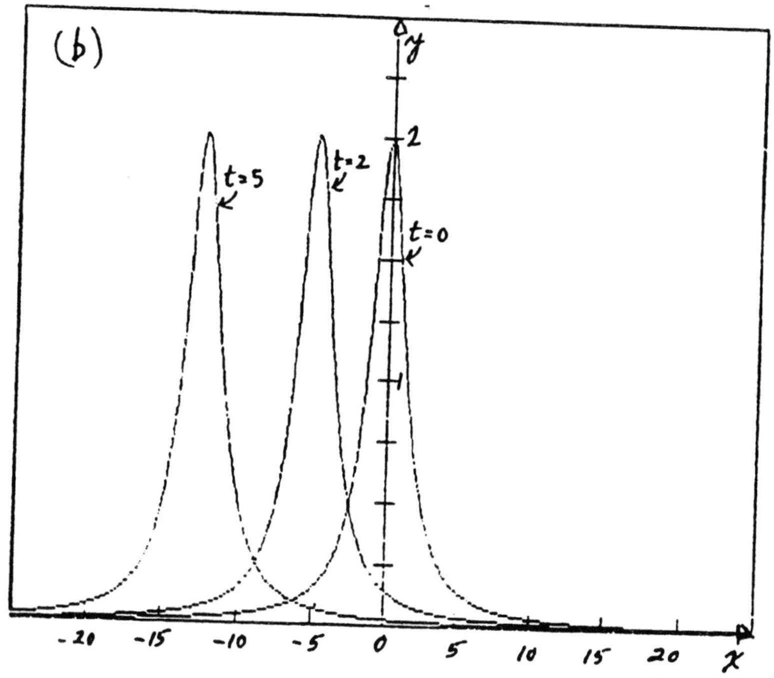


8-3.

(1) $y(z,t) = A\sin^2[4\pi(t+z)]$

If $w = z+t$, $y(w) = A\sin^2(4\pi w)$, a travelling wave,

where $z - vt = z+t$

so $V_z = -1$ m/s

(2) $y(x,t) = A(x-t)^2$

If $w = x-t$, $y(w) = Aw^2$, a travelling wave,

where $x-t = x-vt$

so $V_x = +1$ m/s

(3) $y(x,t) = \dfrac{A}{(\sqrt{3}x^2-t)}$ . $y(x,t) \neq f(x-vt)$ : not a travelling wave.

Also, with more labor, one can show that cases (1) and (2) satisfy the wave equation (8-2), but case (3) does not.

8-4. $y = \dfrac{100\,e^{x^2-20xt+100t}}{x-10t} = \dfrac{100\,e^{w^2}}{w} = f(w)$, where $w = x-10t$.

Thus it represents a traveling wave, with $x - vt = x-10t$, or $V_x = +10$ m/s

8-5. $K = \dfrac{2\pi}{\lambda} = \dfrac{2\pi}{5}\,m^{-1}$ $\quad v = f\lambda = \dfrac{\lambda}{T} = \dfrac{5}{3}$ m/s

(a) $y = A\sin 2\pi\left(\frac{z}{\lambda} \pm \frac{t}{T}\right) = 2\sin 2\pi\left(\frac{z}{5}+\frac{t}{3}\right)$

(b) $y = A\sin K(x \pm vt) = 2\sin\left(\frac{2\pi}{5}\right)\left(x+\frac{5}{3}t\right)$

(c) $y = Ae^{i(Kx\pm\omega t)} = 2e^{i(2\pi x/5+2\pi t/3)} = 2e^{2\pi i\left(\frac{x}{5}+\frac{t}{3}\right)}$

8-6. (a) $y = A\sin 2\pi\left(\frac{x}{\lambda} \pm \frac{t}{T}\right) = 5\sin(2\pi x/50) = 5\sin(\pi x/25)$

8-6. (cont'd.)

(b) $y = 5\sin 2\pi\left(\frac{x}{50} + \frac{4}{25}\right) = 5\sin\left[\left(\frac{\pi}{25}\right)(x+8)\right]$

where $\nu = \frac{v}{\lambda} = \frac{2}{50} = \frac{1}{25}$ and $T = \frac{1}{f} = 25$

8-7. $y = A\sin 2\pi\left(\frac{x}{\lambda} - \frac{t}{T}\right)$
$y = 10\sin(628.3x - 6283t)$ } compare

(a) $2\pi/\lambda = 628.3$ or $\lambda = 0.01\,cm$

(b) $\nu = 1/T$ ; $2\pi/T = 6283$ or $T = 0.001$ and $\nu = 1000\ Hz$

(c) $K = \frac{2\pi}{\lambda} = \frac{2\pi}{.01} = 628.3\ cm^{-1}$

(d) $\omega = 2\pi\nu = 2\pi(1000) = 6283\ s^{-1}$

(e) $T = 0.001s = 1\ ms$

(f) $v = \lambda\nu = (.01)(1000) = 10\ cm/s$

(g) $A = 10\,cm$

8-8. (a) $f(y,t) = A(y-t)^2$
$y - t = const$
$dy - dt = 0$
$V_y = \frac{dy}{dt} = +1\ m/s$

(b) $f(x,t) = A(Bx + Ct + D)^2$
$Bx + Ct + D = const.$
$Bdx + Cdt = 0$
$V_x = \frac{dx}{dt} = -\frac{C}{B}\ \left[\frac{(1/t)}{(1/\ell)} = \frac{\ell}{t}\right]$

(c) $f(z,t) = Ae^{(Bz^2 + BC^2t^2 - 2BCzt)}$
$f(z,t) = Ae^{(\sqrt{B}z - \sqrt{B}Ct)^2}$
$\sqrt{B}z - \sqrt{B}Ct = const$
$\sqrt{B}dz - \sqrt{B}Cdt = 0$
$V_z = \frac{dz}{dt} = C$

From given function, dimensions are
$B \sim 1/\ell^2$
$BC^2 \sim 1/t^2$
$\therefore\ C^2 \sim \ell^2/t^2$
$C \sim \ell/t$

8-9. At $\left\{\begin{matrix} t=0 \\ x=0\end{matrix}\right\}$, $y = 13$ and at $\left\{\begin{matrix} t=0 \\ x=3\lambda/4\end{matrix}\right\}$, $y = -7.5$

In general, at $t=0$, $y = A\sin(2\pi x/\lambda + \varphi)$

1st condition: $13 = A\sin\varphi$
2nd condition: $-7.5 = A\sin\left[\frac{2\pi}{\lambda}\left(\frac{3\lambda}{4}\right) + \varphi\right] = A\sin\left(\frac{3\pi}{2} + \varphi\right)$

But $\sin(\varphi + 3\pi/2) = -\cos\varphi$, so

$\left\{\begin{matrix} 13 = A\sin\varphi \\ +7.5 = A\cos\varphi\end{matrix}\right\}$ or, dividing, $\tan\varphi = \frac{13}{7.5}$ and $\varphi \cong \pi/3$

Then, from $13 = A\sin(\pi/3)$, $A = 15$ and

$y = 15\sin\left(\frac{2\pi x}{\lambda} + \frac{\pi}{3}\right) = 15\sin 2\pi\left(\frac{x}{\lambda} + \frac{1}{6}\right)$

$y = 15\sin(Kx + \pi/3)$

8-10. $y = y_{max} = A$ at $t=0$

(a) $y = A \sin\left(\frac{2\pi x_0}{\lambda} + \varphi_0\right)$. At $y = A$, $\frac{2\pi x_0}{\lambda} + \varphi_0 = \sin^{-1}(1) = \pi/2$

Thus $\varphi_0 = \frac{\pi}{2} - \left(\frac{2\pi}{\lambda}\right)x_0$

(b) $\lambda = 10$ cm

$x = 0: \quad \varphi_0 = \pi/2 = 90°$

$x = 5/6: \quad \varphi_0 = \pi/2 - \frac{2\pi}{\lambda} \cdot \frac{5}{6} = 60°$

$x = 5/2: \quad \varphi_0 = \pi/2 - \frac{2\pi}{\lambda} \cdot \frac{5}{2} = 0°$

$x = 5: \quad \varphi_0 = \frac{\pi}{2} - \frac{2\pi}{\lambda} \cdot 5 = -90°$

$x = -1/2: \quad \varphi_0 = \frac{\pi}{2} - \frac{2\pi}{\lambda}\left(-\frac{1}{2}\right) = 108°$

(c) When $y = A\cos\left(\frac{2\pi x}{\lambda} + \varphi_0\right)$, the same argument as in (b) requires $\cos^{-1}(1) = 0° = 2\pi x_0/\lambda + \varphi_0$, or $90°$ less than when sin is used. Thus we should subtract $90°$ from answers in (b).

$\varphi_0$ (cosine wave) $= \varphi_0$ (sine wave) $- 90°$

8-11. $\vec{k} \cdot \vec{r} = (k_x, k_y, k_z) \cdot (x, y, z)$

(a) Along $+z$-axis, $\vec{k} = (0, 0, k_z)$ and $\vec{k} \cdot \vec{r} = (0, 0, k_z) \cdot (x, y, z) = z k_z$ where $k_z = 2\pi/\lambda$.

$\psi = A \sin(k \cdot r - \omega t) = A \sin(z k_z - \omega t) = A \sin \frac{2\pi}{\lambda}(z - vt)$

or $\psi = A \sin 2\pi(z/\lambda - \nu t)$ — alternate forms

(b) Along $x = y$, $z = 0$ line: $\vec{k} = (k_x, k_y, 0)$ with $k_x = k_y = |k|/\sqrt{2}$

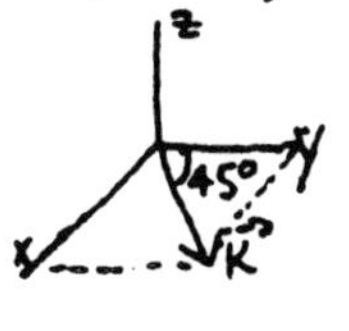


$k \cdot r = (k_x, k_y, 0) \cdot (x, y, z) = x k_x + y k_y$. But $x = y$

$k \cdot r = 2x k_x = \frac{2|k|}{\sqrt{2}} x = \sqrt{2}\left(\frac{2\pi}{\lambda}\right) x$

$\psi = A \sin[x(k_x + k_y) \pm \omega t] = A \sin\left[\frac{2\sqrt{2}\pi}{\lambda} x \pm \omega t\right]$

or $\psi = A \sin \frac{2\pi}{\lambda}(\sqrt{2}x \pm vt)$

(c) $\perp$ planes $x + y + z = $ const.

$\vec{k} = |\vec{k}|\hat{k} = |k| \frac{(1,1,1)}{\sqrt{3}}$, where $\hat{k}$ is unit vector along $\vec{k}$ or $\perp$ surfaces $x + y + z = $ const.

$k \cdot r = \frac{|k|}{\sqrt{3}}(1,1,1) \cdot (x, y, z) = \frac{2\pi}{\lambda} \frac{1}{\sqrt{3}}(x + y + z)$

$\psi = A \sin \frac{2\pi}{\lambda}\left[\frac{\sqrt{3}}{3}(x + y + z) \pm vt\right]$

8-12. $\tilde{z} = a + ib$

$$\begin{cases} \tilde{z} = \mathrm{Re}(\tilde{z}) + i\,\mathrm{Im}(\tilde{z}) \\ \tilde{z}^* = \mathrm{Re}(\tilde{z}) - i\,\mathrm{Im}(\tilde{z}) \end{cases}$$

8-12. (cont'd.)

(a) Adding, $Re(\tilde{z}) = \frac{\tilde{z}+\tilde{z}^*}{2}$ (b) Subtracting, $Im(\tilde{z}) = \frac{\tilde{z}-\tilde{z}^*}{2}$

(c) $\tilde{z} = e^{i\theta} = \cos\theta + i\sin\theta$ so $Re(\tilde{z}) = \cos\theta$ and $Im(\tilde{z}) = \sin\theta$

Applying results of (a), $\cos\theta = \frac{e^{i\theta}+e^{-i\theta}}{2}$, and

(d) Applying (b), $\sin\theta = \frac{e^{i\theta}-e^{-i\theta}}{2}$

8-13.

(a) $\psi = Ae^{i(k\cdot r-\omega t)}$

$i\psi = iAe^{i(k\cdot r-\omega t)} = e^{i\pi/2}Ae^{i(k\cdot r-\omega t)} = Ae^{i(k\cdot r-\omega t+\pi/2)}$

(b) $-\psi = -Ae^{i(k\cdot r-\omega t)} = e^{i\pi}Ae^{i(k\cdot r-\omega t)} = Ae^{i(k\cdot r-\omega t+\pi)}$

8-14. $\psi = A\sin(ky+\omega t) + A\sin(ky-\omega t+\pi)$

$\psi = Im\left[Ae^{i(ky+\omega t)} - Ae^{i(ky-\omega t)}\right]$

$\psi = A\ Im\left[e^{iky}\right]\left[e^{i\omega t}-e^{-i\omega t}\right] = A\ Im\left[e^{iky}(2i\sin\omega t)\right]$

$\psi = A\ Im\left[2i\sin\omega t\,(\cos ky + i\sin ky)\right]$

$\psi = A\,(2\sin\omega t\cos ky)$

8-15.

$E_e = \frac{1}{2}\epsilon_0 c E_0^2$

$1.4\times10^3\ \frac{W}{m^2} = \frac{\epsilon_0 c}{2}E_0^2$

$E_0 = \left[\frac{2.8\times10^3}{\epsilon_0 c}\right]^{1/2} = 1027\ V/m$

$B_0 = E_0/c$

$B_0 = 1027/2.998\times10^8$

$B_0 = 3.43\times10^{-6}\ T$

8-16. $n = 1.50$

$E_0 = 100\ V/m$

(a) $B_0 = E_0/v = E_0 n/c = \frac{(100)(1.50)}{c} = 5.003\times10^{-7}\ T$

(b) $E_e = \langle |S| \rangle = \frac{\epsilon_0 c^2}{2}E_0 B_0 = \frac{\epsilon_0 c^2}{2}(100)(5.003\times10^{-7})$

$\langle |S| \rangle = 19.9\ W/m^2$

8-17. $E_e = 0.135\ W/cm^2$

$\lambda_{av} = 700\ nm$

(a) $E_0 = \sqrt{\frac{2E_e}{\epsilon_0 c}} = \sqrt{\frac{2(1350)}{\epsilon_0 c}} = 1.01\times10^3\ V/m$

$B_0 = E_0/c = 3.36\times10^{-6}\ T$

(b) $n = \frac{E_e}{h\nu} = \frac{E_e}{hc/\lambda} = \frac{1350\ J/m^2\text{-}s}{hc/700\times10^{-9}m} = 4.76\times10^{21}$ photons/m²-s

(c) $k = \frac{2\pi}{\lambda} = \frac{2\pi}{700\times10^{-9}} = 1.43\times10^6\ m^{-1}$ and $\nu = c/\lambda = 4.28\times10^{14}\ s^{-1}$

$\therefore E = 1010\sin 2\pi\,(1.43\times10^{-6}r \pm 4.28\times10^{14}t)$

8-18. (a) $E_e = P/A = \frac{220 \times .05}{4\pi(10)^2} = 8.75 \times 10^{-3}\, W/m^2$

$E_0 = \sqrt{\frac{2E_e}{\epsilon_0 c}} = 2.57\ V/m$

(b) $E_e = P/A = \frac{2000\ W}{10^{-10}\, m^2} = 2 \times 10^{13}\, W/m^2$ and $E_0 = \sqrt{\frac{2E_e}{\epsilon_0 c}} = 1.23 \times 10^{8}\, \frac{V}{m}$

$B_0 = E_0/c = 0.409\ T$

8-19.

The flux per unit area must be the same at all radii in order to be conserved. Thus

$$\frac{\Phi_e}{A} = \frac{\Phi_e}{2\pi r L} = \text{constant}$$

Therefore, $\Phi_e \propto \frac{1}{r}$, but $\Phi_e\,(\text{Watts}) \propto E_0^2$. So $E_0^2 \propto \frac{1}{r}$ and $E_0 \propto \frac{1}{\sqrt{r}}$ Q.E.D.

8-20. $\lambda' = \lambda\left[\frac{1-v/c}{1+v/c}\right]^{1/2} = \lambda\left[\left(1-\frac{v}{c}\right)\left(1+\frac{v}{c}\right)^{-1}\right]^{1/2} \cong \lambda\left[\left(1-\frac{v}{c}\right)\left(1-\frac{v}{c}\right)\right]^{1/2}$

$\lambda' \cong \lambda\left(1-\frac{v}{c}\right)$ Q.E.D.

8-21. $\frac{\lambda'}{\lambda} = \frac{540}{640} = \left[\frac{1-v/c}{1+v/c}\right]^{1/2}$ or $v = 0.168c$

8-22. $\frac{\lambda'}{\lambda} = 4.8 = \left[\frac{1-v/c}{1+v/c}\right]^{1/2}$ or $v = -0.917c$

8-23.

$$v_{rms} = \sqrt{\frac{3RT}{M}} = \left[\frac{3(8.31)(1000)}{4 \times 10^{-3}}\right]^{1/2} = 2497\ m/s$$

Since speeds are small compared with c, we can use

$$\frac{\lambda'}{\lambda} \cong 1 - \frac{v}{c} \quad \text{or} \quad \Delta\lambda = \frac{v}{c}\lambda$$

$$\Delta\lambda = \left(\frac{2497}{3 \times 10^8}\right)\left(706.52 \times 10^{-9}\right) = 0.059\ \text{Å}$$

$\Delta\lambda$ is added to $\lambda_0$ for receding atoms and subtracted for approaching atoms. Thus an estimation of the Doppler broadening is $2\Delta\lambda = 0.12\ \text{Å}$

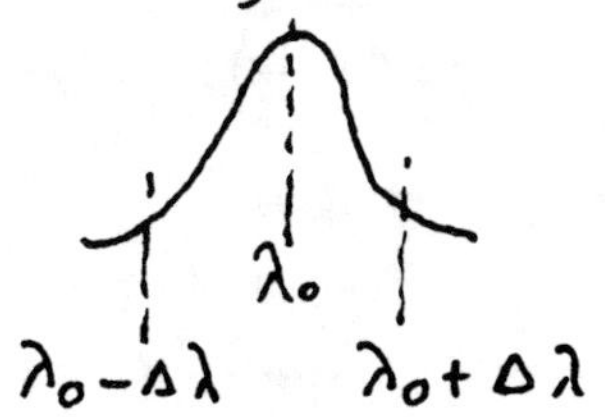

# Chapter 9 - Superposition of Waves

**9-1.** (a) $3x - 4t = \text{const.}$ $\qquad$ $3x + 4t - 6 = \text{const.}$

$3dx - 4dt = 0$ $\qquad$ $3dx + 4dt = 0$

$V_1 = \frac{dx}{dt} = +\frac{4}{3}\ m/s$ $\qquad$ $V_2 = \frac{dx}{dt} = -\frac{4}{3}\ m/s$

The waves move in opposite directions along the x-axis, with equal speeds of 4/3 m/s.

(b) $E_1 + E_2 = 0$ when $(3x-4t)^2 = (3x+4t-6)^2$. Since this must hold everywhere, set $x=0$: Then

$$16t^2 = 16t^2 - 48t + 36 \quad \text{and} \quad t = 3/4\ s$$

(c) Since $E_1 + E_2 = 0$ for all $t$, choose $t = 0$. Then

$$(3x)^2 = (3x-6)^2 \quad \text{or} \quad x = 1\ m$$

**9-2.**

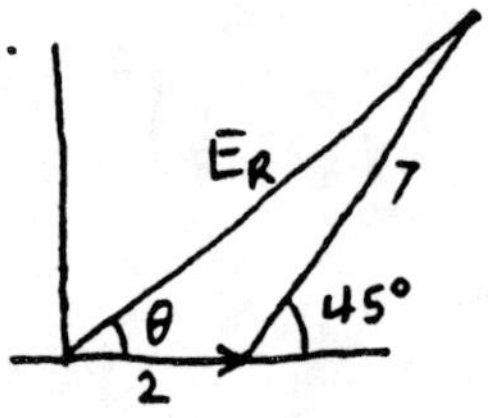


(a) $E_R^2 = (2 + 7\cos 45°)^2 + (0 + 7\sin 45°)^2 = 72.8$

$E_R = 8.53$ and $\tan\theta = \frac{7\sin 45°}{2 + 7\cos 45°} = 0.7122$

or $\theta = 35.46° = 0.2\pi$ radians.

(b) $E_R = 8.53 \sin(\omega t + 0.2\pi)$

**9-3.**

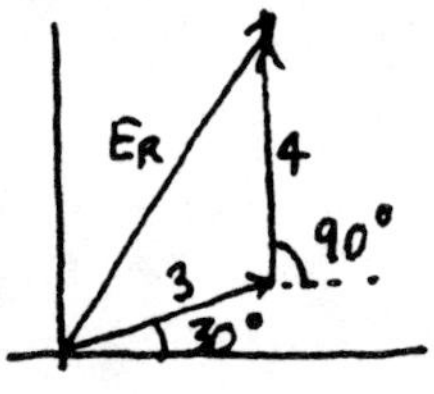


$E_R^2 = (3\cos 30° + 0)^2 + (3\sin 30° + 4)^2 = 37$ or $E_R = 6.08$

$\tan\theta = \frac{3\sin 30° + 4}{3\cos 30°} = 2.11695$ or $\theta = 64.7° = 1.13$ rad.

For $T = 1\,s$, $\omega = 2\pi/T = 2\pi$

then $E_R = 6.08\sin(\omega t + 1.13) = 6.08 \sin 2\pi(t + 0.18)$

**9-4.** $y_1 = 5\sin(\omega t + \pi/2)$ $\qquad$ $A^2 = (5\cos\frac{\pi}{2} + 7\cos\frac{\pi}{3})^2 + (5\sin\frac{\pi}{2} + 7\sin\frac{\pi}{3})^2$

$y_2 = 7\sin(\omega t + \pi/3)$ $\qquad$ $A = 11.60$

$\tan\theta = \frac{5 + 7\sqrt{3}/2}{7/2} = 3.1606$ or $\theta = 0.402\pi$ rad.

Then $y = 11.6 \sin(\omega t + 0.402\pi)$

**9-5.** $E_1 = \sin(\omega t - 10°)$ and $E_2 = 3\cos(\omega t + 100°) = 3\sin(\omega t + 100° + 90°)$

$E_3 = 2\sin(\omega t - 30°)$

$$E_0^2 = [\overbrace{\sin(-10) + 3\sin(190) + 2\sin(-30)}^{E_{oy}}]^2 + [\overbrace{\cos(-10) + 3\cos(190) + 2\cos(-30)}^{E_{ox}}]^2 \quad \text{OR} \quad E_0 = 1.71$$

$\tan\alpha = \frac{E_{oy}}{E_{ox}} = 7.133$ or $\alpha = 262°$

(Note: Since $\tan\alpha > 0$, $\alpha$ is in Quadrant I or III. But both

9-5 (cont'd). $E_{0x}$ and $E_{0y}$ are negative, indicating Q III. Thus $\alpha = 82 + 180 = 262°$) Now $262° = 4.57$ rad, so

$$E_R = 1.71 \sin(\pi t + 4.57) \quad \text{where } \omega = \frac{2\pi}{T} = \pi$$

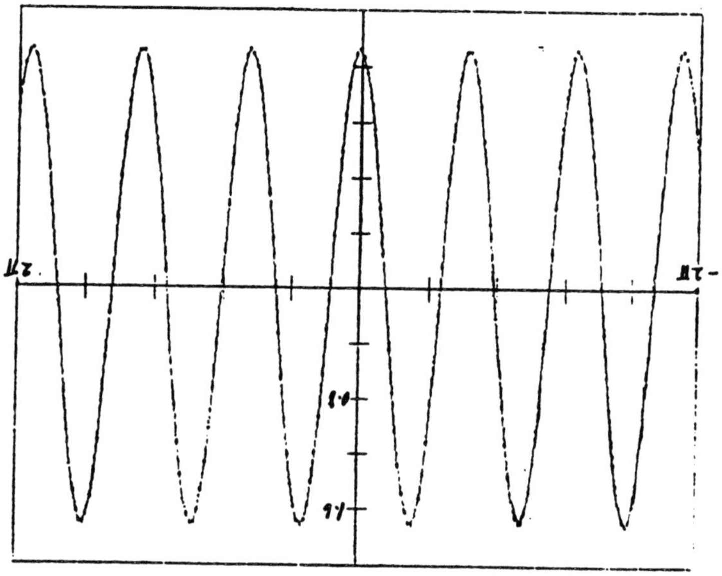

9-6. $E = 0.02 \sin(\omega t + \epsilon)$ V/m

(a) in phase : $E_R = 100(0.02) = 2$ V/m

(b) random : $E_R^2 = 100\, E_0^2 = 100(0.02)^2 = 0.04$

$E_R = 0.2$ V/m

9-7. $\psi_1(x,t) = 4 \sin[20t + \frac{\pi}{3}x + \pi]$ and $\psi_2(y,t) = 2 \sin[20t + \frac{\pi}{4}y + \pi]$

At $(x,y) = (5,2)$, $\psi_1 = 4 \sin(20t + 8\pi/3)$

$\psi_2 = 2 \sin(20t + 3\pi/2)$

$$A^2 = \left(4\cos\frac{8\pi}{3} + 2\cos\frac{3\pi}{2}\right)^2 + \left(4\sin\frac{8\pi}{3} + 2\sin\frac{3\pi}{2}\right)^2 = 6.144 \text{ or } A = 2.48$$

$$\theta = \tan^{-1}\left(\frac{4\sin 8\pi/3 + 2\sin 3\pi/2}{4\cos 8\pi/3 + 2\cos 3\pi/2}\right) = -0.6319 \text{ rad} = -0.20\pi \text{ rad}$$

$$\psi_R = 2.48 \sin(20t - 0.2\pi)$$

9-8. $v_g = v_p - \lambda(dv/d\lambda)$ where $v_p = c/n$

(a) $\lambda = \frac{c}{\nu} = \frac{2\pi c}{\omega}$ and $\frac{dv}{d\lambda} = \frac{d(c/n)}{d(2\pi c/\omega)} = \frac{-c\, dn/n^2}{-2\pi c\, d\omega/\omega^2} = \frac{\omega^2}{2\pi n^2}\frac{dn}{d\omega}$

Thus $v_g = v_p - \left(\frac{2\pi c}{\omega}\right)\left(\frac{\omega^2}{2\pi n^2}\right)\frac{dn}{d\omega} = v_p\left(1 - \frac{\omega}{n}\frac{dn}{d\omega}\right)$

(b) For normal dispersion, $dn/d\lambda < 0$. Then $dn/d\omega > 0$ and $v_g < v_p$

9-9. $\Delta \equiv \frac{n_F - n_C}{n_D - 1} = \frac{1}{30}$ and $\begin{cases} \lambda_C = 6563\,\text{Å},\ \lambda_D = 5890\,\text{Å},\ \lambda_F = 4861\,\text{Å} \\ n_D = 1.50 \end{cases}$

$$v_g = v_p\left[1 + \frac{\lambda}{n}\frac{dn}{d\lambda}\right] \cong v_p\left[1 + \frac{\lambda_D}{n_D}\frac{\Delta n}{\Delta\lambda}\right]$$

where $-\Delta n = n_C - n_F = \Delta(n_D - 1) = \frac{1}{30}(1.50 - 1) = 1/60$

and $\Delta\lambda = \lambda_C - \lambda_F = 6563 - 4861 = 1702\,\text{Å}$

$$v_g = \frac{c}{n_D}\left[1 + \frac{\lambda_D}{n_D}\frac{\Delta n}{\Delta\lambda}\right] = \frac{c}{1.50}\left[1 - \frac{5890}{1.50}\,\frac{1}{60(1702)}\right] = \frac{c}{1.56}$$

9-10. $n = A + B/\lambda^2$ $\qquad v_g = v_p\left[1 + \frac{\lambda}{n}\frac{dn}{d\lambda}\right]$

$$\frac{dn}{d\lambda} = -\frac{2B}{\lambda^3} = -\frac{2(2.5\times10^6)}{(5000)^3}\,\text{Å}^{-1} = -4\times10^{-5}\,\text{Å}^{-1}$$

then $v_p = \frac{c}{n} = \frac{c}{1.50}$ and $v_g = \frac{c}{1.50}\left[1 + \frac{5000}{1.50}(-4\times10^{-5})\right] = \frac{c}{1.73}$

9-11. (a) $K = n^2$ and $v_g = v_p\left(1 + \frac{\lambda}{n}\frac{dn}{d\lambda}\right)$

$$v_p = \frac{c}{n} = \frac{c}{\sqrt{K}} \qquad \frac{dn}{n} = \frac{d(\sqrt{K})}{\sqrt{K}} = \frac{\frac{1}{2}K^{-1/2}dK}{K^{1/2}} = \frac{dK}{2K}$$

Also, $v = \lambda\nu$ or $dv = \lambda\,d\nu + \nu\,d\lambda$. At a particular velocity,

$$\lambda\,d\nu = -\nu\,d\lambda \quad \text{or} \quad \frac{\lambda}{d\lambda} = -\frac{\nu}{d\nu} = -\frac{\omega}{d\omega}$$

Thus $v_g = \frac{c}{\sqrt{K}}\left[1 + \frac{dK}{\sqrt{K}}\left(-\frac{\omega}{d\omega}\right)\right] = \frac{c}{\sqrt{K}}\left(1 - \frac{\omega}{2K}\frac{dK}{d\omega}\right)$ Q.E.D.

(b) $K = 1 + \frac{A}{\omega_0^2 - \omega^2}$ $\qquad$ For $K \cong 1$, $\sqrt{K} \cong 1$

$$\frac{dK}{d\omega} = \frac{-A(-2\omega)}{(\omega_0^2 - \omega^2)^2} = \frac{2A\omega}{(\omega_0^2 - \omega^2)^2}$$

then $v_g \cong c\left[1 - \frac{\omega}{2}\frac{2A\omega}{(\omega_0^2 - \omega^2)^2}\right]$, using the result of (a)

or $v_g \cong c\left(1 - \frac{A\omega^2}{(\omega_0^2 - \omega^2)^2}\right)$ Q.E.D.

9-12. (a) $v_g = \frac{d\omega}{dk} = v_p + k\frac{dv_p}{dk}$ $\qquad$ (Eq. 9-33)

$k = 2\pi/\lambda$ and $dk = -\frac{2\pi}{\lambda^2}d\lambda$

thus $v_g = v_p + \frac{2\pi}{\lambda}\frac{dv_p}{-2\pi}\frac{\lambda^2}{d\lambda} = v_p - \lambda\frac{dv_p}{d\lambda}$ Q.E.D.

9-12. (cont'd.)

(b) $v_g = v_p - \lambda \frac{dv_p}{d\lambda} = (A+B\lambda) - \lambda B = A = \text{const.}$

Since group velocity is independent of wavelength, any waveform constructed from harmonic waves of different wavelengths is transmitted by the medium without a change in shape.

9-13. $v_g = v_p - \lambda \frac{dv_p}{d\lambda}$ as in Prob. 9-12 (a).

Long $\lambda$: $\frac{dv_p}{d\lambda} = \frac{d}{d\lambda}\sqrt{\frac{g\lambda}{2\pi}} = \frac{1}{2}\sqrt{\frac{g}{2\pi\lambda}}$

$$v_g = \sqrt{\frac{g\lambda}{2\pi}} - \frac{\lambda}{2}\sqrt{\frac{g}{2\pi\lambda}} = \frac{1}{2}\sqrt{\frac{g\lambda}{2\pi}} = \frac{1}{2}v_p \quad \text{Q.E.D.}$$

Short $\lambda$: $\frac{dv_p}{d\lambda} = \frac{d}{d\lambda}\left(\frac{2\pi T}{\lambda\rho}\right)^{1/2} = -\frac{1}{2\lambda}\left(\frac{2\pi T}{\rho\lambda}\right)^{1/2}$

$$v_g = \left(\frac{2\pi T}{\lambda\rho}\right)^{1/2} + \frac{1}{2}\left(\frac{2\pi T}{\lambda\rho}\right)^{1/2} = \frac{3}{2}\left(\frac{2\pi T}{\lambda\rho}\right)^{1/2} = \frac{3}{2}v_p \quad \text{Q.E.D.}$$

9-14. Frequency received by mirror $\nu_1' = \nu_0/(1+v/c)$ since $\lambda'/\lambda = \nu/\nu' = 1 - \frac{v}{c}$ and $v<0$ due to recession. The reflected beam is also due to a "source" in recession, so the reflected frequency

$$\nu_2' = \frac{\nu_1'}{1+v/c}$$

Thus, $\nu_2' = \left(\frac{\nu_0}{1+v/c}\right)\left(\frac{1}{1+v/c}\right) = \frac{\nu_0}{(1+v/c)^2} = \nu_0\left(1+\frac{v}{c}\right)^{-2}$

$\nu_2' \cong \nu_0(1-2v/c)$

$\nu_2' - \nu_0 = 2\left(\frac{v}{c}\right)\nu_0$ = beat frequency.

9-15. Standing wave: $E_R = 2E_0 \sin kx \cos \omega t$

From "half" the wave, $y = 7 \sin 2\pi\left(\frac{t}{T} - \frac{2}{\pi}x\right)$, we have $k=4$, $E_0 = 7$. Then $E_R = 14 \sin 4x \cos \omega t$.

For this standing wave, $A = 14$; $\lambda = 2\pi/k = \pi/2 = 1.57$ cm; $v = 0$ with nodal separation $\frac{\lambda}{2} = 0.785$ cm; period $= T$ seconds.

9-16. $y = 3\sin(\pi x/10)\cos(50\pi t)$. This is a standing wave, to be compared, in general, with $E_R = 2E_0 \sin kx \cos\omega t$. Then by inspection,

(a) $2E_0 = 3$ or $E_0 = 1.5$ cm ; $\omega t = 50\pi t$, $\omega = 50\pi$ or $\nu = 25$ Hz;
$k = 2\pi/\lambda = \pi/10$, $\lambda = 20$ cm ; $v = \nu\lambda = 25(20) = 500$ cm/s

(b) $\lambda/2 = 10$ cm

(c) $\dot{y} = -150\pi \sin(\pi x/10)\sin(50\pi t)$
$\ddot{y} = -7500\pi^2 \sin(\pi x/10)\cos(50\pi t)$
Thus, at $x = 5$ cm, $t = 0.22$ s,

$$x = 3\sin(\pi/2)\cos(11\pi) = -3 \text{ cm}$$
$$v = \dot{y} = -150\pi \sin(\pi/2)\sin(11\pi) = 0$$
$$a = \ddot{y} = -7500\pi^2 \sin(\pi/2)\cos(11\pi) = 7500\pi^2$$
$$a = 7.40 \times 10^4 \text{ cm/s}^2$$

9-17. $E_1 = E_0\sin(kx - \omega t) \longrightarrow E_1 = \mathrm{Im}\left[E_0 e^{i(kx-\omega t)}\right]$

$E_2 = E_0 \sin(kx + \omega t) \longrightarrow E_2 = \mathrm{Im}\left[E_0 e^{i(kx+\omega t)}\right]$

$$E_R = E_1 + E_2 = E_0\, \mathrm{Im}\left[e^{i(kx-\omega t)} + e^{i(kx+\omega t)}\right]$$
$$= E_0\, \mathrm{Im}\left[e^{ikx}\underbrace{\left(e^{i\omega t} + e^{-i\omega t}\right)}_{2\cos\omega t}\right]$$

$$E_R = 2E_0\, \mathrm{Im}\left[\cos\omega t\,(\cos kx + i\sin kx)\right]$$

$$E_R = 2E_0 \sin kx \cos\omega t$$

## Chapter 10 Interference of Light

10-1. (a) $I_1 = \frac{\epsilon_0 c}{2} E_{01}^2 = \frac{\epsilon_0 c}{2}(3000)^2 = 11{,}945 \text{ W/m}^2$

$I_2 = \frac{\epsilon_0 c}{2} E_{02}^2 = \frac{\epsilon_0 c}{2}(4000)^2 = 21{,}235 \text{ W/m}^2$

(b) $I_{12} = 2\sqrt{I_1 I_2}\cos\delta = 2\sqrt{I_1 I_2}\cos\left[\frac{\pi}{3} - \left(\frac{\pi}{5} - \frac{\pi}{6}\right)\right] = 18{,}723 \text{ W/m}^2$

(c) $I = I_1 + I_2 + I_{12} = 51{,}903 \text{ W/m}^2$

(d) $V = \frac{I_{max} - I_{min}}{I_{max} + I_{min}} = \frac{(I_1 + I_2 + 2\sqrt{I_1 I_2}) - (I_1 + I_2 - 2\sqrt{I_1 I_2})}{(I_1 + I_2 + 2\sqrt{I_1 I_2}) + (I_1 + I_2 - 2\sqrt{I_1 I_2})}$

$V = \frac{4\sqrt{I_1 I_2}}{2(I_1 + I_2)} = \frac{2E_{01}E_{02}}{E_{01}^2 + E_{02}^2} = \frac{2(3)(4)}{3^2 + 4^2} = 0.96$

10-2. $V = \frac{2E_{01}E_{02}}{E_{01}^2 + E_{02}^2}$ (as in 10-1)

$V = \frac{2(1.6)(2.8)}{1.6^2 + 2.8^2} = 0.86$ for parallel E-fields

For perpendicular E-fields, $I_{max} = I_{min}$ since $I_{12} = 0$. Thus $V = 0$

10-3. First, develop general relations between amplitude ratio $R$ and the fringe contrast, or visibility, $\mathcal{V}$:

For coherent beams,

$$\left.\begin{array}{l} E_{max} = E_1 + E_2 \\ E_{min} = E_1 - E_2 \end{array}\right\} \text{ and } \left\{\begin{array}{l} I_{max} \propto (E_1 + E_2)^2 \\ I_{min} \propto (E_1 - E_2)^2 \end{array}\right.$$

thus $\mathcal{V} \equiv \frac{I_{max} - I_{min}}{I_{max} + I_{min}} = \frac{(E_1+E_2)^2 - (E_1 - E_2)^2}{(E_1+E_2)^2 + (E_1 - E_2)^2} = \frac{2E_1E_2}{E_1^2 + E_2^2}$. Dividing numerator & denominator by $E_2^2$,

$$\mathcal{V} = \frac{2R}{R^2 + 1}$$

Solving (a quadratic) explicitly for $R$ in terms of $\mathcal{V}$,

$$R = \frac{1 + \sqrt{1 - \mathcal{V}^2}}{\mathcal{V}}$$

The two roots yield $E_1/E_2$ and $E_2/E_1$ for $R$

Then, for $R = 2$, $\mathcal{V} = \frac{2(2)}{2^2 + 1} = \frac{4}{5} = 0.80$

and for $\mathcal{V} = 0.5$, $R = \frac{1 + \sqrt{1 - (0.5)^2}}{0.5} = 3.73$

10-4. (a) the ratio of irradiances

$$N = I_1/I_2 = E_1^2/E_2^2 = R^2$$

where R is amplitude ratio. From the solution of Prob 10-3

$$\mathcal{V} = \frac{2R}{R^2+1} = \frac{2\sqrt{N}}{N+1} \quad \text{Q.E.D.}$$

(b) Solving explicitly for N in terms of $\mathcal{V}$,

$$N = \left[\frac{\sqrt{1-\mathcal{V}^2}+1}{\mathcal{V}}\right]^2$$

Then for $\mathcal{V} = 0.96$, $N = 1.78$ ; $\mathcal{V} = 0.8$, $N = 4$

$\mathcal{V} = 0.90$, $N = 2.55$ ; $\mathcal{V} = 0.5$, $N = 13.9$

10-5.

Lloyd's Mirror setup.

$$m\lambda = a \sin\theta = ay/s$$

$$\Delta y = \frac{\lambda s}{a}\Delta m$$

Separation of fringes, $\Delta m = 1$, is

$$\Delta y = \frac{(546.1 \times 10^{-7})(100)(1)}{0.2\text{ cm}} = 0.0273\text{ cm}$$

$$I = 4I_0 \cos^2\left[\frac{\pi a y}{\lambda s}\right] = 4I_0 \cos^2\left[\frac{\pi(.2)y}{(546.1 \times 10^{-7})(100)}\right] = 4I_0 \cos^2(115y)$$

To take into account phase change on reflection, giving I=0 at y=0, one can use the sine fn. instead:

$$I = 4I_0 \sin^2(115y)$$

10-6.

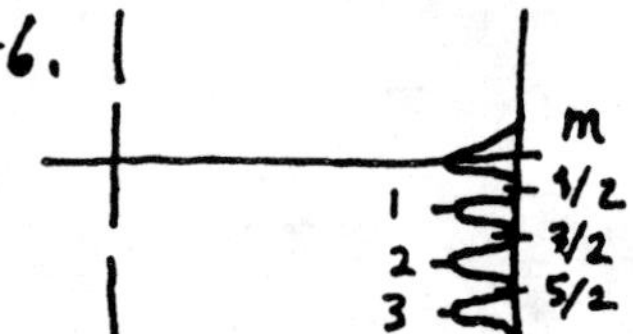


Max: $m\lambda = a\sin\theta$

Min: $(m+1/2)\lambda = a\sin\theta$

When max + min overlap – having the same "$a\sin\theta$", we can write

$$(m_1 + 1/2)\lambda_1 = m_2\lambda$$

$$3.5(436) = 3\lambda \quad \text{OR} \quad \lambda = 508.7\text{ nm}$$

10-7.

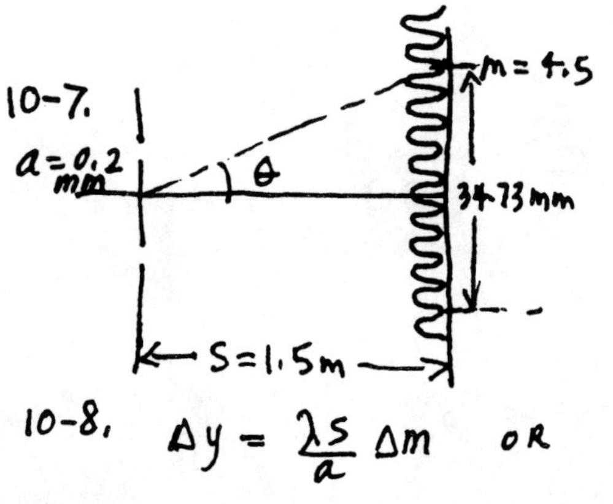


$$(m + 1/2)\lambda = a\sin\theta$$

$$4.5\lambda = (0.02)\left[\frac{3.473/2}{150}\right]$$

$$\lambda = 514.5\text{ nm}$$

10-8. $\Delta y = \frac{\lambda s}{a}\Delta m$ OR $\lambda = \frac{a\,\Delta y}{s\,\Delta m} = \frac{(0.1)(0.56)}{(1000)(1)} = 560\text{ nm}$

10-9. (a) $s = \dfrac{a\,\Delta y}{\lambda\,\Delta m} = \dfrac{(.05)(.1)}{(600\times10^{-7})(1)} = 83.3 \text{ cm}$

(b) Path difference between beams, in general, $\Delta = m\lambda$
Then with and without plate, $\Delta_2 - \Delta_1 = (\Delta m)\lambda$

$$\Delta m = \frac{\Delta_2 - \Delta_1}{\lambda} = \frac{nt - t}{\lambda} = \frac{t(n-1)}{\lambda} = \frac{(100\times10^{-4})(1.5-1)}{600\times10^{-7}} = 83.3 \text{ fringes}$$

(c) $I = 4I_0 \cos^2\left(\dfrac{\pi a y}{\lambda s}\right) = 4I_0\cos^2\left(\dfrac{\pi\Delta}{\lambda}\right)$, where $\Delta = ay/s$

At $\Delta = 0$, $I_{max} = 4I_0$ at a fringe maximum. Then at
$I = 2I_0 = I_{max}/2$, $\quad 2I_0 = 4I_0\cos^2(\pi\Delta/\lambda)$

$$\Delta = \lambda/4 = 150 \text{ nm}$$

10-10. At pinhole, destructive interference occurs for wavelengths given by $\quad (m + 1/2)\lambda = a\sin\theta = \dfrac{ay}{s}$

so $\lambda = \dfrac{y}{(m+1/2)s} = \dfrac{(1.25)(3)}{(m+\frac{1}{2})(1500)} = \dfrac{2500}{m+\frac{1}{2}}$ in nm

In the visible (400 - 700 nm range), m = 4 and m = 5 give two wavelengths: $\lambda = 556$ nm and $\lambda = 455$ nm.

10-11.

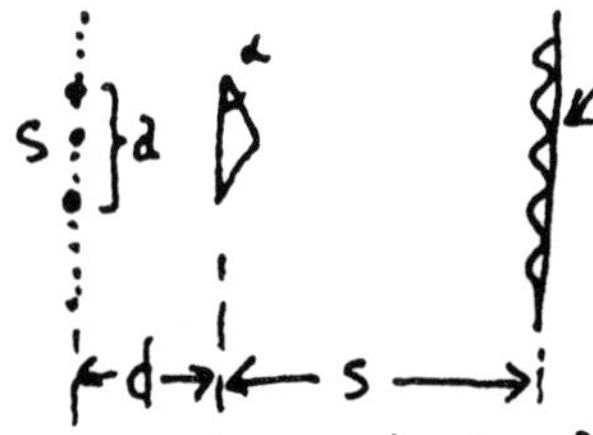


$\Delta y = 0.03$ cm
$s = 2d$
$n = 1.50$

$y = \dfrac{m\lambda(d+s)}{a}$, constr. interf.

$y = \dfrac{m\lambda(3d)}{2d\alpha(n-1)}$ OR $\alpha = \dfrac{3}{2}\dfrac{\lambda}{n-1}\dfrac{\Delta m}{\Delta y}$

$a = 2d\alpha(n-1)$ $\quad \alpha = \dfrac{3}{2}\,\dfrac{589.3\times10^{-9}}{1.5-1}\,\dfrac{1}{3\times10^{-4}} = .005893$ rad

$$\alpha = 0.3376^\circ = 20.3'$$

10-12. $y_m = \dfrac{m\lambda s}{2\theta d}$ OR $\theta = \dfrac{m\lambda s}{2d\,y_m} = \dfrac{\lambda s}{2d}\,\dfrac{\Delta m}{\Delta y_m}$

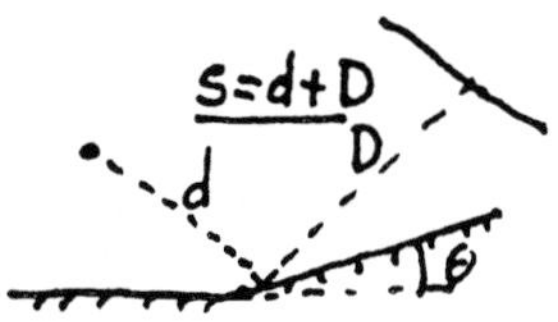


For $\Delta m = 1$, $\quad \theta = \dfrac{(589.3\times10^{-7})(50+100)}{2(50)(.05)} = 0.001768 \text{ rad} = 6'5''$

10-13. $\alpha = \dfrac{\lambda(d+s)}{2d(n-1)\,\Delta y_m}$, where $\Delta y = 0.5$ cm for 20 fringes or $\Delta m = 19$

$$\alpha = \frac{(546.1\times10^{-7})(d+4d)}{2d\,(1.5-1)(0.5/19)} = 0.010376 \text{ rad} = 35'40''$$

10-14. Minima condition: $2nt + 0 = (m + \frac{1}{2})\lambda$

$\Delta_p + \Delta_r = (m+\frac{1}{2})\lambda$

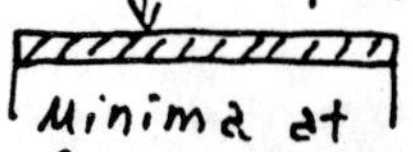


Minima at $\lambda = 525, 675$ nm

$$\begin{cases} 2.6t = (m_1 + \frac{1}{2})525 \\ 2.6t = (m_2 + \frac{1}{2})675 \end{cases}$$

2 Eq. in 3 unknowns. But we know $m_1$ and $m_2$ are integers, and $m_1 > m_2$

$$(m_1 + 1/2)525 = (m_2 + \tfrac{1}{2})675$$

$$\frac{m_1 + 1/2}{m_2 + 1/2} = \frac{675}{525} = 1.2857$$

By trial + error, we find $m_1 = 4$, $m_2 = 3$ satisfies the equation. Thus $t = (m_1 + \frac{1}{2})(525)/2.6$ or $t = 908.65$ nm with order $m = 4$ for 525nm and $m = 3$ for 675 nm.

10-15.

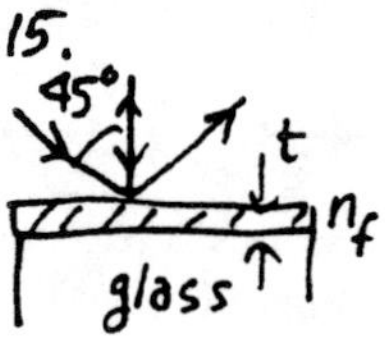


$n_f = 1.38$

$\lambda = 580$ nm

At normal incidence: $(m + \frac{1}{2})\lambda = 2n_F t$

this determines film thickness $t = \frac{(m+\frac{1}{2})\lambda}{2n_F}$

At 45° incidence: $(m + \frac{1}{2})\lambda' = 2n_F t \cos\theta_t$

By Snell's law, $\sin 45 = n_F \sin\theta_t$

so $\sin\theta_t = \frac{1}{\sqrt{2}\, n_F}$

and $\cos\theta_t = \frac{\sqrt{2n_F^2 - 1}}{\sqrt{2}\, n_F}$

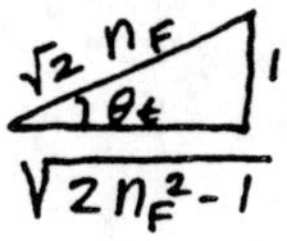


one way To get $\cos\theta_t$ from $\sin\theta_t$

Substituting for $t$ and $\cos\theta_t$,

$$(m+\tfrac{1}{2})\lambda' = 2n_F \frac{(m+\frac{1}{2})\lambda}{2n_F} \frac{\sqrt{2n_F^2 - 1}}{\sqrt{2}\, n_F}$$

$$\lambda' = \lambda \cos\theta_t = \sqrt{\frac{2n_F^2 - 1}{2n_F^2}}\, \lambda = \left[\frac{2(1.38)^2 - 1}{2(1.38)^2}\right]^{1/2}(580)$$

$$\lambda' = 498 \text{ nm}$$

10-16. $n_F = \sqrt{n_0 n_s} = \sqrt{(1)(1.78)} = 1.33$

$$t = \frac{\lambda_m}{4} = \frac{\lambda/n}{4} = \frac{550/1.33}{4} = 103 \text{ nm}$$

10-17. (a) $r = \frac{1-n}{1+n}$ where $n = \frac{n_2}{n_1}$. So $r = \frac{1-1.4}{1+1.4} = -\frac{1}{6}$ and $r^2 = 2.78\%$

(b) $t = \lambda n/4 = \frac{500/1.4}{4} = 89.3$ nm

(c) $r_{top} = -\frac{1}{6}$ ; $r_{bottom} = \frac{1 - 1.6/1.4}{1 + 1.6/1.4} = -\frac{1}{15}$

$r_{effective} = |r_{top}| - |r_{bottom}|$ because they are out of phase.

$r_{eff} = \frac{1}{6} - \frac{1}{15} = 0.1$ so % eff. reflection $= (0.1)^2 = 1\%$

This calculation neglects another interior reflection at top surface as the second beam emerges — a very small part of total.

10-18.

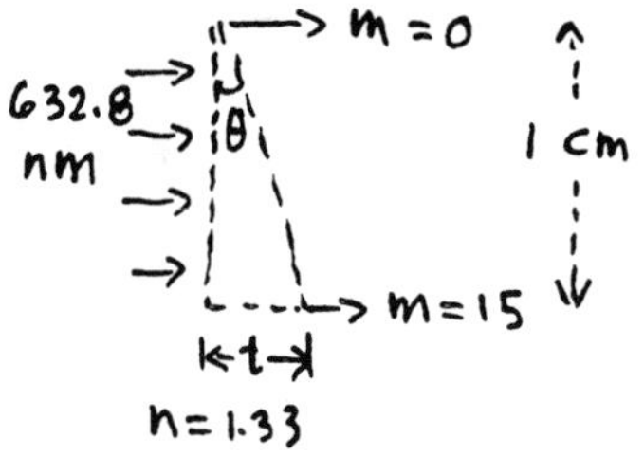


The soap film forms a wedge-like structure as water tends to collect at bottom. We assume a wedge of angle $\theta$. Interference occurs by reflection of the incident 632.8 nm light.

Consider dark fringes: $m\lambda = 2nt$.
At $m=0$, $\Delta = \lambda/2$ due to phase shift alone. At the film bottom, where $m = 15$,

$$(15)\lambda = 2(1.33)t \cong 2(1.33)\theta$$

$$\theta \cong \frac{15\lambda}{2.66} = \frac{15(632.8\times10^{-7})}{2.66} = 3.5684\times10^{-4}\text{ rad}$$

$$\theta \cong 1'14''$$

10-19.

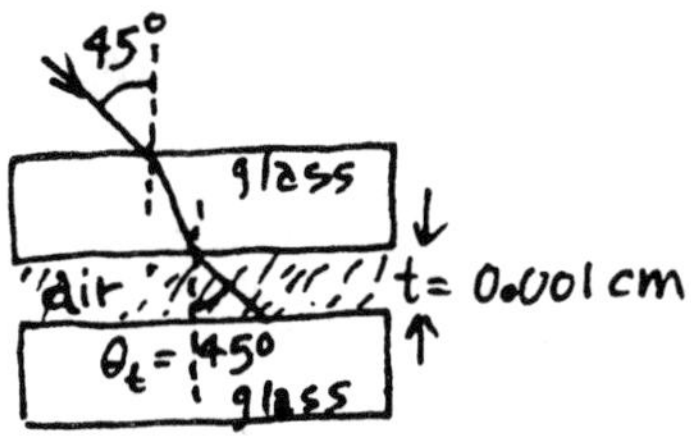


The "dark lines" are wavelengths for which destructive interference occurs on reflection, and so missing from the reflected light. These satisfy

$$m\lambda = 2nt\cos\theta_t$$

$$m\lambda = 2(1)(1\times10^{4}\text{nm})\frac{1}{\sqrt{2}}$$

$$\lambda = \frac{14142}{m}\ (\text{nm})$$

Thus $\lambda$ corresponds to all wavelengths between 400 and 700 nm for $m$ ranging from 20.2 to 35.4, i.e., a total of 15 orders from 21 to 35. Thus the spectrum includes "dark lines" at $\lambda = 673.4$ nm ($m=21$), $\lambda = 642.8$ nm ($m=22$), ..., $\lambda = 404.1$ nm ($m=35$).

10-20. $\lambda = 589.3$ nm

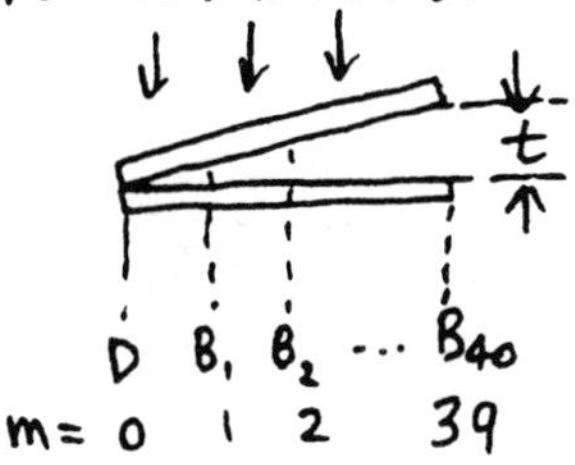


Constructive interference: $(m + 1/2)\lambda = 2t$.
40 bright fringes correspond to $m = 39$ since $m=0$ gives first bright fringe.
then $39.5\lambda = 2t$ and $t = \dfrac{(39.5)(589\times10^{-7})}{2}$

$$t = 1.16\times10^{-3}\text{ cm}$$

10-21.

$$2nt + \frac{\lambda}{2} = (m + \tfrac{1}{2})\lambda \quad \text{OR} \quad t = m\lambda/2n$$

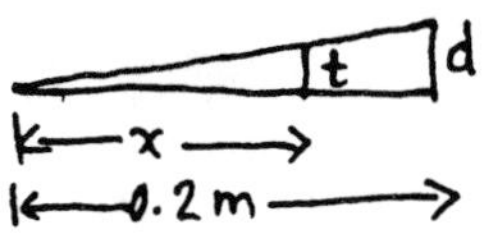


$$\frac{x}{t} = \frac{0.2}{d} \quad \text{so} \quad x = \frac{0.2t}{d} = \frac{0.2}{d}\left(\frac{m\lambda}{2n}\right)$$

For $\Delta m = 1$, $\Delta x = \dfrac{0.1\lambda}{nd} = \dfrac{(0.1)(546.1\times10^{-9})}{(1)(.05\times10^{-3})} = 1.09$ mm

Also, solving for $m = \dfrac{xd}{0.1\lambda} = \dfrac{(.2)(.05\times10^{-3})}{(.1)(546.1\times10^{-9})} = 183.1$

Counting the $m=0$ dark fringe, $m$ (integer) $= 184$

10-22.

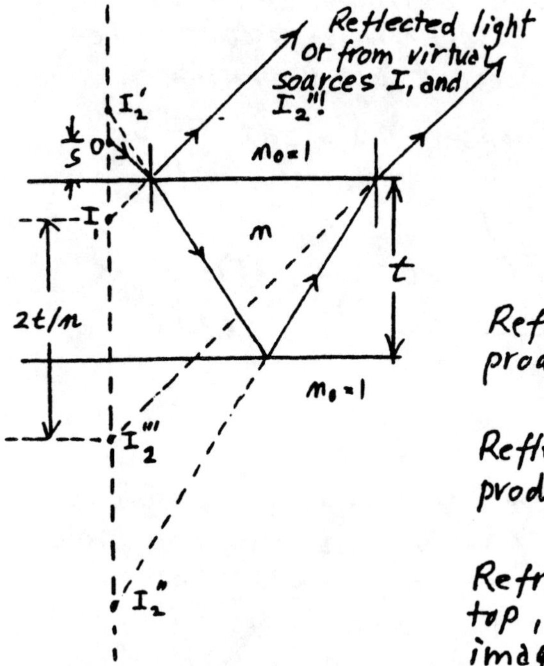


We calculate the two image positions (the "virtual sources") step-by-step. The point source is O. The virtual source $I_1$ due to top surface reflection, is $s_1' = -s$

or s below the top surface.

The virtual source $I_2'''$ is formed in 3 steps:

Reflection at top, producing image $I_2'$: $\dfrac{n_0}{s} + \dfrac{n}{s_2'} = 0$, $s_2' = -ns$

Reflection at bottom producing image $I_2''$: $s_2 = t - s_2' = t + ns$, $s_2'' = -s_2 = -(t+ns)$

Refraction out at top, producing image $I_2'''$: $s_2 = t - s_2'' = 2t + ns$, $\dfrac{n}{s_2} + \dfrac{n_0}{s_2'''} = 0$, $s_2''' = s + \dfrac{2t}{n}$ below top surface

Thus the separation of the virtual sources, as shown, is

$$s_2''' - s_1' = \left(s + \frac{2t}{n}\right) - s = \frac{2t}{n} \quad \text{Q.E.D.}$$

10-23.

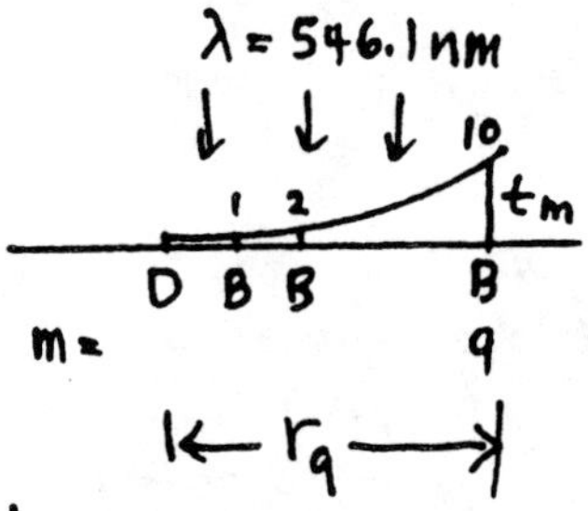


$d_9 = 7.89$ mm

Bright rings: $(m + \frac{1}{2})\lambda = 2t_m$

$$t_9 = \frac{9.5\lambda}{2}$$

$$R_m = \frac{r_m^2 + t_m^2}{2t_m}$$

$$R_9 = \frac{r_9^2 + t_9^2}{2t_9} = \frac{\left(\frac{.789}{2}\right)^2 + \left(\frac{9.5 \times 546.1 \times 10^{-7}}{2}\right)^2}{2\left(\frac{9.5 \times 546.1 \times 10^{-7}}{2}\right)}$$

$R_9 = 300$ cm

$t_9 = 2.594 \times 10^{-4}$ cm

$r_9 = 0.3945$ cm

10-24.

Air: $(r_m^2)_0 \cong 2Rt_m = 2R\,(m + \frac{1}{2})\frac{\lambda}{2}$

Liquid: $(r_m^2)_\ell \cong 2Rt_m = 2R\,(m + \frac{1}{2})\frac{\lambda}{2n}$

$$\left(\frac{r_{mo}}{r_{m\ell}}\right)^2 = n \qquad \frac{r_{mo}}{r_{m\ell}} = \sqrt{n} \qquad \text{Q.E.D.}$$

10-25. Bright rings : $(m + 1/2)\lambda = 2t_m$ and $2Rt_m \cong r_m^2$

$\lambda_1 = 546$ nm $\quad$ 11th bright ring : $m = 10$

$\lambda_2 = ?$ $\quad$ 10th " " : $m = 9$

Thus $(10 + .5)\lambda_1 = 2t_m = 9.5\lambda_2$

$$\lambda_2 = \frac{10.5}{9.5}(546\,\text{nm}) = 603.5\,\text{nm}$$

$$t_m = \frac{10.5\lambda_1}{2} = \frac{10.5(546)}{2} = 2.87 \times 10^{-4}\,\text{cm}$$

$$r_m = \sqrt{2Rt_m} = \sqrt{2(100)(2.87 \times 10^{-4})} = 0.240\,\text{cm}.$$

10-26.

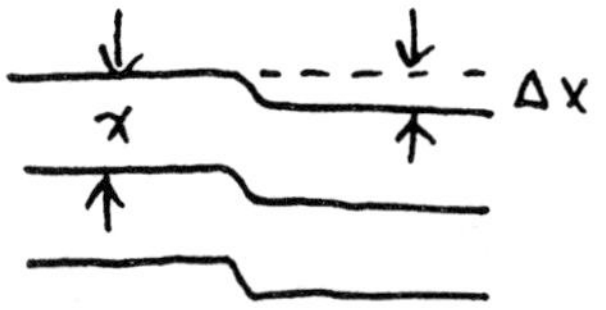


$x = 1$ mm

$\Delta x = 3.4$ mm

$$\Delta m = \frac{\Delta x}{x} = \frac{3.4}{1} = 3.4$$

$$t = \Delta m\left(\frac{\lambda}{2}\right) = 3.4\left(\frac{546.1 \times 10^{-7}}{2}\right)$$

$$t = 9.28 \times 10^{-7}\,\text{cm} = 928.4\,\text{nm}$$

## Chapter 11 - Optical Interferometry

11-1. $(\Delta x)_{OPT} = 2\Delta x = \lambda \Delta m$

$$\lambda = \frac{2\Delta x}{\Delta m} = \frac{2(0.0114\text{ cm})}{523} = 4.359 \times 10^{-5}\text{ cm} = 436\text{ nm}$$

11-2. Straight fringes are due to a wedge between one mirror and the image of the other ($M2$ and $M1'$ in Fig. 11-1). Interference then occurs as from reflection by an air wedge.

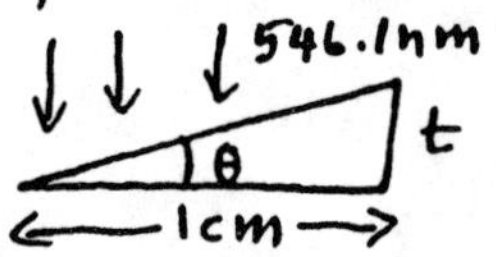


12 fringes/cm ~ 11 fringe spaces/cm

$$\theta\,(\text{rad}) = \frac{t\,(\text{cm})}{1\,(\text{cm})} = t$$

$$m\lambda = 2t \text{ or } t = \frac{m\lambda}{2} = \frac{11\lambda}{2} = 5.5\lambda$$

$\therefore \theta = 5.5\lambda = 5.5\,(5.461 \times 10^{-5}\text{ cm}) = 3.00355 \times 10^{-4}\text{ rad} = 0.0172°$

or $\theta = 1'2''$

11-3. $\Delta = m\lambda = 2(nt - t) = 2t(n-1)$

$$t = \frac{m\lambda}{2(n-1)} = \frac{(35)(589 \times 10^{-9})}{2\,(1.434-1)} = 23.75 \times 10^{-6}\text{ m} = 23.75\,\mu\text{m}$$

11-4. $\lambda = 500\text{ nm}$

(a) $m_{max} = \dfrac{2d}{\lambda} = \dfrac{2(2\text{ cm})}{500 \times 10^{-7}\text{ cm}} = 80{,}000$

(b) $m = m_{max} - 6 = 79{,}994$

11-5. (a) $\Delta = N\lambda = 2nL - 2L = 2L(n-1)$ OR $n = 1 + \dfrac{N\lambda}{2L}$

(b) $1.00045 = 1 + \dfrac{N(589 \times 10^{-7}\text{ cm})}{2(10\text{ cm})}$ OR $N = 153$

11-6. At $\theta = 0°$, $m = \dfrac{2d}{\lambda} = \dfrac{20\,\mu\text{m}}{0.6328\,\mu\text{m}} = 31.6$

thus smallest diameter dark ring corresponds to $m = 31$. Using $m\lambda = 2d\cos\theta_m$,

$$\cos\theta_{31} = \frac{31\lambda}{2d} = \frac{31(0.6328)}{20} = 0.98084 \text{ and } \theta_{31} = 11.23°$$

The 10th dark ring is then of order $m = 22$:

$$\cos\theta_{22} = \frac{22\lambda}{2d} = \frac{22\,(0.6328)}{20} = 0.69608 \text{ and } \theta_{22} = 45.89°$$

11-7. In general, for a path-length difference of $d$, $m\lambda = 2d$. A defect of depth $\Delta d$ then satisfies $2\Delta d = \lambda \Delta m$

So $\Delta d = \Delta m \dfrac{\lambda}{2} = \dfrac{1}{4}\,\dfrac{(632.8\text{ nm})}{2} = 79.1\text{ nm}$ or $\lambda/8$.

11-8.

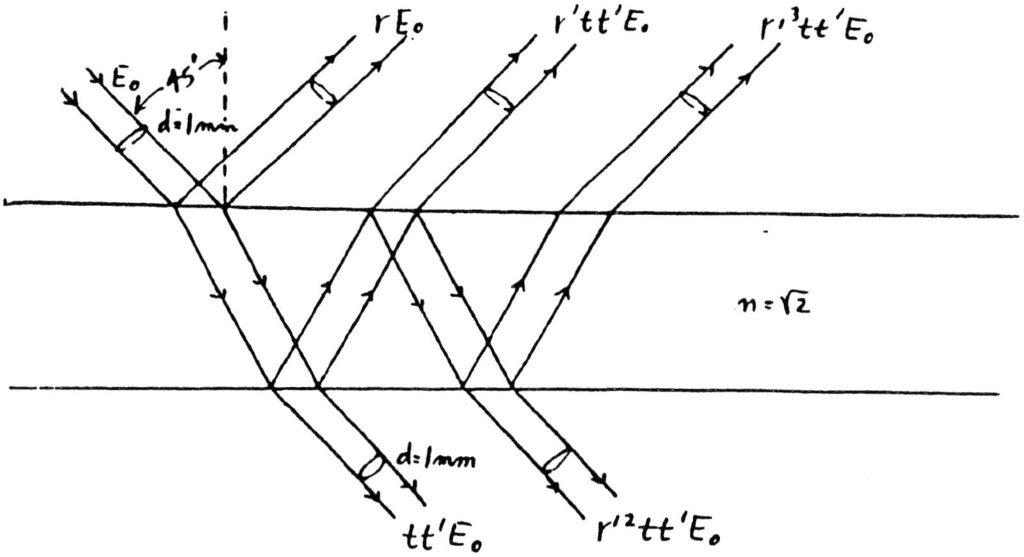


The cross section of the beam is the same in the incident beam, the emergent transmitted beam, and the emergent reflected beam. Inside the film, the cross section is modified due to refraction.

(a) $E_e = \frac{P}{A} = \frac{P}{\pi r^2} = \frac{10^{-3}\,W}{\pi(.5\times10^{-3})^2\,m^2} = 1273.24\ W/m^2$

$E_e = \frac{1}{2}\epsilon_0 c E_0^2$ or $E_0 = (2E_e/\epsilon_0 c)^{1/2} = 979.5\ V/m$

(b) (1) $\sin 45° = \sqrt{2}\sin\theta_R$ OR $\theta_R = 30°$

(c) $r = 0.28$

$r' = -r$ or $|r'| = 0.28$

$tt' = 1 - r^2 = 0.9216$

(d) Reflected beams:

$E_1 = rE_0 = 0.28(980) = 274\ V/m$; $(E_1/E_0)^2 = 7.8\%$

$E_2 = r'tt'E_0 = 0.28(0.9216)(980) = 253\ V/m$; $(E_2/E_0)^2 = 6.7\%$

$E_3 = r'^3tt'E_0 = (0.28)^3(0.9216)(980) = 19.8\ V/m$; $(E_3/E_0)^2 = 0.041\%$

(e) Transmitted beams:

$E_1 = tt'E_0 = 0.9216(980) = 903\ V/m$; $(E_1/E_0)^2 = 85\%$

$E_2 = r'^2tt'E_0 = (0.28)^2(0.9216)(980) = 70.8\ V/m$; $(E_2/E_0)^2 = 0.52\%$

(f) $m\lambda = 2n_F t\cos\theta_t$

$t = \frac{\lambda}{2n_F\cos\theta_t} = \frac{632.8\times10^{-9}}{2\sqrt{2}\cos 30°} = 258\,nm$

11-9. $n_g = 1.52$ ; $n = n_2/n_1 = 1.52/1 = 1.52$ ; $E_0 = 1$

$|r'| = |r| = (1-n)/(1+n) = (1-1.52)/(1+1.52) = 0.20635$

$tt' = 1 - r^2 = 0.95742$

(a) Reflected beams

$E_1 = rE_0 = 0.206\ V/m$

$E_2 = tt'r'E_0 = (.95742)(.20635) = 0.198\ V/m$

$E_3 = tt'r'^3E_0 = (.95742)(.20635)^3 = 0.0084\ V/m$

Transmitted beams

$E_1 = tt'E_0 = 0.957\ V/m$

$E_2 = tt'r'^2E_0 = 0.041\ V/m$

$E_3 = tt'r'^4E_0 = 0.0017\ V/m$

(b) Reflected: $\frac{E_1}{E_2} = \frac{0.206}{0.198} = 1.044$. Use $V = \frac{2R}{R^2+1}$ (derived in Prob. 10-3)
where R represents this ratio of amplitudes. Then

$$V = \frac{2(1.044)}{(1.044)^2+1} = 0.999$$

Transmitted: $\frac{E_1}{E_2} = \frac{0.957}{0.041} = 23.485$

$$V = \frac{2(23.485)}{(23.485)^2+1} = 0.085$$

11-10. (a) $\mathcal{R} = \frac{\lambda}{\Delta\lambda} = \frac{6563\ \text{Å}}{0.136\ \text{Å}} = 48257 \approx 48{,}260$

(b) $F = \frac{4r^2}{(1-r^2)^2} = 9899.75$

$\mathcal{R} = \frac{\pi}{2} m\sqrt{F}$ or $m = \frac{2\mathcal{R}}{\pi\sqrt{F}} = \frac{2(48260)}{\pi(9899.75)^{1/2}} = 308.78$

$m_{max} = \frac{2t}{\lambda}$ or $t = \frac{m\lambda}{2} = \frac{(308.78)(6.563\times10^{-5}\ cm)}{2} = 0.01013\ cm$

11-11. (a) $F = \frac{4r^2}{(1-r^2)^2} = \frac{4(.999)}{(1-.999)^2} = 3.996\times10^6$

(b) $|df| = \frac{c}{\lambda^2}d\lambda$ OR $d\lambda = \frac{\lambda^2 df}{c} = \frac{(632.8\times10^{-9})^2(150\times10^6)}{c}$

$$d\lambda = 2.004\times10^{-13}\ m$$

$\mathcal{R} = \frac{\lambda}{d\lambda} = \frac{632.8\times10^{-9}}{2.004\times10^{-13}} = 3.158\times10^6$

11-11 (cont'd.)

(c) $m = \frac{2\mathcal{R}}{\pi\sqrt{F}} = \frac{2(3.158\times10^6)}{\pi\sqrt{3.996\times10^6}} = 1006$; $t = \frac{m\lambda}{2} = \frac{(1006)(6.328\times10^{-5})}{2}$

$t = 0.0318\ cm$

(d) $(\Delta\lambda)_{fsr} = \frac{\lambda^2}{2t} = \frac{(6328\ Å)^2}{2(.0318\times10^8\ Å)} = 6.30\ Å$

(e) $(\Delta\lambda)_{min} = \frac{2\lambda}{m\pi\sqrt{F}} = \frac{2(632.8\ nm)}{1006(\pi)\sqrt{3.996\times10^6}} = 0.0002\ nm = 0.002\ Å$

11-12. (a) $m_{max} = \frac{2nt}{\lambda} = \frac{2(4.5)(2\ cm)}{5.46\times10^{-5}\ cm} = 329{,}670$

(b) $\frac{T_{max}}{T_{min}} = \frac{1}{1/(1+F)} = 1+F = 1+\frac{4R}{(1-R)^2}$

$\frac{T_{max}}{T_{min}} = 1+\frac{4(.9)}{(1-.9)^2} = 361$ so $F = 360$

(c) $\mathcal{R} = \frac{\pi}{2} m\sqrt{F} = \frac{\pi}{2}(329{,}670)\sqrt{360} = 9.83\times10^6$

11-13. Under these conditions, $\Delta\lambda$ corresponds to the free spectral range. Using Eq (11-42),

$t = \frac{\lambda^2}{2(\Delta\lambda)_{fsr}} = \frac{(490\times10^{-7}\ cm)^2}{2(0.0055\times10^{-7})} = 2.18\ cm$

11-14. $F = \frac{4r^2}{(1-r^2)^2} = \frac{4(.6)}{(1-.6^2)^2} = 15$

$\frac{T_{max}}{T_{min}} = 1+F = 16$

11-15. The bright bands due to white light satisfy $m\lambda = 2t\cos\theta_m$ where $\theta_m = 0°$. Thus,

$m_1\lambda_1 = m_2\lambda_2 = 2t$ and $m_1 - m_2 = 149$

Solved simultaneously, $m_2 = 588.7 \rightarrow 588$.
Then $(588)(546.1) = 2t$ and $t = 0.161\ mm$

11-16. $I = 4I_0\cos^2(\delta/2)$

(a) Fringe max: $I = 4I_0$ for $\cos^2(\delta/2) = 1$; $\cos(\delta/2) = \pm1$; $\delta = \pm 2m\pi$ thus fringe maxima are separated by $2\pi$ ($\Delta m = 1$).

(b) 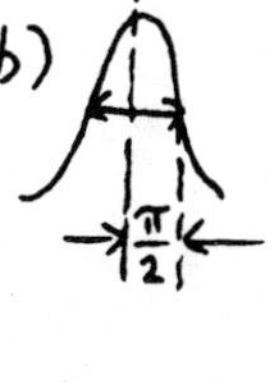


At half max, $I = 2I_0$; $\cos^2(\delta/2) = \frac{1}{2}$; $\cos(\delta/2) = \frac{1}{\sqrt{2}}$

$\frac{\delta}{2} = \frac{\pi}{4}$ and $\delta = \frac{\pi}{2}$. thus $\Delta\delta_{FWHM} = \pi$.

11-16. (cont'd.) (c) $\mathcal{F} = \frac{2\pi}{\pi} = 2$

11-17.

Case (1): $I_1 = (.2)(.8) I_0 = 0.16\, I_0$
$I_2 = (.8)(.2) I_0 = 0.16\, I_0$ } $I_1 = I_2$

Fringe contrast $= \frac{I_{max} - I_{min}}{I_{max} + I_{min}} = \frac{2\sqrt{I_1 I_2}}{I_1 + I_2} = \frac{2 I_2}{2 I_2} = 1$

Case (2): $I_1 = (.2)(.2) I_0 = 0.04\, I_0$
$I_2 = (.8)(.8) I_0 = 0.64\, I_0$ } $I_2 = 16 I_1$

Fringe contrast $= \frac{2\sqrt{16 I_1^2}}{I_1 + 16 I_1} = \frac{8}{17} = 0.47$

# Chapter 12 – Coherence

12-1.

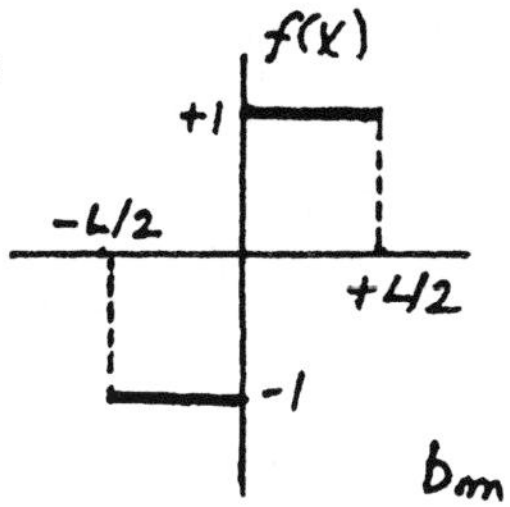


$$f(x) = \begin{cases} -1, & -L/2 < x < 0 \\ +1, & 0 < x < L/2 \end{cases}$$

Odd function: $a_0 = a_n = 0$

$$f(x) = \sum_{m=1}^{\infty} b_m \sin mKx\,, \text{ where } b_m = \frac{2}{L}\int_{-L/2}^{+L/2} f(x)\sin mKx\,dx$$

$$b_m = \frac{2}{L}\left\{ \int_{-L/2}^{0} -\sin mKx\,dx + \int_{0}^{L/2} \sin mKx\,dx \right\}$$

$$b_m = \frac{2}{mKL}\left\{ \Big[\cos mKx\Big]_{-L/2}^{0} - \Big[\cos mKx\Big]_{0}^{L/2} \right\} = \frac{2}{mKL}\left\{ 1 - \cos\frac{mKL}{2} - \cos\frac{mKL}{2} + 1 \right\}$$

$$b_m = \frac{4}{mKL}\left[1 - \cos\left(\frac{mKL}{2}\right)\right] \xrightarrow{K = 2\pi/L} \frac{2}{m\pi}(1 - \cos m\pi)$$

$$f(x) = \frac{2}{\pi}\sum_{m=1}^{\infty}\left(\frac{1-\cos m\pi}{m}\right)\sin\frac{2\pi m x}{L} = \frac{2}{\pi}\left(2\sin\left(\frac{2\pi x}{L}\right) + \frac{2}{3}\sin\left(\frac{6\pi x}{L}\right) + \dots\right)$$

or $f(x) = \frac{4}{\pi}\left(\frac{\sin Kx}{1} + \frac{\sin 3Kx}{3} + \frac{\sin 5Kx}{5} + \dots\right)$

12-2.

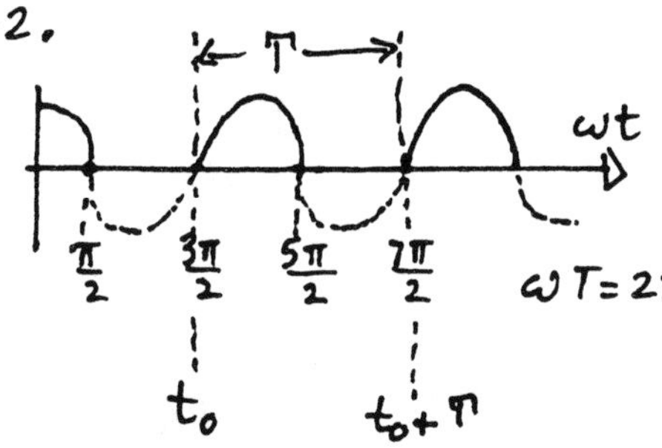


$$f(t) = \begin{cases} E_0 \cos\omega t\,, & \tfrac{3}{2}\pi < \omega t < \tfrac{5}{2}\pi \\ 0 & , \tfrac{5}{2}\pi < \omega t < \tfrac{7}{2}\pi \end{cases}$$

$$f(t) = \frac{a_0}{2} + \sum_{m=1}^{\infty} a_m \cos m\omega t$$

where $\begin{cases} a_0 = \frac{2}{T}\int_{t_0}^{t_0+T} f(t)\,dt \\ a_m = \frac{2}{T}\int_{t_0}^{t_0+T} f(t)\cos m\omega t\,dt \end{cases}$

$$a_0 = \frac{2}{T}\int_{t_0}^{t_0+T} f(t)\,dt = \frac{2}{\omega T}\int E_0\cos\omega t\,d(\omega t) = \frac{2E_0}{\omega T}\sin\omega t\Big]_{3\pi/2}^{5\pi/2} = \frac{2E_0}{\pi}$$

$$a_m = \frac{2E_0}{\omega T}\int_{3\pi/2}^{5\pi/2}\cos\omega t\cos m\omega t\,d(\omega t)$$

$$m=1: \quad a_1 = \frac{2E_0}{\omega T}\int_{3\pi/2}^{5\pi/2}\cos^2\omega t\,d(\omega t) = \frac{2E_0}{2\pi}\left[\frac{\omega t}{2} + \frac{\sin 2\omega t}{4}\right]_{3\pi/2}^{5\pi/2} = \frac{E_0}{2}$$

$$m \neq 1: \quad a_m = \frac{2E_0}{\omega T}\left[\frac{\sin(m-1)\omega t}{2(m-1)} + \frac{\sin(m+1)\omega t}{2(m+1)}\right]_{3\pi/2}^{5\pi/2}$$

$$m=2: \quad a_2 = \frac{2E_0}{2\pi}\left[\frac{\sin\omega t}{2} + \frac{\sin 3\omega t}{6}\right]_{3\pi/2}^{5\pi/2} = \frac{2E_0}{3\pi}$$

$$m=3: \quad a_3 = a_5 = a_7 = \dots = 0$$

$$m=4: \quad a_4 = \frac{E_0}{\pi}\left[\frac{\sin 3\omega t}{6} + \frac{\sin 5\omega t}{10}\right]_{3\pi/2}^{5\pi/2} = -\frac{2E_0}{15\pi}$$

12-2. (cont'd.)

All $b_m = 0$ since function is even or, more tediously, by integration.

Thus

$$f(t) = \frac{E_0}{\pi} + \frac{E_0}{2}\cos\omega t + \frac{2E_0}{3\pi}\cos 2\omega t - \frac{2E_0}{15\pi}\cos 4\omega t + \ldots$$

12-3. $g(\omega) = \frac{1}{2\pi}\int_{-\infty}^{\infty} f(t)e^{i\omega t}dt = \frac{1}{2\pi}\int_{-\infty}^{\infty} h e^{-t^2/2\sigma^2} e^{i\omega t} dt$

$$g(\omega) = \frac{h}{2\pi}\int_{-\infty}^{\infty} e^{-\left[\frac{t^2}{2\sigma^2} - i\omega t\right]} dt$$

Complete the square: $\frac{t^2}{2\sigma^2} - i\omega t = \left(\frac{t}{\sqrt{2}\sigma} - \frac{i\sigma\omega}{\sqrt{2}}\right)^2 + \frac{\sigma^2\omega^2}{2}$

$$g(\omega) = \frac{h}{2\pi}\int_{-\infty}^{\infty} e^{-\left[\left(\frac{t}{\sqrt{2}\sigma} - \frac{i\sigma\omega}{\sqrt{2}}\right)^2 + \frac{\sigma^2\omega^2}{2}\right]} dt = \frac{h}{2\pi} e^{-\frac{\sigma^2\omega^2}{2}}\int_{-\infty}^{\infty} e^{-\left(\frac{t}{\sqrt{2}\sigma} - \frac{i\sigma\omega}{\sqrt{2}}\right)^2} dt$$

Let $x \equiv \frac{t}{\sqrt{2}\sigma} - \frac{i\sigma\omega}{\sqrt{2}}$ so $dx = \frac{dt}{\sqrt{2}\sigma}$

$$g(\omega) = \frac{h}{2\pi} e^{-\frac{\sigma^2\omega^2}{2}}\int_{-\infty}^{\infty} e^{-x^2}\sqrt{2}\sigma\, dx = \frac{h}{2\pi} e^{-\frac{\sigma^2\omega^2}{2}}\sqrt{2}\sigma \underbrace{\int_{-\infty}^{\infty} e^{-x^2} dx}_{\sqrt{\pi}}$$

$$g(\omega) = \frac{\sigma h}{\sqrt{2\pi}} e^{-\sigma^2\omega^2/2} \qquad \text{Q.E.D.}$$

12-4.

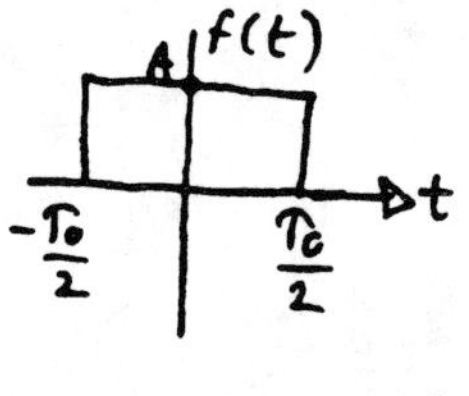


$f(t) = \int_{-\infty}^{\infty} g(\omega)e^{-i\omega t}d\omega$ where $g(\omega) = \frac{1}{2\pi}\int_{-\infty}^{\infty} f(t)e^{i\omega t}dt$

$$g(\omega) = \frac{1}{2\pi}\int_{-T_0/2}^{T_0/2} A e^{i\omega t}dt = \frac{A}{2\pi}\left[\frac{e^{i\omega t}}{i\omega}\right]_{-T_0/2}^{T_0/2}$$

$$g(\omega) = \frac{A}{\pi\omega}\left[\frac{e^{i\omega T_0/2} - e^{-i\omega T_0/2}}{2i}\right] = \frac{A}{\pi\omega}\sin\left(\frac{\omega T_0}{2}\right) = \frac{AT_0}{2\pi}\text{sinc}\left(\frac{\omega T_0}{2}\right)$$

$$|g(\omega)|^2 = \frac{A^2T_0^2}{4\pi^2}\text{sinc}^2(\omega T_0/2)$$

$\Delta\omega \cong \frac{2\pi}{T_0}$

$2\pi\Delta f \cong 2\pi/T_0$

$\Delta f \cong \frac{1}{T_0}$ Q.E.D.

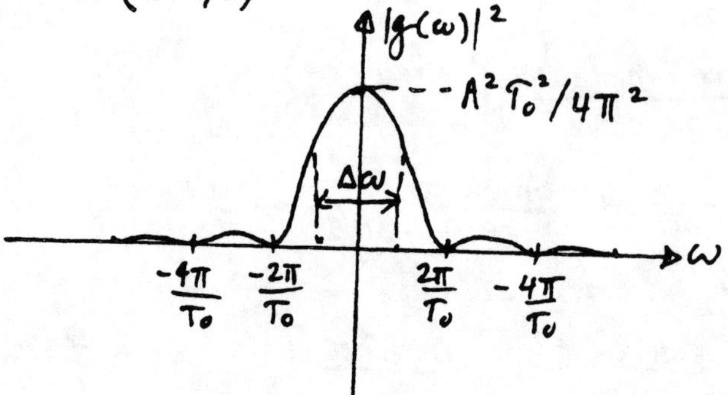

12-5.

$$\ell_t = \lambda^2/\Delta\lambda$$

$$(\ell_t)_1 = \frac{(590)^2}{100} = 3.48\times10^{-4}\,m$$

$$(\ell_t)_2 = \frac{(590)^2}{10} = 3.48\times10^{-5}\,m$$

Use longer coherence-length light, thus shorter-bandwidth filter.

12-6. $\ell_t = c\tau_0 = c(0.1\times10^{-9}) = 3\ cm$

$$\Delta f = \frac{1}{\tau_0} = \frac{1}{0.1\times10^{-9}} = 10^{10}\,Hz$$

$$\Delta\lambda = \frac{\lambda^2}{\ell_t} = \frac{(632.8\times10^{-7}\,cm)^2}{3\,cm} = 0.013\,nm$$

12-7.

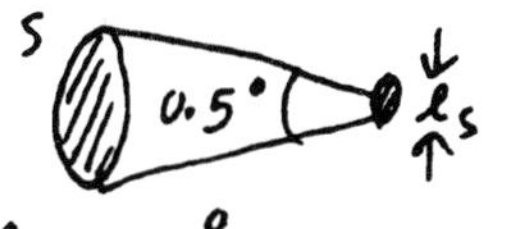


$\theta = 0.5° = 0.008727\,rad$

$$\ell_s < \frac{1.22\lambda}{\theta} = \frac{1.22\,(550\times10^{-7}\,cm)}{0.008727} = 0.00769\,cm$$

$\ell_s < 0.0769\,mm$

If $\ell_s$ is the diameter of a circle of coherence, then "good" coherence exists over an area of 10% the area, or a diameter of $\sqrt{0.1}\,\ell_s$. $\sqrt{.1}\,\ell_s < \sqrt{.1}\,(0.0769) = 0.0243\,mm$

12-8. (a) $\Delta\lambda = \dfrac{\lambda^2}{\ell_t} = \dfrac{(643.8\,nm)^2}{30\times10^7\,nm} = 0.00138\,nm$

(b) $\tau_c = \dfrac{\ell_t}{c} = \dfrac{30\,cm}{c} = 1\,ns$

12-9. $\lambda = \lambda_0 \pm \Delta\lambda/2$

$\lambda = 5000 \pm 0.5\ Å$

$$\ell_t = \frac{\lambda^2}{\Delta\lambda} = \frac{(5000\ Å)^2}{1\ Å} = 0.25\ cm = 2.5\,mm$$

12-10.

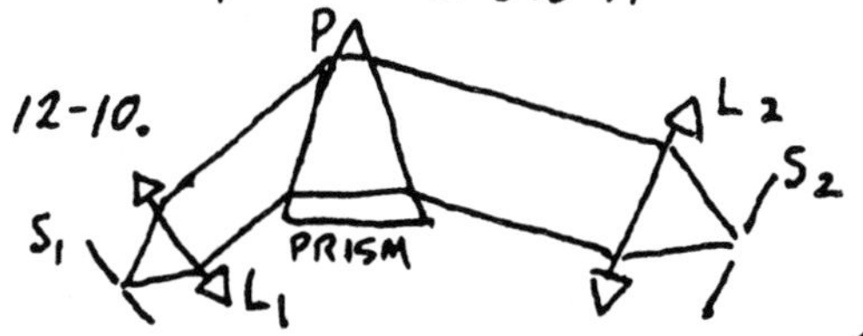


$20\ Å/mm \times 0.2\,mm = 4\ Å$

Thus, $\lambda = 5000\ Å$ and $\Delta\lambda = 4\ Å$

$$\ell_t = \frac{\lambda^2}{\Delta\lambda} = \frac{(5\times10^{-5}\,cm)^2}{4\times10^{-8}\,cm} = 0.0625\,cm$$

$$\tau_0 = \ell_t/c = 0.0625\,cm/c = 2.08\times10^{-12}\,s$$

12-11.

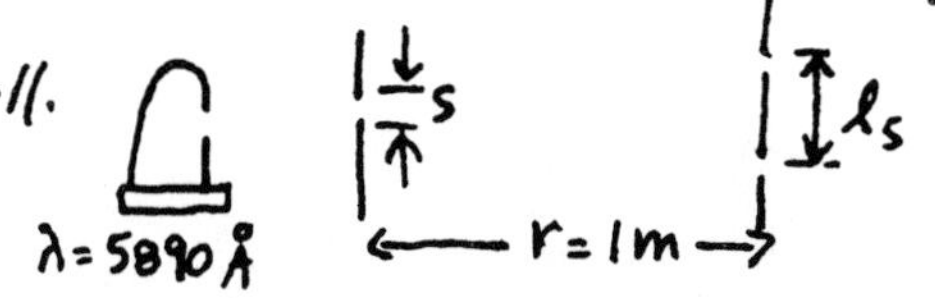


$$\ell_s < \frac{1.22\,r\lambda}{s} = \frac{1.22\,(100\,cm)(5.89\times10^{-5}\,cm)}{0.05\,cm}$$

$\ell_s < 0.144\,cm$

12-12. $\Delta\lambda = \dfrac{\lambda^2}{\ell_t} = \dfrac{(6328\times10^{-10}\,m)^2}{10^4\,m} = 4\times10^{-7}\ Å$

$$\Delta f = \frac{1}{\tau_0} = \frac{c}{\ell_t} = \frac{c}{10^4\,m} = 3\times10^4\,Hz$$

12-13. $\Delta\lambda = 20\,\text{Å/mm} \times \underbrace{200\times10^{-3}\,\text{mm}}_{200\,\mu m} = 4\,\text{Å}$

(a) $\ell_t = \dfrac{\lambda^2}{\Delta\lambda} = \dfrac{(500\times10^{-7}\,cm)^2}{4\times10^{-8}\,cm} = 0.0625\,cm$

$\tau_0 = \ell_t/c = 0.0625\,cm/c = 2.08\times10^{-12}\,s$ } as in Prob. 12-10

(b) $\Delta = 0.4\,mm$

normalized correlation fn $= |\gamma_{12}(\tau)| = 1 - \tau/\tau_0$

But $\tau/\tau_0 = \Delta\ell/\ell_t = \dfrac{0.4\,mm}{0.625\,mm} = 0.64$

Thus $|\gamma_{12}(\tau)| = 1 - \tau/\tau_0 = 1 - 0.64 = 0.36$

Visibility $\mathcal{V} = |\gamma_{12}(\tau)| = 0.36$

(c) $\mathcal{V} = \dfrac{I_{max} - I_{min}}{I_{max} + I_{min}} = 0.36 = \dfrac{100 - I_{min}}{100 + I_{min}}$ or $I_{min} = 47.06$

thus $I_{max} - I_{min} = 100 - 47 = 53$

12-14.

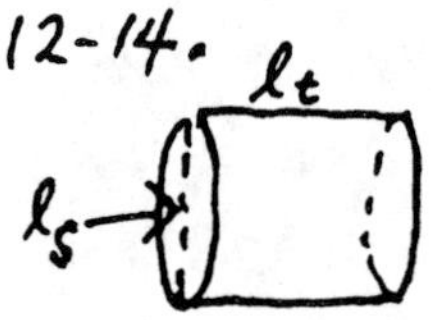


$\ell_t = \dfrac{\lambda^2}{\Delta\lambda} = \dfrac{550^2}{700-400} = 1.0083\times10^{-4}\,cm = 1.83\,\lambda_{av}$

$\ell_s = \dfrac{1.22\lambda}{\theta} = \dfrac{1.22(550)}{0.008727} = 76890\,nm = 7.689\times10^{-3}\,cm$

"Good" $\ell_s = 0.25\,(7.689\times10^{-3}) = 1.922\times10^{-3}\,cm = 35\,\lambda_{av}$

$A_{base} = \dfrac{\pi d^2}{4} = \dfrac{\pi}{4}\ell_s^2 = \dfrac{\pi}{4}(1.922\times10^{-3})^2 = 2.90\times10^{-6}\,cm^2$

12-15.

(a) For unequal beams and partial coherence,

$$I_p = I_1 + I_2 + 2\sqrt{I_1 I_2}\,\text{Re}(\gamma_{12})$$

where $\text{Re}(\gamma_{12}) = \text{Re}\,(1 - \tau/\tau_0)e^{i\omega\tau} = (1 - \tau/\tau_0)\cos\omega\tau = |\gamma_{12}|\cos\omega\tau$

Then $I_p = I_1 + I_2 + 2\sqrt{I_1 I_2}\,|\gamma_{12}|\cos\omega\tau$

so $I_{max} = I_1 + I_2 + 2\sqrt{I_1 I_2}\,|\gamma_{12}|$; $I_{min} = I_1 + I_2 - 2\sqrt{I_1 I_2}\,|\gamma_{12}|$

Then fringe visibility $\mathcal{V} = \dfrac{I_{max} - I_{min}}{I_{max} + I_{min}} = \dfrac{4\sqrt{I_1 I_2}\,|\gamma_{12}|}{2(I_1 + I_2)}$

or $\mathcal{V} = \dfrac{2\sqrt{I_1 I_2}\,|\gamma_{12}|}{I_1 + I_2}$ Q.E.D.

(b) For equal beams, $\mathcal{V}_{eq} = \dfrac{2\sqrt{I_0^2}\,|\gamma_{12}|}{2I_0} = |\gamma_{12}|$

when $\mathcal{V} = 0.9\,\mathcal{V}_{eq} = 0.9\,|\gamma_{12}|$, we have $\dfrac{2\sqrt{I_1 I_2}\,|\gamma_{12}|}{I_1 + I_2} = 0.9\,|\gamma_{12}|$

$4 I_1 I_2 = 0.81(I_1 + I_2)^2 = 0.81(I_1/I_2 + 1)^2$ or a quadratic in $R = I_1/I_2$:

$$0.81R^2 - 2.38R + 0.81 = 0$$

$$R = 2.55$$

12-16.

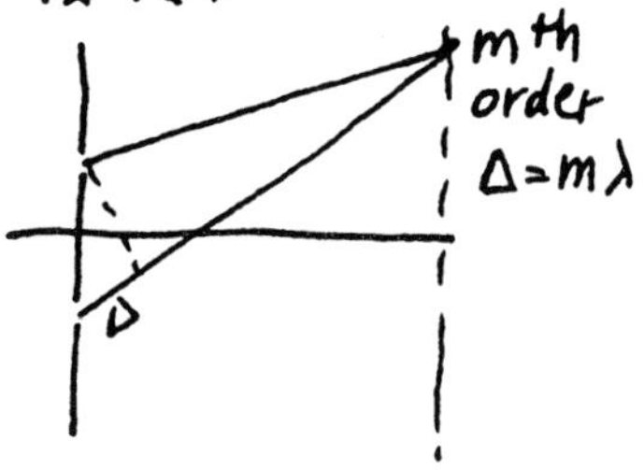


$$\mathcal{V} = 1 - \hat{\tau}/\tau_0$$

$$\frac{\hat{\tau}}{\tau_0} = \frac{\Delta}{l_c} = \frac{\Delta}{\lambda^2/\Delta\lambda} = \frac{m\lambda}{\lambda^2/\Delta\lambda} = \frac{m\,\Delta\lambda}{\lambda}$$

$$\mathcal{V} = 1 - \frac{m\,\Delta\lambda}{\lambda} \qquad \text{Q.E.D.}$$

12-17. $l_c = \lambda^2/\Delta\lambda = (546.1)^2/0.05 = 5.965 \times 10^6\ nm$

$\Delta = m\lambda = 20\lambda$

$$\mathcal{V} = 1 - \frac{m\,\Delta\lambda}{\lambda} = 1 - \frac{20(0.05)}{546.1} = 0.998 \quad \text{filtered Hg lamp}$$

With filtered white light, $\lambda_{av} = 546\ nm$ and $\Delta\lambda = 10\ nm$

$$\mathcal{V} = 1 - \frac{20(10)}{546} = 0.63$$

12-18. $\Delta = m\lambda = 2 \times 1\ cm = 2 \times 10^7\ nm$

$$\mathcal{V} = 1 - m\frac{\Delta\lambda}{\lambda} = 1 - \frac{(\Delta)(\Delta\lambda)}{\lambda^2} = 1 - \frac{(2\times10^7)(.0013)}{(643.847)^2} = 0.937$$

For a 5-cm movement, $\Delta = 2 \times 5\ cm = 10^8\ nm$, and

$$\mathcal{V} = 1 - \frac{(10^8)(0.0013)}{(643.847)^2} = 0.686$$

$\mathcal{V} \to 0$ when $1 - \frac{(2d)(\Delta\lambda)}{\lambda^2} \to 0$ or when $d = \lambda^2/2\Delta\lambda$

$$d = \frac{(643.847)^2}{2(.0013)} = 15.94\ cm$$

12-19. (a) $d = 1\ cm$

$$\mathcal{V} = 1 - \frac{(2\times10^7)(0.025)}{(546.1)^2} < 0 \quad \text{or } \mathcal{V} = 0 \qquad \text{(see Prob. 12-16)}$$

$d = 5\ cm$ : ditto

$$\mathcal{V} = 0 \text{ first when } d = \frac{\lambda^2}{2\Delta\lambda} = \frac{(546.1)^2}{2(0.025)} = 0.596\ cm$$

(b) $\mathcal{V} = 0.85 = 1 - 2d\frac{\Delta\lambda}{\lambda^2}$ or $d = 0.15\left(\frac{\lambda^2}{2\Delta\lambda}\right) = \frac{(0.15)(546.1)^2}{2(0.025)}$

$d = 0.0895\ cm$

## Chapter 13 Holography

13-1.

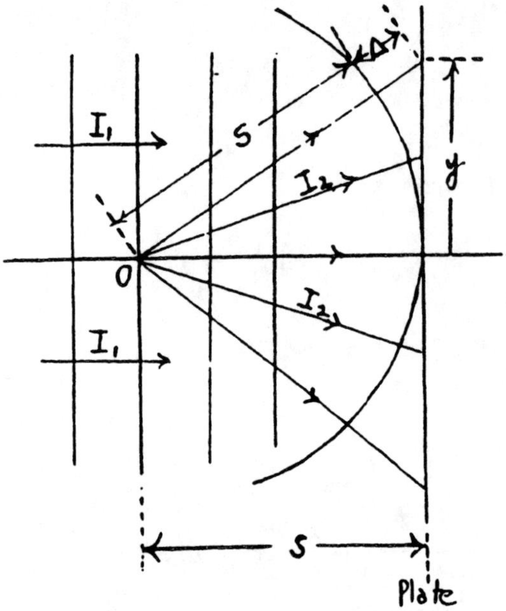


$I_1$ : plane waves

$I_2$ : spherical waves from O

Eq. (10-13):

$$I = I_1 + I_2 + 2\sqrt{I_1 I_2}\cos\delta$$

Write $\cos\delta \equiv 2\cos^2(\frac{\delta}{2}) - 1$

$$I = I_1 + I_2 + 2\sqrt{I_1 I_2}\left(2\cos^2(\tfrac{\delta}{2}) - 1\right)$$

$\delta = 2\pi(\frac{\Delta}{\lambda})$, where, from the diagram,

$$(s+\Delta)^2 = y^2 + s^2 \text{ , or}$$

$$s^2 + 2s\Delta + \Delta^2 = y^2 + s^2$$

$$\Delta(2s + \Delta) = y^2$$

But, for $\Delta << s$,

$$\Delta \cong \frac{y^2}{2s}$$

and $\delta \cong \frac{\pi y^2}{\lambda s}$

then $I = I_1 + I_2 + 2\sqrt{I_1 I_2}\left[2\cos^2\left(\frac{\pi y^2}{2\lambda s}\right) - 1\right]$

$$I = \underbrace{\left[I_1 + I_2 - 2\sqrt{I_1 I_2}\right]}_{A} + \left[\underbrace{4\sqrt{I_1 I_2}}_{B}\cos^2\underbrace{\left(\frac{\pi y^2}{2\lambda s}\right)}_{a y^2}\right]$$

$I = A + B\cos^2(a y^2)$, where $y = r$ = radius of zones

13-2.

(a) For $\left(\frac{E_R}{E_S}\right)^2 = N$, $\mathcal{V} = \frac{2\sqrt{N}}{N+1}$ (shown in Prob 10-4)

(b) $N = 3$ : $\mathcal{V} = \frac{2\sqrt{3}}{3+1} = 0.866$

13-3. (See Figure, next page)

From the center right triangle, $\sin\theta = \frac{\lambda_n}{2d} = \frac{\lambda_0}{2nd}$

OR $d = \frac{\lambda_0}{2n\sin\theta}$ Q.E.D.

For $\lambda_0 = 488\text{ nm}$, $n = 1$, $2\theta = 120^\circ$

$$\frac{1}{d} = \frac{2n\sin\theta}{\lambda_0} = \frac{2(1)\sin 60^\circ}{488 \times 10^{-7}\text{ cm}} = 3549 \text{ grooves/mm}$$

13-3 (cont'd.)

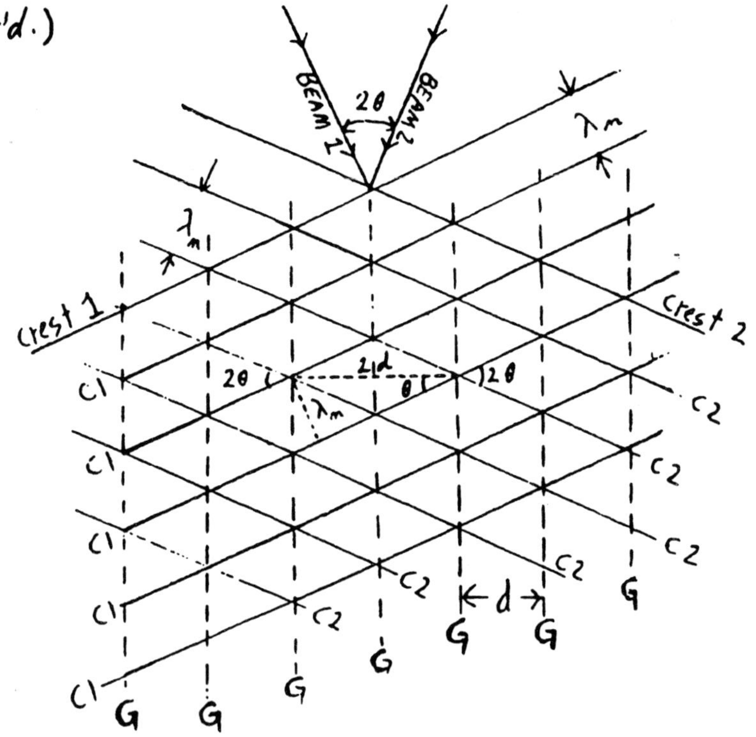


13-4. $d = \frac{\lambda n}{2 \sin \theta} = \frac{633\ nm}{2 \sin 10^\circ} = 1823\ nm = 1.82\ \mu m$

13-5. $V = \frac{x}{t} = \frac{\lambda/10}{10^{-9}} = \frac{633 \times 10^{-10}\ m}{10^{-9}\ s} = 63.3\ m/s$

13-6. $\frac{I_{max}}{I_{min}} = \left[\frac{A_R + A_S}{A_R - A_S}\right]^2 = \left[\frac{A_R/A_S + 1}{A_R/A_S - 1}\right]^2 = \left(\frac{8+1}{8-1}\right)^2 = 1.65$

13-7. $N_b = \frac{V}{\lambda_m^3} = \frac{1\ mm^3}{(492 nm/1.30)^3} = \frac{(10^{-3})^3\ m^3}{(492 \times 10^{-9}/1.30)^3\ m^3} = 1.8 \times 10^{10}$ bits

13-8.

(a) 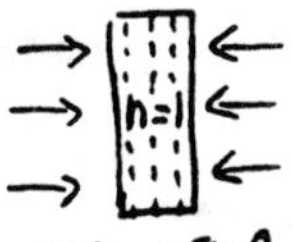


$\lambda = 550 nm$

$2\theta = 180^\circ$

$d = \frac{\lambda_0}{2n \sin\theta_0} = \frac{500\ nm}{2(1) \sin 90^\circ} = 250\ nm$

(b) $m\lambda = 2d$ OR $\lambda = \frac{2d}{m} = \frac{2(250\ nm)}{1} = 500\ nm$

(c) $m\lambda = 2n_F d \cos\theta_t = 2(1)(250\ nm) \cos 30^\circ = 433\ nm$

13-9. (a) See Prob 13-3.

(b) $d = \frac{\lambda_0}{2n \sin\theta} = \frac{633\ nm}{2(1)\sin 60°} = 365\ nm$

(c) $m\lambda = 2n_F d \cos\theta_t$ OR $\cos\theta_t = \frac{m\lambda}{2n_F d}$

$\cos\theta_t = \frac{(1)(450 nm)}{2(1)(365 nm)} = 0.61644$

$\theta_t = 51.9°$ relative to normal, or $38.1°$ relative to silver planes.

13-10. $\lambda = 430\ nm$

$d_0 = \frac{\lambda}{2 \sin 90} = \frac{430}{2} = 215 nm$

$d = d_0 - 0.15 d_0 = 0.85(215)$

$d = 182.75\ nm$

$\lambda = 2d \sin 90 = 2(182.75)(1)$

$\lambda = 365.5\ nm$

Blue components shift into uv and appear missing.

13-11. (a) $m = \frac{\lambda_R}{\lambda_c} = \frac{633}{337} = 1.88\ X$

(b) $m = \frac{\lambda_R}{\lambda_c} = \frac{633}{0.10} = 6330\ X$

13-12. (a) $E_R = re^{i\omega t}$ and $E_S = \frac{s}{R} e^{i(\omega t+\delta)}$; $E_F = E_R + E_S$

$I_F = |E_F|^2 = E_R^2 + E_S^2 + E_R E_S^* + E_R^* E_S = r^2 + \frac{s^2}{R^2} + \frac{rs}{R} e^{-i\delta} + \frac{rs}{R} e^{i\delta}$

$E_H \propto I_F E_R = \underbrace{(r^2 + \frac{s^2}{R^2}) E_R}_{E_{H1}} + \underbrace{\frac{r^2 s}{R} e^{i(\omega t - \delta)}}_{E_{H3}} + \underbrace{\frac{r^2 s}{R} e^{i(\omega t+\delta)}}_{E_{H2}}$

$E_{H1}$: amplitude-modulated reference beam

$E_{H3}$: phase-reversed subject beam (real image)

$E_{H2}$: amplitude modulated subject beam (virtual image)

(b) $\delta = \frac{\pi y^2}{\lambda d}$: derived in Prob 13-1, with $s \equiv d$

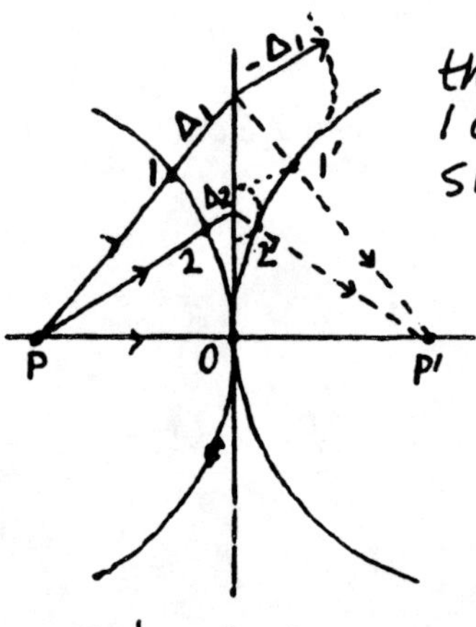


When the diverging spherical wave front (from P) on the left touches point O on the plate, phases of points 1 and 2 on the expanding wavefront – for example – show lags related to the path difference:

$\Delta_1 > \Delta_2 > \Delta_0 = 0$

When these differences are reversed, i.e., promoted to advances relative to O, then points such as 1' and 2', shown along the direction of reinforcement, (toward P') become appropriate. The points 0, 1', 2', ... are consistent with the spherical wavefront converging toward (real object) P'.

# Chapter 14 – Matrix Treatment of Polarization

14-1.

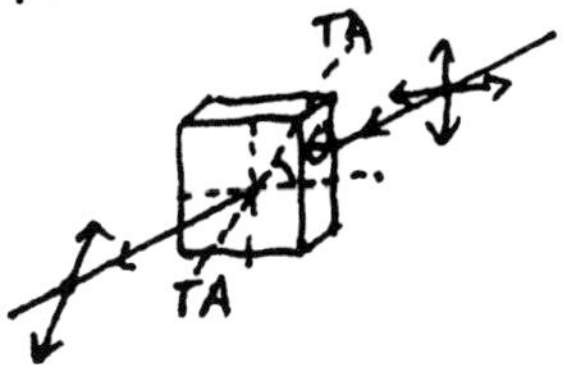


The four equations that specify the matrix elements are found from

$$\begin{pmatrix} a & b \\ c & d \end{pmatrix}\begin{pmatrix} \cos\theta \\ \sin\theta \end{pmatrix} = \begin{pmatrix} \cos\theta \\ \sin\theta \end{pmatrix} \quad \text{and} \quad \begin{pmatrix} a & b \\ c & d \end{pmatrix}\begin{pmatrix} \sin\theta \\ -\cos\theta \end{pmatrix} = \begin{pmatrix} 0 \\ 0 \end{pmatrix}$$

(polarized along TA) (transmitted) (polarized ⊥ TA) (No transmission)

OR (1) $a\cos\theta + b\sin\theta = \cos\theta$

(2) $c\cos\theta + d\sin\theta = \sin\theta$

(3) $a\sin\theta - b\cos\theta = 0$

(4) $c\sin\theta - d\cos\theta = 0$

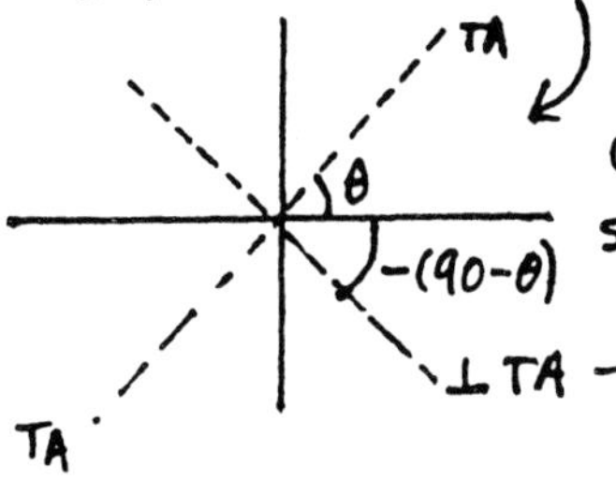


One way to solve:

Multiply (1) by $\sin\theta$

(3) by $\cos\theta$

$$a\sin\theta\cos\theta + b\sin^2\theta = \sin\theta\cos\theta$$
$$a\sin\theta\cos\theta - b\cos^2\theta = 0$$

Subtract: $b(\sin^2\theta + \cos^2\theta) = \sin\theta\cos\theta$ OR $b = \sin\theta\cos\theta$

Continuing this approach, one finds

$$M = \begin{pmatrix} \cos^2\theta & \sin\theta\cos\theta \\ \sin\theta\cos\theta & \sin^2\theta \end{pmatrix}$$

14-2. (a) $\vec{E} = \hat{i}E_0\cos(kz-\omega t) - \hat{j}E_0\cos(kz-\omega t)$

$$E = \begin{pmatrix} E_0 \\ -E_0 \end{pmatrix} = E_0\begin{pmatrix} 1 \\ -1 \end{pmatrix} \rightarrow \frac{1}{\sqrt{2}}\begin{pmatrix} 1 \\ -1 \end{pmatrix}:$$ Linear Pol. at −45°

(b) $\vec{E} = \hat{i}E_0\sin 2\pi\left(\frac{z}{\lambda} - ft\right) + \hat{j}E_0\sin 2\pi\left(\frac{z}{\lambda} - ft\right)$

$$E = \begin{pmatrix} E_0 \\ E_0 \end{pmatrix} = E_0\begin{pmatrix} 1 \\ 1 \end{pmatrix} \rightarrow \frac{1}{\sqrt{2}}\begin{pmatrix} 1 \\ 1 \end{pmatrix}:$$ Linear Pol. at +45°

(c) $\vec{E} = \hat{i}E_0\sin(kz-\omega t) + \hat{j}E_0\sin(kz-\omega t - \pi/4)$

$$E = \begin{pmatrix} E_0 \\ E_0 e^{-i\pi/4} \end{pmatrix} = E_0\begin{pmatrix} 1 \\ \cos\frac{\pi}{4} - i\sin\frac{\pi}{4} \end{pmatrix} \rightarrow \frac{1}{\sqrt{2}}\begin{pmatrix} 1 \\ \frac{1}{\sqrt{2}}(1-i) \end{pmatrix}$$

$$\tan 2\alpha = \frac{2E_{0x}E_{0y}\cos\epsilon}{E_{0x}^2 - E_{0y}^2} = \frac{2(1)(1)\frac{1}{\sqrt{2}}}{0} \rightarrow \infty; \quad 2\alpha = 90° \text{ OR } \alpha = 45°$$

Right elliptically pol. at 45°.

(d) $E = \hat{i}E_0\cos(kz-\omega t) + \hat{j}E_0\cos(kz-\omega t + \pi/2)$

$$E = \begin{pmatrix} E_0 \\ E_0 e^{i\pi/2} \end{pmatrix} = E_0\begin{pmatrix} 1 \\ i \end{pmatrix} \rightarrow \frac{1}{\sqrt{2}}\begin{pmatrix} 1 \\ i \end{pmatrix}$$ Left-circularly polarized.

14-3. (a) $\vec{E} = 2E_0 \hat{i}\, e^{i(kz-\omega t)}$

$E = \begin{pmatrix} 2E_0 \\ 0 \end{pmatrix} = 2E_0 \begin{pmatrix} 1 \\ 0 \end{pmatrix}$

$A = 2E_0\sqrt{1^2+0^2} = 2E_0$

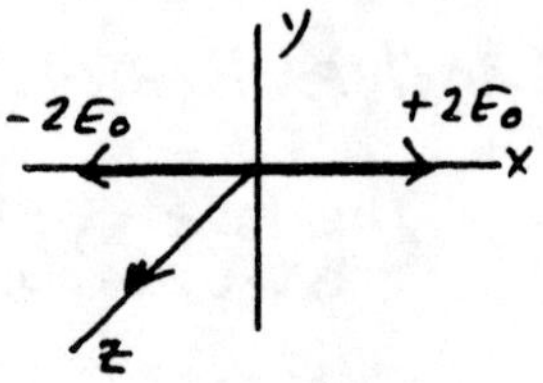


Velocity: +z
LP along x-axis
Amplitude $2E_0$

(b) $\vec{E} = E_0(3\hat{i} + 4\hat{j})e^{i(kz-\omega t)}$

$E = \begin{pmatrix} 3E_0 \\ 4E_0 \end{pmatrix} = E_0 \begin{pmatrix} 3 \\ 4 \end{pmatrix}$

$\tan\alpha = 4/3$ OR $\alpha = 53.13°$

$A = E_0\sqrt{3^2+4^2} = 5E_0$

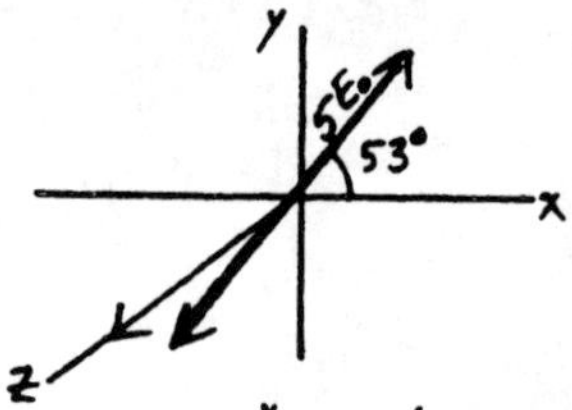


Velocity: +z
LP at 53° to x-axis
Amplitude = $5E_0$

(c) $\vec{E} = 5E_0(\hat{i} - i\hat{j})e^{i(kz-\omega t)}$

$E = \begin{pmatrix} 5E_0 \\ -5iE_0 \end{pmatrix} = 5E_0 \begin{pmatrix} 1 \\ -i \end{pmatrix}$

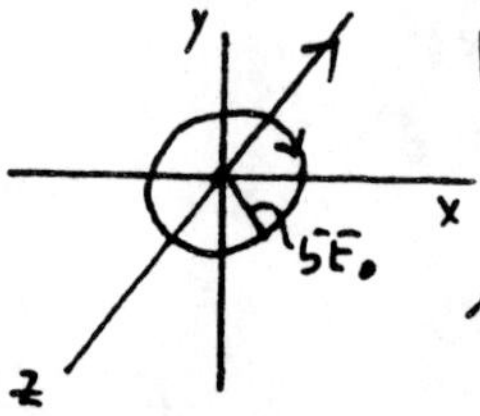


Velocity: −z dir.
Right Circ. Pol.
Amplitude = $5E_0$

14-4. (a) $E_1 = \begin{pmatrix} E_{01} \\ -E_{01} \end{pmatrix} = E_{01}\begin{pmatrix} 1 \\ -1 \end{pmatrix}$: Linearly polarized at −45°

$A = E_{01}\sqrt{1^2+(-1)^2} = \sqrt{2}\,E_{01}$

$E_2 = \begin{pmatrix} \sqrt{3}E_{02} \\ E_{02} \end{pmatrix} = E_{02}\begin{pmatrix} \sqrt{3} \\ 1 \end{pmatrix}$ Linearly polarized at $\tan^{-1}(1/\sqrt{3}) = +30°$

$A = E_{02}\sqrt{(\sqrt{3})^2+1^2} = 2E_{02}$

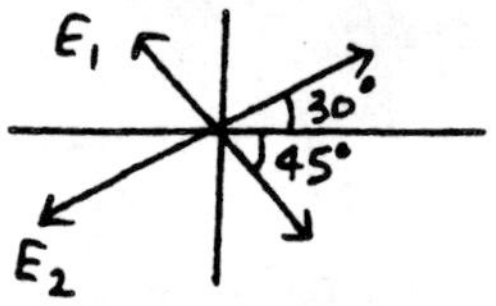


Thus, angle between them is 30°+45° OR 75° (or 105°).

(b) $\vec{E}_{01} \cdot \vec{E}_{02} = |E_{01}||E_{02}|\cos(E_{01}, E_{02})$

$E_{01}(1,-1) \cdot E_{02}(\sqrt{3},1) = (\sqrt{2}E_{01})(2E_{02})\cos\theta$

$E_{01}E_{02}(\sqrt{3}-1) = 2\sqrt{2}E_{01}E_{02}\cos\theta$ OR $\cos\theta = \dfrac{\sqrt{3}-1}{2\sqrt{2}}$ and $\theta = 75°$

14-5. Since we have not determined a matrix for a HWP with FA at arbitrary angle θ (here, 45°), we do the problem in two steps to avoid having to find this matrix.

First, consider the effect of passing LP light at −45° through a HWP <u>with FA vertical</u>.

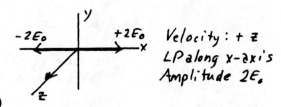

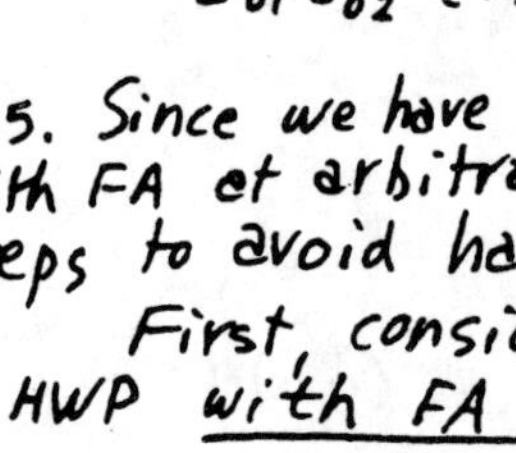


$\underbrace{\begin{pmatrix} 1 & 0 \\ 0 & -1 \end{pmatrix}}_{\text{HWP FA-vert}}\underbrace{\begin{pmatrix} 1 \\ -1 \end{pmatrix}}_{\text{LP at }-45°} = \begin{pmatrix} 1 \\ 1 \end{pmatrix}$ OR LP at +45°

Thus the first step rotates the LP light through 2×45° = 90°. If the LP light is originally vertical, it comes through the original HWP (SA at 45°) <u>horizontal</u>. The next two steps can be handled without change in orientation:

$\overbrace{\begin{pmatrix} 1 & 0 \\ 0 & -i \end{pmatrix}}^{\text{QWP}}\overbrace{\begin{pmatrix} 1 & 1 \\ 1 & 1 \end{pmatrix}}^{\text{LP}}\begin{pmatrix} 1 \\ 0 \end{pmatrix} = \begin{pmatrix} 1 & 1 \\ -i & -i \end{pmatrix}\begin{pmatrix} 1 \\ 0 \end{pmatrix} = \begin{pmatrix} 1 \\ -i \end{pmatrix}$ OR right circ. polarization

14-6. (a) Velocity: $+x$ so phase is $(Kx - \omega t)$

$\alpha = 30°$ $\quad \tan 30 = \frac{E_{oz}}{E_{oy}} = \frac{1}{\sqrt{3}}$

$\vec{E} = E_0(\sqrt{3}\hat{j} + \hat{k})\, e^{i(kx - \omega t)}$

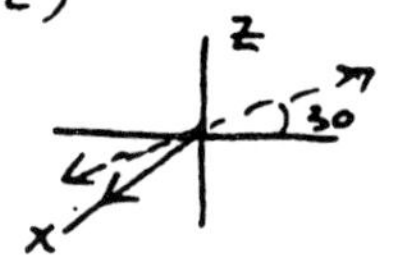

(b) Velocity: $+y$ so phase is $(Ky - \omega t)$

$\begin{pmatrix} E_{oz} \\ E_{ox} \end{pmatrix} \rightarrow \begin{pmatrix} A \\ -iB \end{pmatrix}$ with $A = 2B \rightarrow B\begin{pmatrix} 2 \\ -i \end{pmatrix}$

$\vec{E} = E_0(2\hat{k} - i\hat{i})\, e^{i(Ky - \omega t)}$

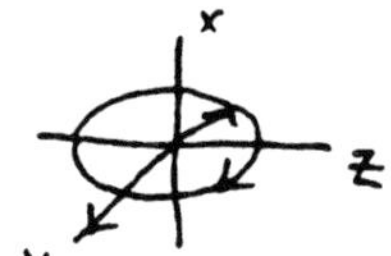

(c) Velocity: Not along an axis. Phase is $(K \cdot r - \omega t)$

where $\vec{K} = |k|\hat{K} = |K| \frac{(1,1,0)}{\sqrt{2}}$ and $\vec{K} \cdot \vec{r} = \frac{|K|}{2}(1,1,0)\cdot(x,y,z)$

$\vec{K} \cdot \vec{r} = \frac{|K|}{\sqrt{2}}(x+y)$

$E = E_0 \hat{K}\, e^{i\left[\frac{|K|}{\sqrt{2}}(x+y) - \omega t\right]}$

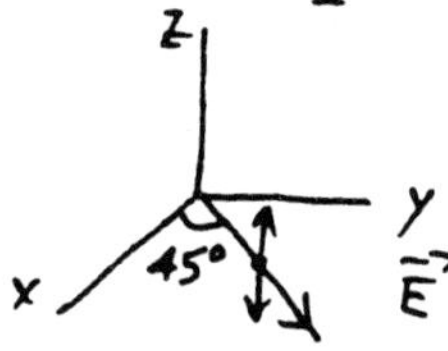

$\vec{E} = E_0 \hat{K}$

14-7. $\tilde{E}_0 = \begin{vmatrix} A \\ B + iC \end{vmatrix}$ (a) linearly polarized: $C = 0$ or $\tilde{E}_0 = \begin{vmatrix} A \\ B \end{vmatrix}$. Phase difference must be either 0° or 180° (or multiples): $m\pi$

(b) Elliptically polarized, major axis along coordinate axis: $B = 0$ or $\tilde{E}_0 = \begin{pmatrix} A \\ iC \end{pmatrix}$, with phase difference of $(m + 1/2)\pi$.

(c) Circularly polarized: $B = 0$ and $C = \pm A$, or $\tilde{E}_0 = A\begin{pmatrix} 1 \\ \pm i \end{pmatrix}$ with phase difference of $(m + 1/2)\pi$.

14-8. Ellipse: $\left(\frac{E_x}{E_{ox}}\right)^2 + \left(\frac{E_y}{E_{oy}}\right)^2 - 2\left(\frac{E_x}{E_{ox}}\right)\left(\frac{E_y}{E_{oy}}\right)\cos\epsilon = \sin^2\epsilon$, having the form of the quadratic,

$$E_y^2 + bE_y + c = 0$$

if $b = -2\left(\frac{E_{oy}}{E_{ox}}\right)(\cos\epsilon)E_x$ and $c = E_{oy}^2\left(\frac{E_x^2}{E_{ox}^2} - \sin^2\epsilon\right)$

As shown in text, when $M = \begin{pmatrix} A \\ B + iC \end{pmatrix}$, $E_{ox} = A$, $E_{oy} = \sqrt{B^2 + C^2}$, $\epsilon = \tan^{-1}(C/B)$. Thus the quadratic in $E_y$ can be solved once the Jones matrix is known. A basic program such as the following could be used:

```
INPUT "A,B,C= ? "; A1, B1, C1
XO= A1 : YO = SQR(B1↑2 + C1↑2)
E= ATN (C1/B1) : R= YO/XO
20 INPUT "EX = ?"; X
B= -2*R*COSE*X
C= R↑2*X↑2 - YO↑2*(SINE)↑2
D= SQR (B↑2 - 4*C)
Y1= (-B+D)/2 : Y2= (-B-D)/2
PRINT Y1; Y2
GOTO 20
END
```

14-8. (cont'd.)

In the program, matrix elements are called A1, B1, C1 to distinguish them from coefficients of the quadratic equation, a, b, c. Also, $X0 \equiv E_{ox}$ $E \equiv \epsilon$ $X \equiv E_x$

$Y0 \equiv E_{oy}$ $R \equiv E_{oy}/E_{ox}$ Y1 and Y2 $\equiv E_y$

Sample numerical values and a partial plot:

| $E_x$ | $E_y$ |
|---|---|
| 0 | 1, −1 |
| 0.5 | 1.32, −0.653 |
| 1 | 1.61, −0.276 |
| 1.5 | 1.87, 0.134 |
| 2 | 2.08, 0.588 |
| 2.5 | 2.22, 1.11 |
| 3 | 2, 2 |

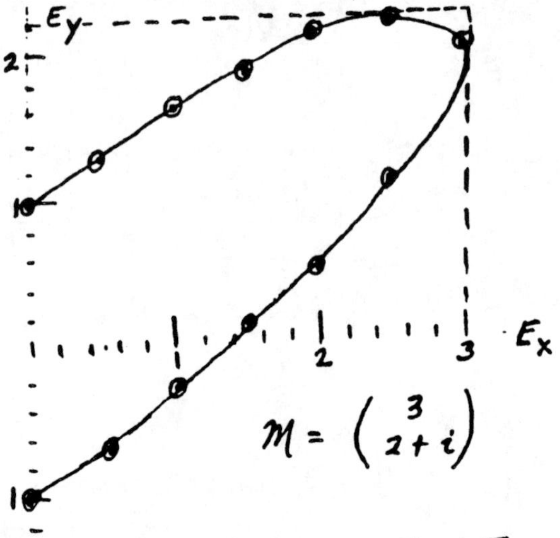


14-9. (a) $\begin{pmatrix} 3i \\ i \end{pmatrix} \rightarrow \begin{pmatrix} 3 \\ 1 \end{pmatrix}$ LP at $\tan^{-1}(1/3) = 18.4°$ ; $A = \sqrt{3^2+1^2} = \sqrt{10}$

(b) $\begin{pmatrix} i \\ 1 \end{pmatrix} \rightarrow \begin{pmatrix} -1 \\ i \end{pmatrix} \rightarrow \begin{pmatrix} 1 \\ -i \end{pmatrix}$ Right-Circular, A = 1

(c) $\begin{pmatrix} 4i \\ 5 \end{pmatrix} \rightarrow \begin{pmatrix} -4 \\ 5i \end{pmatrix} \rightarrow \begin{pmatrix} 4 \\ -5i \end{pmatrix}$ Right-Elliptical

(d) $\begin{pmatrix} 5 \\ 0 \end{pmatrix} \rightarrow$ LP along x, A = 5

(e) $\begin{pmatrix} 2 \\ 2i \end{pmatrix} \rightarrow 2\begin{pmatrix} 1 \\ i \end{pmatrix}$ Left circular, A = 2

(f) $\begin{pmatrix} 2 \\ 3 \end{pmatrix}$ LP at $\tan^{-1}(3/2) = 56.3°$ ; $A = \sqrt{2^2+3^2} = \sqrt{13}$

(g) $\begin{pmatrix} 2 \\ 6+8i \end{pmatrix} = 2\begin{pmatrix} 1 \\ 3+4i \end{pmatrix}$ Left-elliptical with $E_{ox} = 2$ ;

$E_{oy} = 2\sqrt{3^2+4^2} = 10$ ; $\epsilon = \tan^{-1}\left(\frac{4}{3}\right) = 53.1°$

$\tan 2\alpha = \dfrac{(2)(1)(5)\cos 53.1°}{1^2 - 5^2}$ OR $\alpha = -7.02°$

14-10. $\underbrace{\begin{pmatrix} 1 & 0 \\ 0 & -i \end{pmatrix}}_{\substack{QWP \\ SA\text{-}horiz}} \underbrace{\begin{pmatrix} \sqrt{3} \\ 1 \end{pmatrix}}_{\substack{LP \\ 30°}} = \begin{pmatrix} \sqrt{3} \\ -i \end{pmatrix}$ : Right Elliptical, $\frac{E_{ox}}{E_{oy}} = \sqrt{3}$

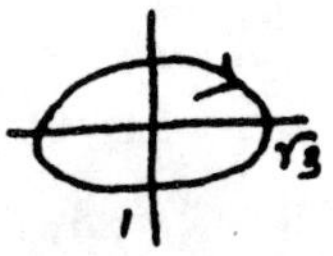


14-11. $\underbrace{\begin{pmatrix} 1 & 0 \\ 0 & -1 \end{pmatrix}}_{HWP} \underbrace{\begin{pmatrix} \cos\alpha \\ \sin\alpha \end{pmatrix}}_{LP\ at\ \alpha} = \begin{pmatrix} \cos\alpha \\ -\sin\alpha \end{pmatrix} = \underbrace{\begin{pmatrix} \cos(-\alpha) \\ \sin(-\alpha) \end{pmatrix}}_{LP\ at\ (-\alpha)}$

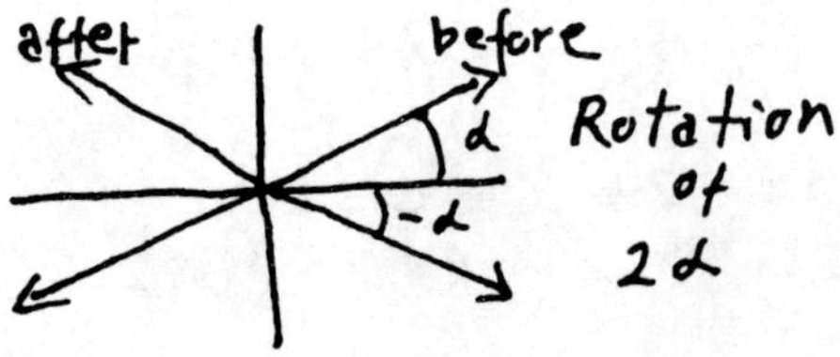

14-12. Light from the 45° LP passes through the QWP twice, before and after reflection. Thus it passes through (equivalently) a HWP that rotates the direction of polarization by 2 × 45° (see Prob. 14-11) or 90°. It then returns to the LP ⊥ to its TA. Result: No light returns from the reflector through the LP.

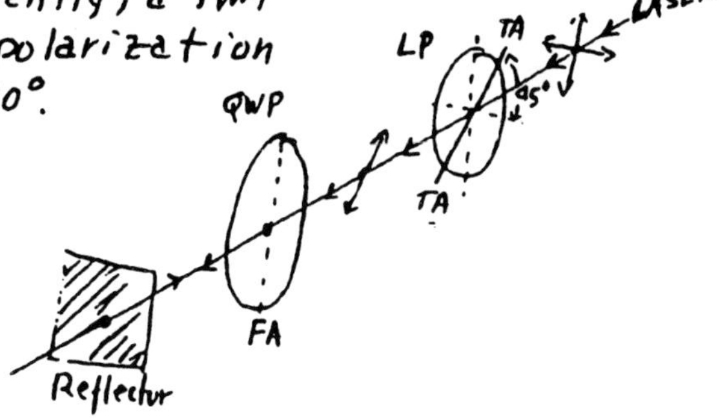


14-13. $\underbrace{\begin{pmatrix} 1 & 0 \\ 0 & -i \end{pmatrix}}_{\text{QWP SA-horiz}} \underbrace{\begin{pmatrix} 1 & 1 \\ 1 & 1 \end{pmatrix}}_{\text{LP TA at } 45°} \begin{pmatrix} 1 \\ 0 \end{pmatrix} = \begin{pmatrix} 1 & 1 \\ -i & -i \end{pmatrix} \begin{pmatrix} 1 \\ 0 \end{pmatrix} = \begin{pmatrix} 1 \\ -i \end{pmatrix}$ : Right Circular

14-4. $\underbrace{\begin{pmatrix} 0 & 0 \\ 0 & 1 \end{pmatrix}}_{\text{LP TA-vert}} \underbrace{\begin{pmatrix} 1 & 0 \\ 0 & -1 \end{pmatrix}}_{\text{HWP}} \underbrace{\begin{pmatrix} 1 & 0 \\ 0 & 0 \end{pmatrix}}_{\text{LP TA hor.}} \underbrace{\begin{pmatrix} 1 & 0 \\ 0 & i \end{pmatrix}}_{\text{QWP FA-hor}} \underbrace{\begin{pmatrix} 1 \\ 1 \end{pmatrix}}_{\text{LP at } 45°} = \begin{pmatrix} 0 & 0 \\ 0 & -1 \end{pmatrix} \begin{pmatrix} 1 & 0 \\ 0 & 0 \end{pmatrix} \begin{pmatrix} 1 \\ 1 \end{pmatrix} = \begin{pmatrix} 0 \\ 0 \end{pmatrix}$ No light

14-15.

$$\underbrace{\begin{pmatrix} 0 & 0 \\ 0 & 1 \end{pmatrix}}_{\text{LP, TA-y}} \underbrace{\begin{pmatrix} 1 & 0 \\ 0 & -i \end{pmatrix}}_{\text{QWP, SA-X}} \underbrace{\begin{pmatrix} \cos 30 \\ \sin 30 \end{pmatrix}}_{\text{Light from LP}} = \begin{pmatrix} 0 & 0 \\ 0 & 1 \end{pmatrix} \begin{pmatrix} \sqrt{3} \\ -i \end{pmatrix} = \begin{pmatrix} 0 \\ -i \end{pmatrix} = -i \begin{pmatrix} 0 \\ 1 \end{pmatrix}$$

(a) Right Elliptical (for $\begin{pmatrix} \sqrt{3} \\ -i \end{pmatrix}$)

(b) linearly pol-vert. (for $\begin{pmatrix} 0 \\ 1 \end{pmatrix}$)

14-16. (a) all cases, the result is linearly polarized light at ±45°:

SA-x, LCP: $\begin{pmatrix} 1 & 0 \\ 0 & -i \end{pmatrix} \begin{pmatrix} 1 \\ i \end{pmatrix} = \begin{pmatrix} 1 \\ 1 \end{pmatrix}$ : LP at +45°

SA-x, RCP: $\begin{pmatrix} 1 & 0 \\ 0 & -i \end{pmatrix} \begin{pmatrix} 1 \\ -i \end{pmatrix} = \begin{pmatrix} 1 \\ -1 \end{pmatrix}$ : LP at −45°

SA-y, LCP: $\begin{pmatrix} 1 & 0 \\ 0 & i \end{pmatrix} \begin{pmatrix} 1 \\ i \end{pmatrix} = \begin{pmatrix} 1 \\ -1 \end{pmatrix}$ : LP at −45°

SA-y, RCP: $\begin{pmatrix} 1 & 0 \\ 0 & i \end{pmatrix} \begin{pmatrix} 1 \\ -i \end{pmatrix} = \begin{pmatrix} 1 \\ 1 \end{pmatrix}$ : LP at +45°

14-16. (cont'd.)

(b) Eighth wave plate: $|\epsilon_y - \epsilon_x| = \frac{2\pi}{8} = \frac{\pi}{4}$

then $\mathcal{M}_{1/8} = \begin{pmatrix} 1 & 0 \\ 0 & e^{\pm i\pi/4} \end{pmatrix}$ for either $\epsilon_y > \epsilon_x$ or $\epsilon_y < \epsilon_x$

$$\begin{pmatrix} 1 & 0 \\ 0 & e^{\pm i\pi/4} \end{pmatrix} \underbrace{\begin{pmatrix} 1 \\ i \end{pmatrix}}_{LCP} = \begin{pmatrix} 1 \\ i e^{\pm i\pi/4} \end{pmatrix} = \begin{pmatrix} 1 \\ e^{i(\pi/2 \pm \pi/4)} \end{pmatrix} = \begin{pmatrix} 1 \\ e^{\pm 3i\pi/4} \end{pmatrix}$$

OR
$$\begin{pmatrix} 1 & 0 \\ 0 & e^{\pm i\pi/4} \end{pmatrix} \underbrace{\begin{pmatrix} 1 \\ -i \end{pmatrix}}_{RCP} = \begin{pmatrix} 1 \\ -i e^{\pm i\pi/4} \end{pmatrix} = \begin{pmatrix} 1 \\ e^{i(-\pi/2 \pm \pi/4)} \end{pmatrix} = \begin{pmatrix} 1 \\ e^{\pm i\pi/4} \end{pmatrix}$$

the results, using Euler's theorem, can also be expressed as

$$\begin{pmatrix} 1 \\ -\frac{\sqrt{2}}{2} \pm i\frac{\sqrt{2}}{2} \end{pmatrix} \text{ OR } \begin{pmatrix} 1 \\ \frac{\sqrt{2}}{2} \pm i\frac{\sqrt{2}}{2} \end{pmatrix} \; : \; \text{Form of } \begin{pmatrix} A \\ \pm B \pm iC \end{pmatrix}$$

where $A = 1$ and $|B| = |C| = \sqrt{2}/2$. Thus the result is elliptical pol.

14-17. $$\underbrace{\begin{pmatrix} 1 & i \\ -i & 1 \end{pmatrix}}_{\text{"Right Circ. Polarizer"}} \underbrace{\begin{pmatrix} A \\ B + iC \end{pmatrix}}_{\text{general pol. light}} = \begin{pmatrix} A + iB - C \\ -iA + B + iC \end{pmatrix} = \begin{pmatrix} (A-C) + iB \\ B - i(A-C) \end{pmatrix}$$

$$= [(A-C) + iB] \begin{pmatrix} 1 \\ -i \end{pmatrix} : \text{Right Circular.}$$

For a "left circular polarizer," the result must exhibit $+i$ instead.
Thus we try

$$\begin{pmatrix} 1 & -i \\ i & 1 \end{pmatrix} \begin{pmatrix} A \\ B + iC \end{pmatrix} = \begin{pmatrix} A - iB + C \\ iA + B + iC \end{pmatrix} = \begin{pmatrix} (A+C) - iB \\ B + i(A+C) \end{pmatrix} = [(A+C) - iB] \begin{pmatrix} 1 \\ i \end{pmatrix} \quad \text{Q.E.D.}$$

14-18. $$\underbrace{\begin{pmatrix} 1 \\ \pm i \end{pmatrix}}_{\text{circular}} + \underbrace{\begin{pmatrix} \cos\alpha \\ \sin\alpha \end{pmatrix}}_{\text{linear}} = \begin{pmatrix} \cos\alpha + 1 \\ \sin\alpha \pm i \end{pmatrix} = \underbrace{\begin{pmatrix} A \\ B \pm iC \end{pmatrix}}_{\text{elliptical}}$$

14-19. In general, elliptical polarization, $E_{ox} \neq E_{oy}$ and $\epsilon \neq 0$.

$$E_y = E_{oy} \cos(kz - \omega t) \equiv E_{oy} \cos\alpha$$
$$E_x = E_{ox} \cos(kz - \omega t + \epsilon) = E_{ox} \cos(\alpha + \epsilon)$$

Eliminate $z$ and $t$ through $\alpha$:

$\frac{E_y}{E_{oy}} = \cos\alpha$ and $\frac{E_x}{E_{ox}} = \cos(\alpha + \epsilon) \equiv \cos\alpha\cos\epsilon - \sin\alpha\sin\epsilon$

$E_x/E_{ox} = (E_y/E_{oy})\cos\epsilon - \sin\alpha\sin\epsilon$. Also, $\sin\alpha \equiv \sqrt{1-\cos^2\alpha} = \left[1 - \left(\frac{E_y}{E_{oy}}\right)^2\right]^{\frac{1}{2}}$

$\frac{E_x}{E_{ox}} - \frac{E_y}{E_{oy}}\cos\epsilon = -\sin\epsilon\sqrt{1-(E_y/E_{oy})^2}$. Squaring the equation,

$$\left(\frac{E_x}{E_{ox}}\right)^2 + \left(\frac{E_y}{E_{oy}}\right)^2 \cos^2\epsilon - 2\frac{E_x}{E_{ox}}\frac{E_y}{E_{oy}}\cos\epsilon = \left[1 - \left(\frac{E_y}{E_{oy}}\right)^2\right]\sin^2\epsilon$$

14-19. (cont'd.)

Making use of the identity $\sin^2\epsilon + \cos^2\epsilon \equiv 1$, the result follows:

$$\left(\frac{E_x}{E_{ox}}\right)^2 + \left(\frac{E_y}{E_{oy}}\right)^2 - 2\frac{E_x}{E_{ox}}\frac{E_y}{E_{oy}}\cos\epsilon = \sin^2\epsilon \qquad \text{Q.E.D.}$$

14-20.

(a) $\begin{vmatrix} A \\ B+iC \end{vmatrix} = \begin{vmatrix} 2 \\ 3e^{i\pi/3} \end{vmatrix} = \begin{vmatrix} 2 \\ 3\left(\cos\frac{\pi}{3} + i\sin\frac{\pi}{3}\right) \end{vmatrix} =$

Thus $A = 2$; $B = 3\cos\frac{\pi}{3} = \frac{3}{2}$; $C = 3\sin\frac{\pi}{3} = 3\sqrt{3}/2$

The normalized, standard form is then

$$\frac{1}{\sqrt{A^2+B^2+C^2}}\begin{vmatrix} A \\ B+iC \end{vmatrix} = \frac{1}{\sqrt{13}}\begin{vmatrix} 2 \\ 3/2 + i3\sqrt{3}/2 \end{vmatrix} = \frac{1}{\sqrt{13}}\begin{vmatrix} E_{ox} \\ E_{oy}e^{i\epsilon} \end{vmatrix}$$

This corresponds to elliptical polarization, with

$E_{ox} = A = 2$

$E_{oy} = \sqrt{B^2+C^2} = \left[(3/2)^2 + (3\sqrt{3}/2)^2\right]^{1/2} = 3$

$\epsilon = \tan^{-1}(C/B) = \pi/3 = 60°$

$\tan 2\alpha = \dfrac{2E_{ox}E_{oy}\cos\epsilon}{E_{ox}^2 - E_{oy}^2} = \dfrac{2(2)(3)\cos 60°}{2^2 - 3^2}$ OR $\alpha = \dfrac{-50.194°}{2} = -25.1°$

(b) Modification by the rotator is given by

$\begin{vmatrix} \cos\beta & -\sin\beta \\ \sin\beta & \cos\beta \end{vmatrix}\begin{vmatrix} 2 \\ 3e^{i\pi/3} \end{vmatrix}$, with $\beta = 30°$

$$\begin{vmatrix} \sqrt{3}/2 & -1/2 \\ 1/2 & \sqrt{3}/2 \end{vmatrix}\begin{vmatrix} 2 \\ 3e^{i\pi/3} \end{vmatrix} = \begin{vmatrix} \sqrt{3} - 3/2\, e^{i\pi/3} \\ 1 + 3\sqrt{3}/2\, e^{i\pi/3} \end{vmatrix} = \begin{vmatrix} \sqrt{3} - 3/2\left(\cos\pi/3 + i\sin\pi/3\right) \\ 1 + \frac{3\sqrt{3}}{2}\left(\cos\pi/3 + i\sin\pi/3\right) \end{vmatrix}$$

$$= \begin{vmatrix} (\sqrt{3} - 3/4) - i(3\sqrt{3}/4) \\ (1 + 3\sqrt{3}/4) + i(9/4) \end{vmatrix}$$

Note that, in general,

$$\begin{vmatrix} a - ib \\ a + ib \end{vmatrix} \times \frac{a+ib}{a+ib} \Rightarrow \begin{vmatrix} a^2+b^2 \\ (ac-bd) + i(bc+ad) \end{vmatrix}.$$

In this case, $a = \sqrt{3} - 3/4$, $b = 3\sqrt{3}/4$, $c = 1 + 3\sqrt{3}/4$, $d = 9/4$

so the standard form becomes

$$\begin{vmatrix} A \\ B+iC \end{vmatrix} = \begin{vmatrix} 2.65192 \\ -0.66506 + i(5.19615) \end{vmatrix}$$

$E_{ox} = A = 2.65192$

$E_{oy} = \sqrt{B^2+C^2} = 5.23854$

$\tan 2\alpha = \dfrac{2E_{ox}E_{oy}\cos\epsilon}{E_{ox}^2 - E_{oy}^2}$

$\alpha = +4.90276°$

$\epsilon = \tan^{-1}\left(\frac{C}{B}\right) = -82.7063°$, in Q-II because real part is negative, imag. part is positive

$\epsilon = -82.7063 + 180° = 97.29368°$

the new elliptical polarization is thus rotated by $\alpha_2 - \alpha_1$ or $4.903 - (-25.097) = +30°$, as expected.

14-21. $\left(\frac{E_x}{E_{0x}}\right)^2 + \left(\frac{E_y}{E_{0y}}\right)^2 - 2\left(\frac{E_x}{E_{0x}}\right)\left(\frac{E_y}{E_{0y}}\right)\cos\epsilon = \sin^2\epsilon$   Eq. (14-12)

(a) $\epsilon = \pi/2$. Then $\cos\epsilon = 0$ and $\sin\epsilon = 1$

$\left(\frac{E_x}{E_{0x}}\right)^2 + \left(\frac{E_y}{E_{0y}}\right)^2 = 1$ : Ellipse with semi-axes of $E_{0x}$ and $E_{0y}$ aligned with coordinate axes.

(b) $E_{0x}^2 = E_{0y}^2 = E_0^2$

$$E_x^2 + E_y^2 - 2E_xE_y\cos\epsilon = E_0^2\sin^2\epsilon$$

This is an ellipse with principal axes at 45° to coordinate axes, since

$$\tan 2\alpha = \frac{2E_0^2\cos\epsilon}{E_0^2 - E_0^2} = 0\ ;\ 2\alpha = 90°\ ;\ \alpha = 45°$$

(c) $E_x^2 + E_y^2 = E_0^2$ : circle centered at origin and with radius of $E_0$

(d) $\epsilon = 0$. Then $\cos\epsilon = 1$ and $\sin\epsilon = 0$

$$\left(\frac{E_x}{E_{0x}}\right)^2 + \left(\frac{E_y}{E_{0y}}\right)^2 - 2\left(\frac{E_x}{E_{0x}}\right)\left(\frac{E_y}{E_{0y}}\right) = 0 \quad \text{OR} \quad \left(\frac{E_x}{E_{0x}} - \frac{E_y}{E_{0y}}\right)^2 = 0$$

$E_y = \left(\frac{E_{0y}}{E_{0x}}\right)E_x$ : Straight line of slope $E_{0y}/E_{0x}$

14-22. Set up matrix product: (Analyzer) (QWP)(Light from polarizer)

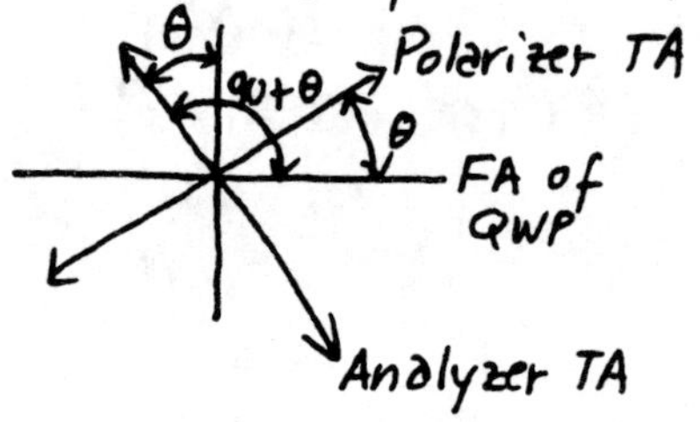


The analyzer is the general linear polarizer whose Jones matrix is

$$\begin{pmatrix} \cos^2\alpha & \sin\alpha\cos\alpha \\ \sin\alpha\cos\alpha & \sin^2\alpha \end{pmatrix}$$

where $\alpha = 90 + \theta$ so $\cos\alpha = -\sin\theta$, $\sin\alpha = \cos\theta$

The product is then

$$\begin{pmatrix} \sin^2\theta & -\sin\theta\cos\theta \\ -\sin\theta\cos\theta & \cos^2\theta \end{pmatrix}\begin{pmatrix} 1 & 0 \\ 0 & i \end{pmatrix}\overbrace{\begin{pmatrix} \cos\theta \\ \sin\theta \end{pmatrix}}^{\text{amplitude}=1} = (1-i)\sin\theta\cos\theta\overbrace{\begin{pmatrix} \sin\theta \\ \cos\theta \end{pmatrix}}^{\text{amplitude}=1}$$

The amplitude is $[(1-i)\sin\theta\cos\theta]$ so irradiance is

$I = [|1-i|^2\sin^2\theta\cos^2\theta]I_0$ where $I_0 = \cos^2\theta + \sin^2\theta = 1$ in this case

$I = (2\sin^2\theta\cos^2\theta)I_0$

# Chapter 15 - Production of Polarized Light

15-1. $I = I_0 \cos^2\theta$ : Malus' law

$$\left.\begin{aligned} I_1 &= \tfrac{1}{2} I_0 \\ I_2 &= I_1 \cos^2(30^\circ - 0^\circ) \\ I_3 &= I_2 \cos^2(60^\circ - 30^\circ) \end{aligned}\right\} \quad \begin{aligned} I_3 &= (\cos^2 30^\circ)(\cos^2 30^\circ)\left(\tfrac{1}{2} I_0\right) \\ I_3 &= 0.28125\, I_0 \text{ or } 28.1\% \text{ of } I_0. \end{aligned}$$

15-2. $\tan\theta_p = \frac{n_2}{n_1}$ when $n_1 = 1$ and $n_2 = 2.42$

Internal reflection: $\theta_p = \tan^{-1}\left(\frac{n_1}{n_2}\right) = \tan^{-1}\left(\frac{1}{2.42}\right) = 22.5^\circ$

External reflection: $\theta_p = \tan^{-1}\left(\frac{n_2}{n_1}\right) = \tan^{-1}\left(\frac{2.42}{1}\right) = 67.5^\circ$

15-3. (a)

$E_{op}$ - orig amplitude ∥ $TA_1$

$E_{on}$ - " " ⊥ $TA_1$

$E_{on}^2 + E_{op}^2 = E_0^2$

$E_{op}^2 = E_{on}^2 = \frac{E_0^2}{2}$

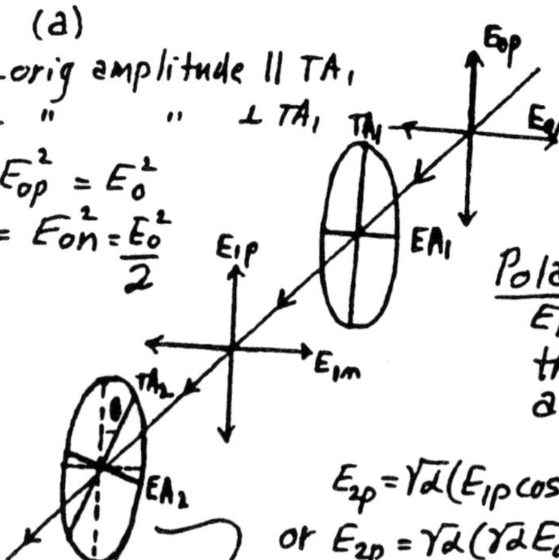


Polarizer 1:
$E_{1p} = \sqrt{\alpha}\, E_{op}$ thru $TA_1$ since energy fraction is $\alpha$. Similarly,
$E_{1m} = \sqrt{\beta}\, E_{om}$ thru $EA_1$

Polarizer 2: Now each component $E_{1p}$ and $E_{1m}$, has a component along both the transmission axis $TA_2$ and extinction axis $EA_2$ of the second polarizer.

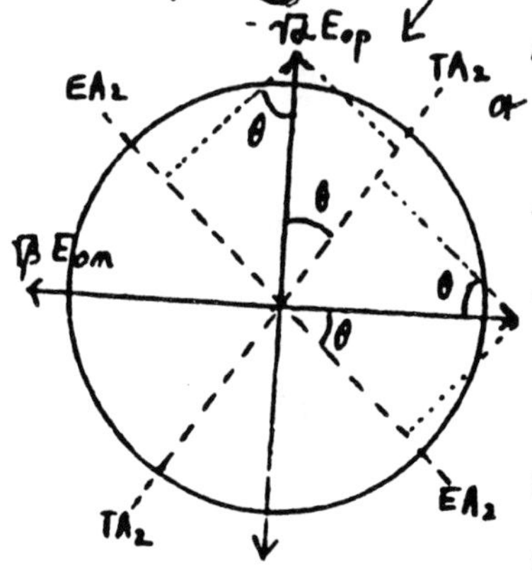


| | |
|---|---|
| $E_{2p} = \sqrt{\alpha}(E_{1p}\cos\theta)$ thru $TA_2$ | $E_{2m} = \sqrt{\alpha}(E_{1m}\sin\theta)$ thru $TA_2$ |
| or $E_{2p} = \sqrt{\alpha}(\sqrt{\alpha}E_{op})\cos\theta$ " | $E_{2m} = \sqrt{\alpha}(\sqrt{\beta}E_{om})\sin\theta$ " |
| $E_{2p} = \sqrt{\beta}(E_{1p}\sin\theta)$ thru $EA_2$ | $E_{2m} = \sqrt{\beta}(E_{1m}\cos\theta)$ thru $EA_2$ |
| or $E_{2p} = \sqrt{\beta}(\sqrt{\alpha}E_{op})\sin\theta$ " | $E_{2m} = \sqrt{\beta}(\sqrt{\beta}E_{om})\cos\theta$ " |
| $I_p = E_p^2 = [E_{2p}(TA)]^2 + [E_{2p}(EA)]^2$ | $I_m = E_m^2 = [E_{2m}(TA)]^2 + [E_{2m}(EA)]^2$ |
| $I_p = \alpha^2 E_{op}^2\cos^2\theta + \alpha\beta E_{op}^2\sin^2\theta$ | $I_m = \alpha\beta E_{om}^2\sin^2\theta + \beta^2 E_{om}^2\cos^2\theta$ |
| $I_p = E_{op}^2(\alpha^2\cos^2\theta + \alpha\beta\sin^2\theta)$ | $I_m = E_{om}^2(\alpha\beta\sin^2\theta + \beta^2\cos^2\theta)$ |

Use: $E_{op}^2 = E_{om}^2 = \frac{E_0^2}{2}$ and $E_0^2 = I_0$
and add all transmitted energies: $I = I_p + I_m$

$$I = \frac{E_0^2}{2}\left[(\alpha + \beta)\cos^2\theta + 2\alpha\beta\sin^2\theta\right]$$

$$I = I_0\left[\tfrac{1}{2}(\alpha + \beta)\cos^2\theta + \alpha\beta\sin^2\theta\right.$$

In the ideal case, $\beta = 0$ and $\alpha = 1$. Then

$$I = \frac{I_0}{2}\cos^2\theta \quad : \text{Malus' law.}$$

(b)

| $\theta$ | ideal | actual | |
|---|---|---|---|
| 0° | 0.5 | 0.4525 | fractions of $I_0$ |
| 30° | 0.375 | 0.351 | |
| 45° | 0.250 | 0.250 | |
| 90° | 0 | 0.0475 | |

$\alpha = 0.95$, $\beta = 0.05$

$I = I_0\left[\tfrac{1}{2}(\alpha^2 + \beta^2)\cos^2\theta + \alpha\beta\sin^2\theta\right]$ : actual

$I = \tfrac{1}{2} I_0 \cos^2\theta$ : ideal

15-4. $\frac{\lambda}{2} = t(\Delta n)$ or $t = \frac{\lambda}{2\,\Delta n} = \frac{632.8 \times 10^{-7}\,\text{cm}}{2(1.599 - 1.594)} = 0.063\,\text{mm}$

15-5. See Answers in text.

15-6. (a) $\Delta_{max} = 2\lambda = (\Delta n)(d_2 - d_1)$ OR $d_2 - d_1 = \frac{2\lambda}{\Delta n} = \frac{2(546.1 \times 10^{-6}\,\text{mm})}{1.555 - 1.546}$

$d_2 - d_1 = 0.12\,\text{mm}$

(b) $\Delta = \frac{\lambda}{4}$ for circularly polarized light

$d_2 - d_1 = \frac{\lambda}{4\,\Delta n} = \frac{546.1 \times 10^{-6}\,\text{mm}}{4(1.555 - 1.546)} = 0.015\,\text{mm}$

15-7.

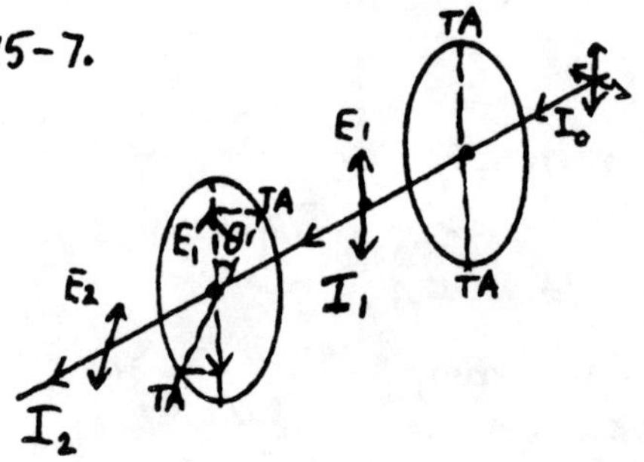


(a) $I_1 = I_0/2$ $\quad E_2 = E_1 \cos\theta$

$I_2 = (E_1 \cos\theta)^2 = I_1 \cos^2\theta$

$I_2 = \frac{I_0}{2}\cos^2\theta$

(b) $\theta = 90° - 0° = 90°$

$I_2 = \frac{I_0}{2}\cos^2 90° = 0$

(c) $I_7 = I_6 \cos^2 15°$

$I_6 = I_5 \cos^2 15°$

$\vdots \qquad \vdots$

$I_1 = \frac{1}{2} I_0$

$I_7 = (\cos^2 15°)^6 \left(\frac{1}{2} I_0\right) = 0.3298\, I_0$

OR 33 % $I_0$

15-8. $\frac{\lambda}{4} = (\Delta n)t$ or $t = \frac{\lambda}{4\,\Delta n} = \frac{589.3 \times 10^{-6}\,\text{mm}}{4(1.5534 - 1.5443)} = 0.0162\,\text{mm}$

15-9.

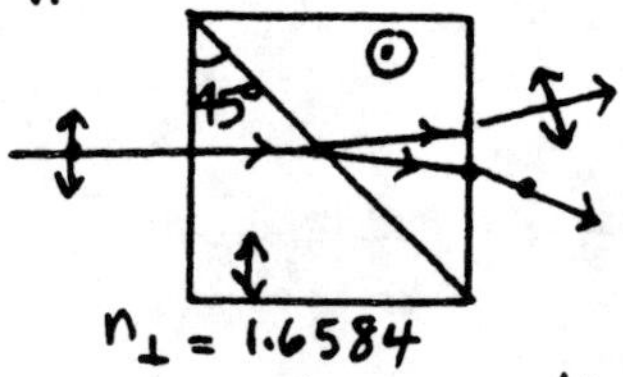


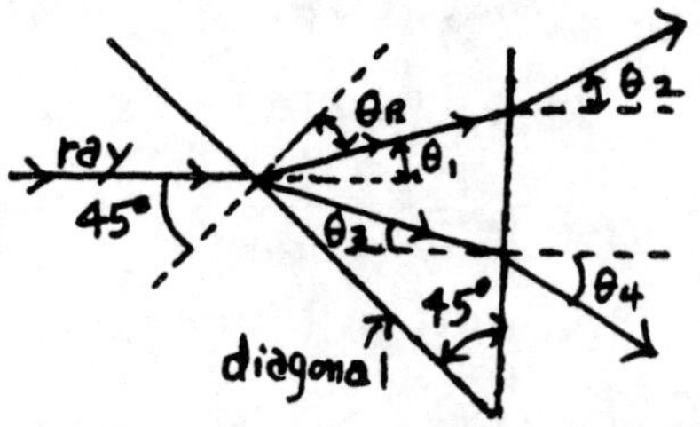


$n_\perp = 1.6584$

$n_\parallel = 1.4864$

At the diagonal interface:

from $n_\parallel$ to $n_\perp$: $1.4864 \sin 45 = 1.6584 \sin\theta_R$

OR $\theta_R = 39.329°$

from $n_\perp$ to $n_\parallel$: $1.6584 \sin 45 = 1.4864 \sin\theta_R'$

OR $\theta_R' = 52.086°$

On Exit:

Upper ray: $\theta_1 = 45 - \theta_R = 5.671°$; $1.6584 \sin 5.671° = (1)\sin\theta_2$ OR $\theta_2 = 9.432°$

Lower ray: $\theta_3 = \theta_R' - 45 = 7.086°$; $1.4864 \sin 7.086° = (1)\sin\theta_4$ OR $\theta_4 = 10.566°$

Deviation: $\theta_2 + \theta_4 = 9.432° + 10.566° = 19.997° \cong 20°$

15-10.

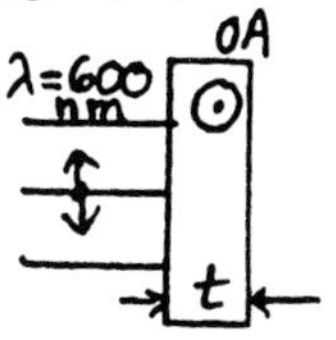


$t = 0.003\,cm$

$$\Delta\varphi = \pi/2 \text{ or } \Delta = \frac{\lambda}{4} = t\,\Delta n$$

$$\Delta n = \frac{\lambda}{4t} = \frac{600 \times 10^{-6}\,mm}{4(0.03\,mm)} = 0.005$$

15-11.

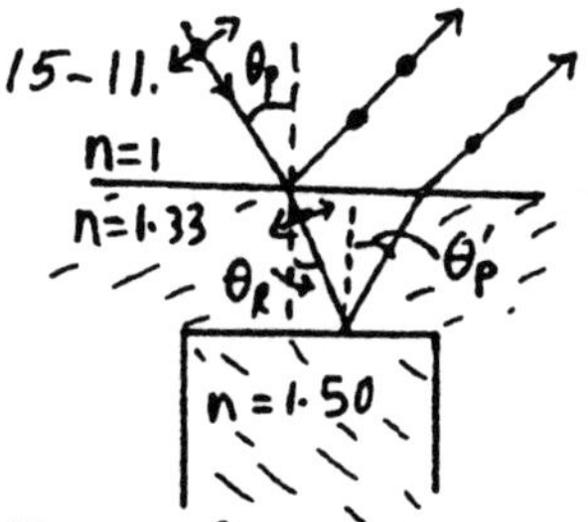


(a) $\tan\theta_p = \frac{n_2}{n_1} = \frac{1.333}{1}$ OR $\theta_p = 53.12°$

(b) $\theta_R = \sin^{-1}\left(\frac{\sin\theta_p}{1.333}\right) = 36.877°$

$\theta_p' = \tan^{-1}\left(\frac{1.50}{1.333}\right) = 48.37°$ for complete polarization

If surfaces were parallel, as in Figure, then $\theta_R = \theta_p' = 36.88°$; however, for complete polarization off the glass, $\theta_p'$ must be $48.37°$. Thus the glass must be tilted by $48.37° - 36.88° = 11.5°$ relative to the water surface.

15-12. (a) With polarizer alone rotating, there is no variation in intensity. This means there can be no linearly polarized, or elliptically polarized, component. The light must be either unpolarized or circularly polarized, or a mixture of both. If pure circularly polarized, then insertion of a QWP should produce extinction at some position. Since minima do not go to zero, the light is a mixture of circularly polarized and unpolarized light.

(See: Meyer-Arendt, for example, for a convenient diagrammatic analysis of such cases.)

(b) Here the rotating polarizer <u>does</u> produce a variation in intensity, so there must be linearly, or elliptically, polarized light or a component of both. Since the intensity never goes to zero, it cannot be a case of <u>pure</u> linearly polarized light. The use of the QWP now produces zero minima, so the light must be elliptically polarized. Any linearly polarized component would not be extinguished under the condition described.

15-13.

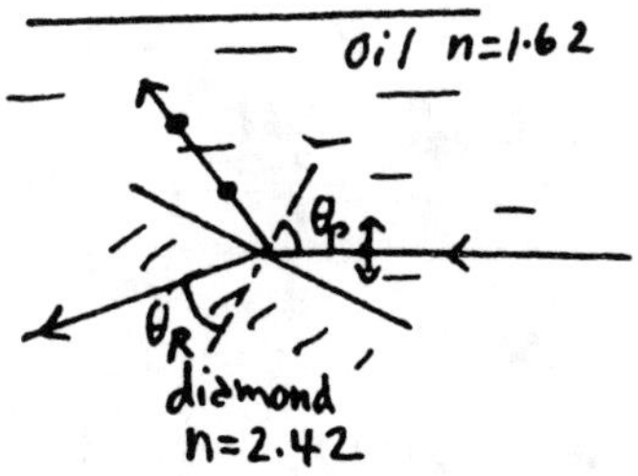


(a) $\theta_p = \tan^{-1}\left(\frac{2.42}{1.62}\right) = 56.2°$

(b) Snell:

$$\theta_R = \sin^{-1}\left[\frac{1.62\sin\theta_p}{2.42}\right]$$

$\theta_R = 33.8°$

15-14. $\beta = \rho L d \propto \frac{1}{\lambda^2}$   (a) $\beta = 1.23^\circ$, $L = 12\,cm = 1.2\,dm$

$\rho = 20.5^\circ$

$$d = \frac{\beta}{\rho L} = \frac{1.23}{(20.5)(1.2)} = 0.05\ g/cc$$

(b) $\frac{\beta_1}{\beta_2} = \frac{\lambda_2^2}{\lambda_1^2}$   If red ~ 700 nm ($\lambda_2$)
violet ~ 400 nm ($\lambda_1$)

$$\beta_1 = \left(\frac{\lambda_2}{\lambda_1}\right)^2 \beta_2 = \left(\frac{700}{400}\right)^2 (15) = 46^\circ$$

15-15. $\beta = \frac{\pi z}{\lambda_0}(n_L - n_R)$   (a) $\beta = 10^\circ = 0.01745$ rad

$$z = \frac{\beta \lambda_0}{\pi (\Delta m)} = \frac{(0.1745)(396.8 \times 10^{-6}\,mm)}{\pi (0.00011)}$$

$z = 0.200\,mm$

(b) $\rho = \beta$ when $z = 1\,mm$

$$\rho = \frac{\pi z}{\lambda_0}\Delta n = \frac{\pi (1mm)}{396.8 \times 10^{-6}\,mm}(0.00011) = 0.8709\ rad = 49.9^\circ$$

Also, by interpolation from Table 15-2, $\rho \cong 50^\circ$

15-16.
(a) $\frac{\lambda}{4} = t\Delta n$ OR $t = \frac{\lambda}{4\Delta n} = \frac{589.3 \times 10^{-6}\,mm}{4\,|1.4864 - 1.6584|} = 8.57 \times 10^{-4}\,mm$

(b) Zircon: From Table 15-1, $n_{\parallel} = 1.968$ and $n_{\perp} = 1.923$
$t = 0.0182\,mm$

To transmit, it must serve as a HWP: $\frac{\lambda}{2} = t\Delta n$, or

$$\lambda = 2t\Delta n = 2(0.00182 cm)(1.968 - 1.923) = 1.638 \times 10^{-4} cm$$
$= 1638\,n$
infra red

In general, $(m + \frac{1}{2})\lambda = t\Delta n$, or

$$\lambda = \frac{t\Delta n}{m + 1/2} = \frac{8.19 \times 10^{-5}}{m + 1/2}$$

For $m = 1$, $\lambda = \frac{8.19 \times 10^{-5}}{1.5} = 546\,nm$ (green)

$m = 2$, $\lambda = 327.6\,nm$ (uviolet)

thus in the visible, green light is transmitted.

15-17.

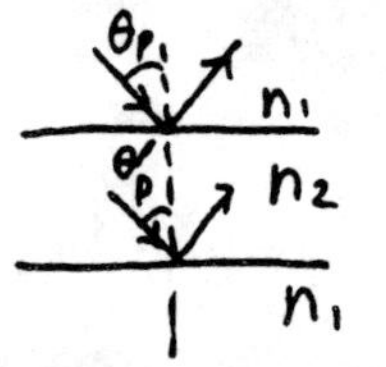


(a) $\theta_p = \tan^{-1} n_2/n_1$ ; $\theta_p' = \tan^{-1} n_1/n_2$

$$\tan\theta_p = \frac{n_2}{n_1} = \frac{1}{\tan\theta_p'} = \cot\theta_p'$$

or $\theta_p = 90 - \theta_p'$  Q.E.D.

(b)

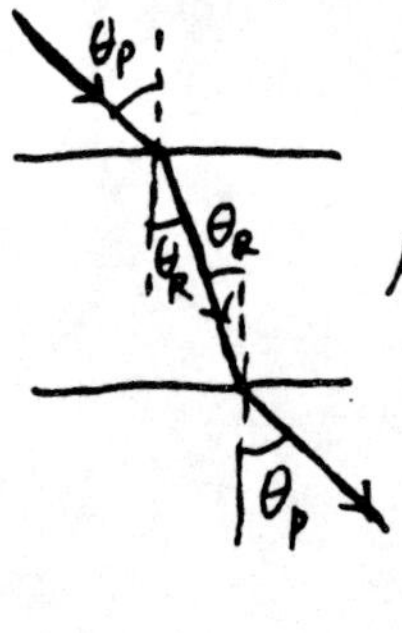


① $\tan\theta_p = n = n_2/n_1$ – Brewster's angle for light in.

Also ② $\sin\theta_p = n\sin\theta_R$ – Snell's law.

Then from ①: $\sin\theta_p = n\cos\theta_p$

Substituting ②: $n\sin\theta_R = n\cos\theta_p$ : $\theta_R$ and $\theta_p$ must be complementary.

$n = \tan\theta_p = \cot\theta_R = \frac{1}{\tan\theta_R}$ and $\tan\theta_R = \frac{1}{n} = \frac{n_1}{n_2}$  Q.E.D.

15-18. (a) $\Delta = t\Delta n$. For $t = \lambda$, $\frac{\Delta}{\lambda} = \Delta n = 1.5553 - 1.5462 = 0.0091$

(b) $\frac{\lambda}{4} = t\Delta n$ OR $t = \frac{546 \times 10^{-6} mm}{4(.0091)} = 0.015 mm = 15 \mu m$

(c) $(m + 1/4)\lambda = t\Delta n$ OR $m + 1/4 = \frac{t\Delta n}{\lambda} = \frac{(0.735 mm)(0.0091)}{546 \times 10^{-6} mm}$

$m + 1/4 = 12.25$ OR $m = 12$

(d) 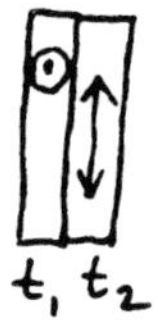 $\Delta_1 = -\Delta_2$  $\Delta_{total} = t_1 \Delta n + t_2(-\Delta n) = \frac{\lambda}{4}$

$t_1 - t_2 = \frac{\lambda}{4\Delta n} = \frac{546 \times 10^{-6} mm}{4(0.0091)} = 0.015 mm = 15 \mu m$

15-19. $\lambda = 500 nm$

$t = 1/16 in = 0.0625 in = 0.15875 cm$

$(m + 1/2)\lambda = t\Delta n$ OR $\Delta n = \frac{(m+1/2)\lambda}{t} = \frac{(m+\frac{1}{2})(500 \times 10^{-6} mm)}{1.5875 mm}$

$\Delta n = (m + 1/2)(3.1496 \times 10^{-4})$

FOR $\Delta m = 1$ between adjacent bands, $\Delta n = 3.15 \times 10^{-4}$

15-20.
From Eq. (15-2), $d = \frac{\lambda_0 \Delta\varphi}{2\pi \Delta n}$; From Table 15-1, $\Delta n = 1.598 - 1.590$
$\Delta n = 0.008$

(a) Plane Pol: $\Delta\varphi = \pi$ and $d = \frac{(0.5893)(\pi)}{2\pi(0.008)} = 36.8 \mu m$

(b) Circular Pol: $\Delta\varphi = \frac{\pi}{2}$ and $d = \frac{36.8 \mu m}{2} = 18.4 \mu m$

15-21. $\rho = 25.535$ deg/mm at 546 nm from Table 15-2.
Then $\beta = \rho L = +25.535 \frac{deg}{mm} \times 1.15 mm = +29.365°$ (ccw)
Thus the HWP must be set at $\beta/2 = +14.68°$, since it converts linearly polarized light at $+\alpha$ to linearly polarized light at $-\alpha$.

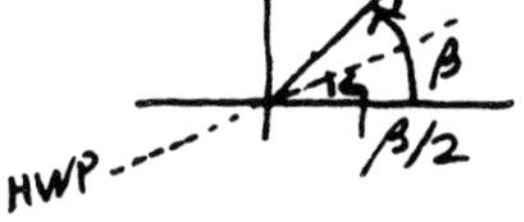


15-22. $\theta_p = \tan^{-1} n = \tan^{-1} n_2/n_1 = \tan^{-1} 1.5 = 56.31°$

(a) $R = \left[\frac{\cos 56.31 - \sqrt{1.5^2 - \sin^2 56.31}}{\cos 56.31 + \sqrt{1.5^2 - \sin^2 56.31}}\right]^2 = 14.79\%$

(b) The incident irradiance divides equally into $I_0/2$ for each mode: Brewster's angle is satisfied at each interface. For the TE mode, 14.8% is reflected, so 85.2% is transmitted at each interface. The TM mode is transmitted throughout at 100%. For N plates, there are 2N interfaces, so for N = 10 we have

% TE transmitted $= (0.852)^{2N} \frac{I_0}{2} = 0.0203 I_0 = 2.03\% I_0$

15-22. (cont'd.)

(c) Since $I_{TM}$ = 50% of $I_o$, or $0.50\, I_o$

$$P = \frac{0.5 - 0.0203}{0.5 + 0.0203} = 0.922$$

15-23.

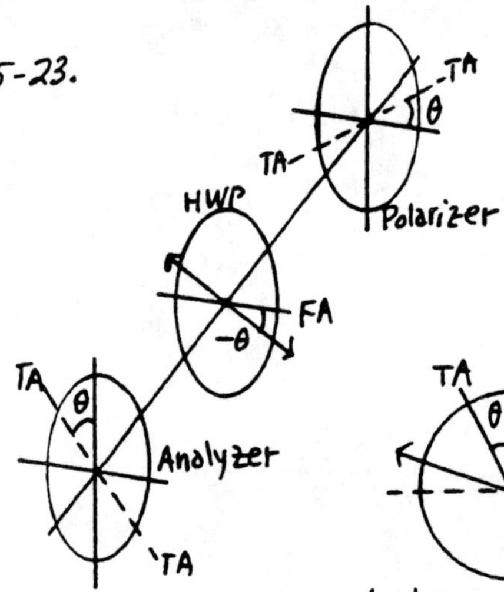


The HWP rotates the LP light from +θ to -θ so that the angle between the analyzer TA and the LP light is 90-2θ, as indicated.

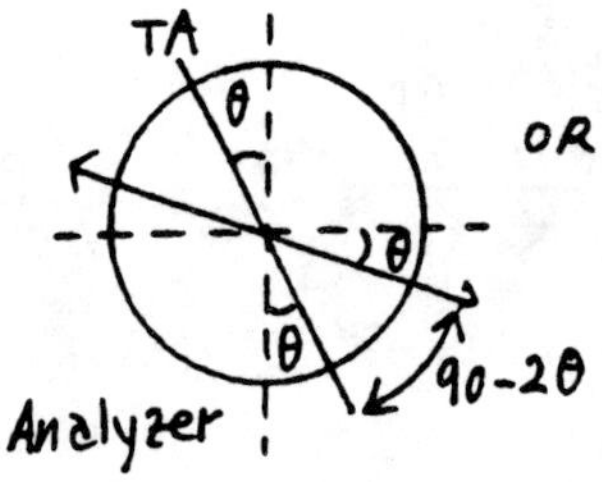


Then, using Malus' law,

$$I = I_o \cos^2(90 - 2\theta)$$

OR $$I = I_o \sin^2(2\theta)$$

This problem can also be worked using matrices, in exactly the manner of Prob. 14-22, replacing the QWP matrix there by the HWP matrix.

15-24. (a) From Eq. (15-10), $\beta = \frac{\pi z}{\lambda_o}(n_L - n_R)$, and Table 15-3,

$$\beta = \frac{\pi (3\times10^{-3})}{762\times10^{-9}}(6\times10^{-5}) = 0.742 \text{ rad} = 42.5^\circ$$

(b) From Eq. (15-3), with $\Delta\varphi = \pi$,

$$d = \frac{\pi \lambda_o}{2\pi |n_\perp - n_\parallel|} = \frac{\lambda_o}{2|n_\perp - n_\parallel|} = z$$

$$\text{so } \beta = \frac{\pi}{\lambda_o}(n_L - n_R)\frac{\lambda_o}{2|n_\perp - n_\parallel|} = \frac{\pi}{2}\frac{n_L - n_R}{|n_\parallel - n_\perp|}$$

$$\beta = \frac{\pi}{2}\frac{6\times10^{-5}}{8.94\times10^{-3}} = 0.0105 \text{ rad}$$

$$\beta = 0.60^\circ$$

# Chapter 16 - Fraunhofer Diffraction

16-1. $m\lambda = b\sin\theta = b\frac{y}{f}$

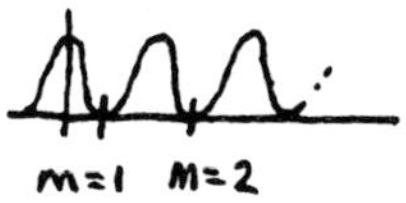


(a) $m = 1$; $y = \frac{\lambda f}{b} = \frac{(546.1\times10^{-6}\,mm)(60\,cm)}{0.015\,cm} = 2.18\,mm$

(b) $\Delta y = \frac{f\lambda\Delta m}{b}$ with $\Delta m = 2 - 1 = 1$

$\Delta y = 2.18\,mm$

16-2.

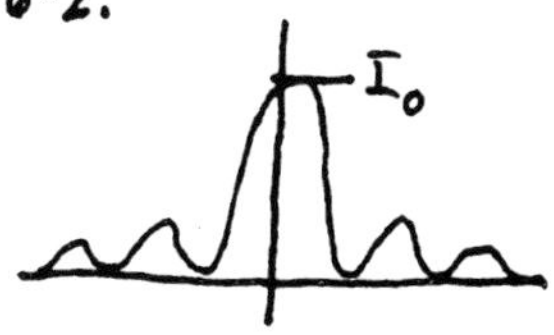


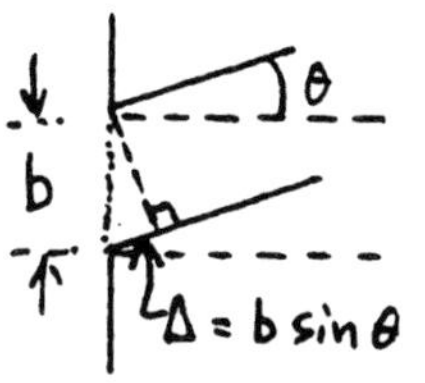


$I = I_0\left(\frac{\sin\beta}{\beta}\right)^2$; $\beta = \frac{2\pi}{\lambda}\frac{b}{2}\sin\theta = \frac{2\pi}{\lambda}\frac{\Delta}{2}$

$\beta = \frac{1}{2}$ phase difference between slit edges.

$\Delta = \frac{3}{4}\lambda$ ; $\beta = \frac{2\pi}{\lambda}\,\frac{3\lambda}{4}\cdot\frac{1}{2} = \frac{3}{4}\pi$

$\frac{\sin\beta}{\beta} = \frac{\sin(3\pi/4)}{(3\pi/4)} = 0.3001$

$I = (.3001)^2 I_0 = 0.090\,I_0$

16-3. (a) $m\lambda = b\sin\theta$

$3\lambda = b\frac{\Delta y}{s}$ or $b = \frac{3\lambda s}{\Delta y} = \frac{3(632.8\times10^{-7})(200)}{(5.625/2)} = 0.135\,mm$

(b) $L_{min} = b^2/2\lambda$

$\frac{L}{L_{min}} = \frac{200\,cm}{(0.0135\,cm)^2/(2)(632.8\times10^{-7}cm)} = 139$ , yes.

16-4. $m = 5$ for $\lambda_1$ $\quad m_1\lambda_1 = m_2\lambda_2 = b\sin\theta$

$m = 4$ for $\lambda_2$ $\quad 5\lambda_1 = 4\lambda_2 = 4\,(620\,nm)$

$\lambda_1 = 496\,nm$

16-5.

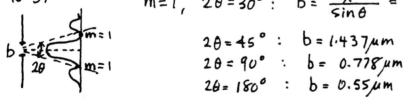

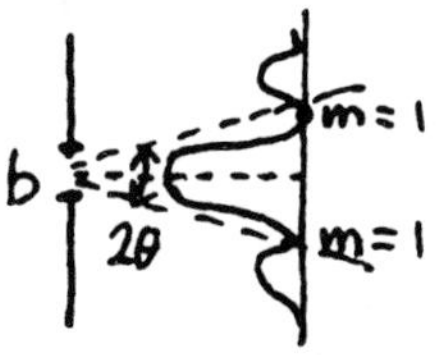


$m = 1$, $2\theta = 30°$ : $b = \frac{\lambda}{\sin\theta} = \frac{550\,nm}{\sin 15°} = 2.125\,\mu m$

$2\theta = 45°$ : $b = 1.437\,\mu m$

$2\theta = 90°$ : $b = 0.778\,\mu m$

$2\theta = 180°$ : $b = 0.55\,\mu m$

16-6. (a) $\sin\theta = \frac{m\lambda}{b} = \frac{(1)(550)}{2125}$ OR $\theta = 15°$

(b) $\beta = \frac{kb}{2}\sin\theta = \frac{\pi b}{\lambda}\sin\theta = \frac{\pi(2.125\,\mu m)}{0.55\,\mu m}\sin\theta = 12.138\sin\theta$

$\frac{I}{I_0} = \left(\frac{\sin\beta}{\beta}\right)^2$

16-6 (cont'd.)  $\beta$ will be in radians!

$\theta = 5°$, $\beta = 1.058$ : $I/I_0 = 0.678$

$\theta = 10°$, $\beta = 2.108$ : $I/I_0 = 0.166$

$\theta = 15°$, $\beta = 3.142$ : $I/I_0 = 2\times10^{-10} \approx 0$

$\theta = 22.5°$, $\beta = 4.645$ : $I/I_0 = 0.0461$

16-7. $\gamma = \frac{k}{2} D \sin\theta = \frac{\pi D}{\lambda}\sin\theta = \frac{\pi D}{\lambda}\frac{y}{f}$, or, all in cm,

$$y = \frac{f\lambda\gamma}{\pi D} = \gamma\left[\frac{(1706.88)(5.5\times10^{-5})}{\pi\,(91.44)}\right] = 3.268\times10^{-4}\gamma$$

1st secondary maximum ($\gamma = 5.14$) : $y = 1.68\times10^{-3}$ cm

2nd " " ($\gamma = 8.42$) : $y = 2.75\times10^{-3}$ cm

16-8. $1.22\lambda = D\sin\theta = D\frac{y}{f}$ OR $y = R = \frac{1.22\lambda f}{D}$

$$y = R = \frac{1.22(5.5\times10^{-5})(150)}{12} = 8.39\times10^{-4}\text{ cm}$$

16-9. 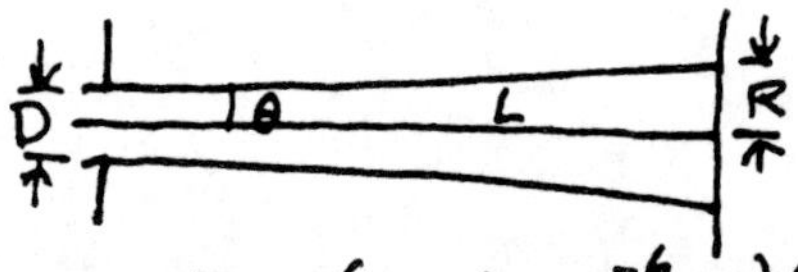


$1.22\lambda = D\sin\theta = D\frac{R}{L}$

$R = 1.22\lambda L/D$

$$R = \frac{1.22\,(10.6\times10^{-6}\text{ m})(3.76\times10^{8}\text{ m})}{10^{-3}\text{ m}} = 4.86\times10^{6}\text{ m}$$

$D(\text{moon}) = 9.7\times10^{6}$ m

$$I = \frac{P}{A} = \frac{P}{\pi R^2} = \frac{2\times10^{3}\text{ W}}{\pi(4.86\times10^{6}\text{ m})^2} = 2.7\times10^{-11}\text{ W/m}^2$$

16-10. $W = 2b = 1.22\left(\frac{2L\lambda}{b}\right)$ 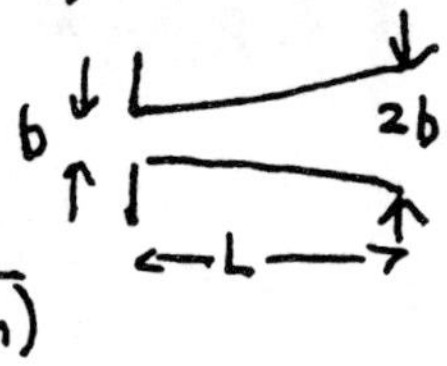


$$L = \frac{b^2}{1.22\lambda} = \frac{(2\times10^{-3}\text{m})^2}{1.22(632.8\times10^{-9}\text{m})}$$

$L = 5.18$ m

16-11. $(\Delta\theta)_{min} = \frac{1.22\lambda}{D}$ ; $\frac{y}{L} = \frac{1.22\lambda}{D}$ or

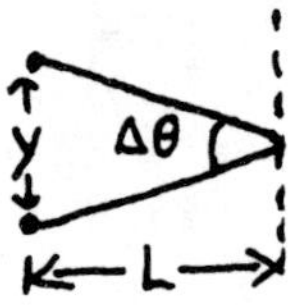


$$L = \frac{yD}{1.22\lambda} = \frac{(45\times2.54\text{ cm})(0.5\text{ cm})}{1.22\,(5.5\times10^{-5}\text{ cm})} = 8.517\times10^{5}\text{ cm}$$

$L = 27{,}943$ ft $\approx$ 5.3 miles

16-12. $L = \left(\frac{D}{1.22\lambda}\right)y$ : From $\left(\frac{0.2}{1.22\lambda}\right)y$ to $\left(\frac{0.7}{1.22\lambda}\right)y$

$$L = \frac{0.2\text{cm}}{1.22(5.5\times10^{-5}\text{cm})}\left(\frac{1}{12}\text{ft}\right) \text{ to } \frac{0.7\text{cm}}{1.22(5.5\times10^{-5}\text{cm})}\left(\frac{1}{12}\text{ft}\right)$$

16-12. (cont'd.)

$L = 285\,ft$ to $869\,ft$ OR $75.7\,m$ to $265\,m$

16-13.

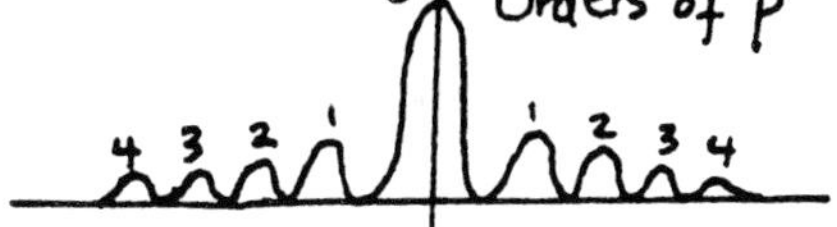


$I = 4I_0\left(\frac{\sin\beta}{\beta}\right)^2(\cos^2\alpha)$

(a) $\frac{a}{b} = 4$ ; $a = 4b = 4(0.1) = 0.4\,mm$

(b) Zeroth order : $I = 4I_0$

Interference maxima : $p\lambda = a\sin\theta$

or $\sin\theta = \pm\frac{p\lambda}{a} = 0, \pm\frac{\lambda}{a}, \pm\frac{2\lambda}{a}, \pm\frac{3\lambda}{a}\ldots$

Also, $\cos^2\alpha = 1$ so $I = 4I_0\left(\frac{\sin\beta}{\beta}\right)^2$

$\beta = \frac{kb}{2}\sin\theta = \frac{\pi b}{\lambda}\sin\theta$

$p=1:\ \sin\theta = \frac{\lambda}{a};\ \beta = \frac{\pi b}{\lambda}\frac{\lambda}{a} = \pi\left(\frac{b}{a}\right);\ \frac{I}{4I_0} = \left(\frac{\sin\beta}{\beta}\right)^2 = \left[\frac{\sin(\pi/4)}{\pi/4}\right]^2 = 0.8106$

$p=2:\ \sin\theta = \frac{2\lambda}{a};\ \beta = \frac{\pi b}{\lambda}\frac{2\lambda}{a} = 2\pi\left(\frac{b}{a}\right);\ \frac{I}{4I_0} = \left(\frac{\sin\beta}{\beta}\right)^2 = \left[\frac{\sin(\pi/2)}{\pi/2}\right]^2 = 0.4053$

$p=3:\ \sin\theta = \frac{3\lambda}{a};\ \beta = \frac{\pi b}{\lambda}\frac{3\lambda}{a} = 3\pi\left(\frac{b}{a}\right);\ \frac{I}{4I_0} = \left(\frac{\sin\beta}{\beta}\right)^2 = \left[\frac{\sin(3\pi/4)}{3\pi/4}\right]^2 = 0.0901$

16-14.

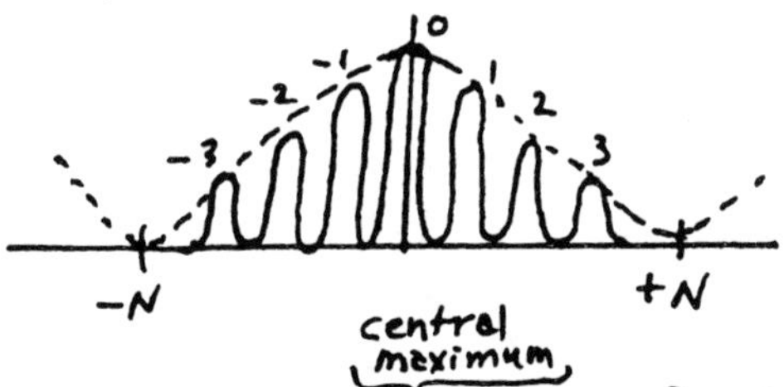


(a) If $a/b$ = integer, $N$, then the $N^{th}$ fringe is missing on either side of the central maximum. If $a/b$ falls between $N-1$ and $N$, then the $(N-1)^{th}$ fringes appear on either side. The total number of fringes is thus

$2(N-1)+1 = 2\left(\frac{a}{b}-1\right)+1 = 2\left(\frac{a}{b}\right)-1$ Q.E.D.

(b) $2\left(\frac{a}{b}\right)-1 = 13$ when $b = 0.3\,mm$

$\frac{a}{b} = 7$ OR $a = 7b = 7(0.3) = 2.1\,mm$

16-15.

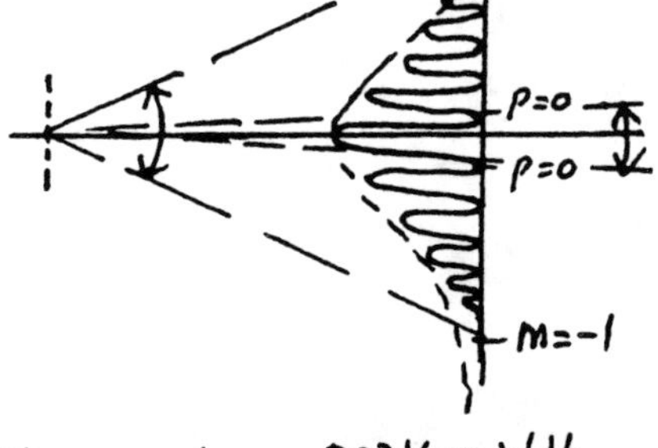


(a) diffraction minima : $m\lambda = b\sin\theta$ $\quad m = \pm1, \pm2, \ldots$

$m\lambda \cong b\theta$ or $\theta_{1/2} = \frac{\lambda}{b}$ for $m=1$

interference minima : $(p+\frac{1}{2})\lambda = a\sin\theta$ $\quad p = 0, \pm1, \pm2, \ldots$

$(p+\frac{1}{2})\lambda \cong a\theta$ or $\theta_{1/2} = \frac{\lambda}{2a}$ when $p=0$

Thus $\frac{(\Delta\theta_{1/2})_{diff}}{(\Delta\theta_{1/2})_{int}} = \frac{\lambda/b}{\lambda/2a} = 2\left(\frac{a}{b}\right)$ Q.E.D.

(b) $a = 10b$ : $\frac{\text{peak width}}{\text{fringe width}} = 2\left(\frac{a}{b}\right) = 2(10) = 20\times$

16-16.

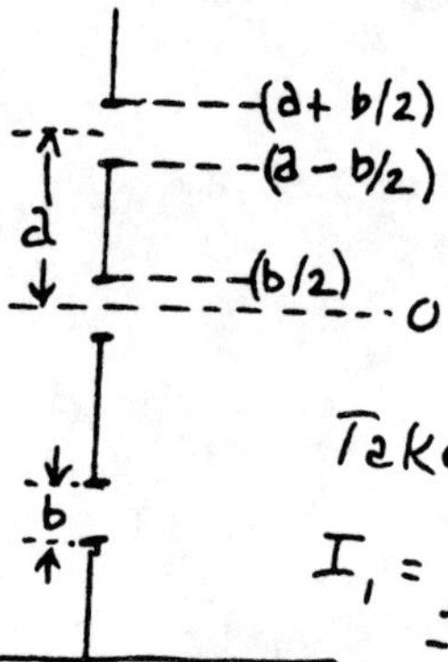


$\beta \equiv \frac{1}{2}Kb\sin\theta$

$\alpha \equiv \frac{1}{2}Ka\sin\theta$

Beginning with Eq. (16-4) and retaining only the amplitude,

$$E_R = \frac{E_L}{r_0}\left\{ \underbrace{\int_{-b/2}^{b/2} e^{isK\sin\theta}\,ds}_{\text{center slit } I_1} + \underbrace{\int_{-a-b/2}^{-a+b/2} e^{isK\sin\theta}\,ds}_{\text{bottom slit } I_2} + \underbrace{\int_{a-b/2}^{a+b/2} e^{isK\sin\theta}\,ds}_{\text{top slit } I_3} \right\}$$

Take the integrals one at a time:

$$I_1 = \int_{-b/2}^{b/2} e^{isK\sin\theta}\,ds = \frac{1}{iK\sin\theta}\left[e^{isK\sin\theta}\right]_{-b/2}^{b/2} = \frac{b}{2i\beta}\left[e^{\frac{2i\beta s}{b}}\right]_{-b/2}^{b/2}$$

$$I_1 = \frac{b}{2i\beta}\left(e^{i\beta} - e^{-i\beta}\right) = \frac{b}{2i\beta}(2i\sin\beta) = b\,\frac{\sin\beta}{\beta}$$

$$I_3 = \int_{-a-b/2}^{-a+b/2} e^{isK\sin\theta}\,ds = \frac{1}{iK\sin\theta}\left[e^{isK\sin\theta}\right]_{a-b/2}^{a+b/2} = \frac{1}{iK\sin\theta}\left[e^{iK\sin\theta(a+\frac{b}{2})} - e^{iK\sin\theta(a-\frac{b}{2})}\right]$$

$$I_3 = \frac{1}{iK\sin\theta}\left\{e^{2i\alpha}e^{i\beta} - e^{2i\alpha}e^{-i\beta}\right\} = \frac{e^{2i\alpha}}{iK\sin\theta}\left(e^{i\beta} - e^{-i\beta}\right) = \frac{e^{2i\alpha}}{iK\sin\theta}\,2i\sin\beta$$

Similarly, with $a \to -a$ and $\alpha \to -\alpha$

$$I_2 = \frac{e^{-2i\alpha}}{iK\sin\theta}\,2i\sin\beta$$

Then $I_2 + I_3 = \dfrac{2i\sin\beta}{iK\sin\theta}\left(e^{2i\alpha} + e^{-2i\alpha}\right) = \dfrac{2\sin\beta}{K\sin\theta}(2\cos 2\alpha) = \dfrac{4\sin\beta}{2\beta/b}\cos 2\alpha$

$$I_2 + I_3 = 2b\,\frac{\sin\beta}{\beta}\cos 2\alpha$$

All together,

$$E_R = \frac{E_L b}{r_0}\left\{\frac{\sin\beta}{\beta} + \frac{2\sin\beta}{\beta}\cos 2\alpha\right\} = \frac{E_L b}{r_0}\,\frac{\sin\beta}{\beta}\left(1 + 2\cos 2\alpha\right)$$

$$I = I_0\left(\frac{\sin\beta}{\beta}\right)^2 \left(1 + 2\cos 2\alpha\right)^2$$

To get the result in the general form, note that

$$1 + 2\cos 2\alpha = 1 + 2\left(1 - 2\sin^2\alpha\right) = 3 - 4\sin^2\alpha$$

$$= \frac{3\sin\alpha - 4\sin^3\alpha}{\sin\alpha}$$

$$= \frac{\sin 3\alpha}{\sin\alpha}$$

thus $I = I_0\left(\dfrac{\sin\beta}{\beta}\right)^2\left(\dfrac{\sin 3\alpha}{\sin\alpha}\right)^2.$

16-17.

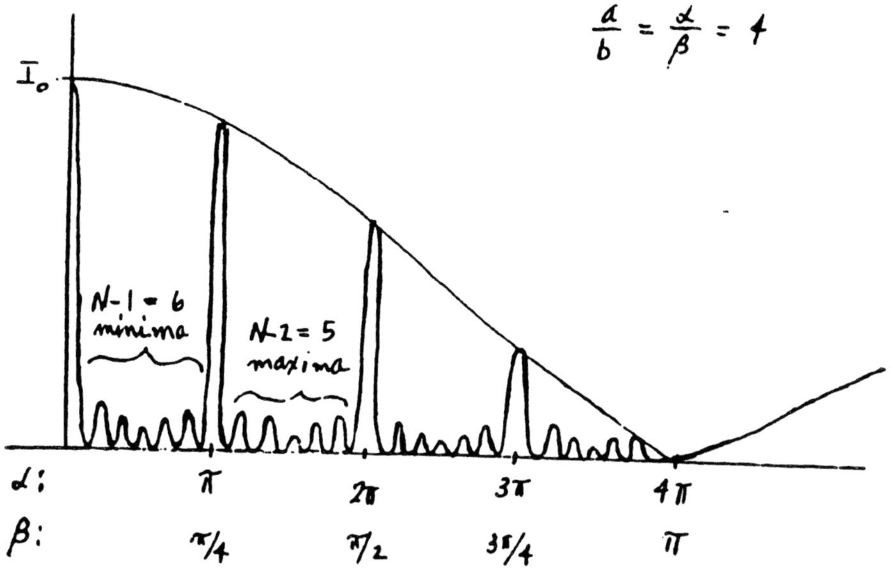


16-18. $I = I_0 \left(\frac{\sin\beta}{\beta}\right)^2 \left(\frac{\sin N\alpha}{\sin\alpha}\right)^2$ $\quad N = 10 \quad b = 1\times10^{-4}\text{ cm}$ $\quad a/b = 5 \quad \lambda = 435.8\text{ nm}$

For interference maxima,

$$\left(\frac{\sin N\alpha}{\sin\alpha}\right)^2 = 1 \quad \text{and} \quad \frac{I}{I_0} = \left(\frac{\sin\beta}{\beta}\right)^2$$

Also, $m\lambda = a\sin\theta$ , $m = 0, \pm1, \pm2, \dots$

$$\sin\theta = \frac{m\lambda}{a} \qquad \beta = \frac{kb}{2}\sin\theta = \frac{\pi b}{\lambda}\sin\theta = \frac{\pi b}{\lambda}\left(\frac{m\lambda}{a}\right) = m\pi\left(\frac{b}{a}\right)$$

$$\beta = m\left(\frac{\pi}{5}\right)$$

Then, for $m=1$: $I/I_0 = \left(\frac{\sin\beta}{\beta}\right)^2 = \left[\frac{\sin(\pi/5)}{\pi/5}\right]^2 = 0.875$

$m=2$: $I/I_0 = \left[\frac{\sin(2\pi/5)}{2\pi/5}\right]^2 = 0.573$

$m=3$: $I/I_0 = \left[\frac{\sin(3\pi/5)}{3\pi/5}\right]^2 = 0.255$

Similarly, $m=4$: $I/I_0 = 0.0547$

$m=5$: $I/I_0 = 0$

16-19.

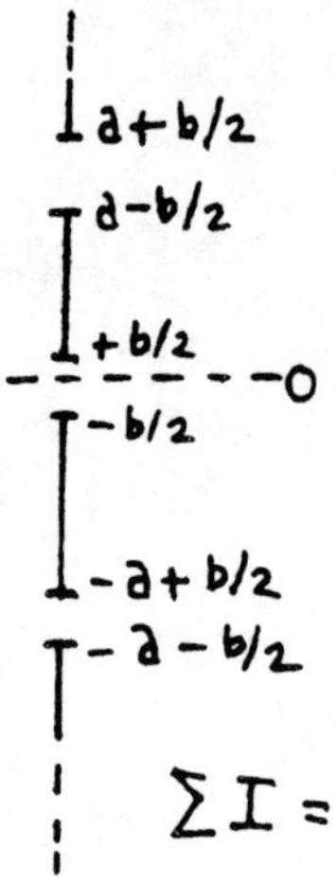


$$E_R = \frac{E_L}{r_0} \underbrace{\sum \int e^{isk\sin\theta} ds}_{\sum I}$$

$$\sum I = \underbrace{\int_{-b/2}^{b/2} e^{isk\sin\theta} ds}_{N=1} + \underbrace{\sum_{j=1}^{\frac{N-1}{2}} \left( \int_{-ja-b/2}^{-ja+b/2} e^{isk\sin\theta} ds + \int_{ja-b/2}^{ja+b/2} e^{isk\sin\theta} ds \right)}_{N = 3,5,7,\ldots \text{ as } j = 1,2,3,\ldots} \quad \text{for } N \text{ slits}$$

Now $\int e^{isk\sin\theta} ds = \frac{1}{ik\sin\theta}\left[e^{isk\sin\theta}\right] = \frac{b}{2i\beta} e^{isk\sin\theta}$

$$\sum I = \frac{b}{2i\beta}\left(e^{ikb\sin\theta/2} - e^{-ikb\sin\theta/2}\right) + \frac{b}{2i\beta}\sum_{j=1}^{(N-1)/2}\left(e^{-i(ja-b/2)k\sin\theta} - e^{-i(ja+b/2)k\sin\theta} + e^{i(ja-b/2)k\sin\theta} - e^{i(ja+b/2)k\sin\theta}\right)$$

$$\sum I = \frac{b}{2i\beta}\left\{(e^{i\beta} - e^{-i\beta}) + \sum_j e^{-ijak\sin\theta}\left(e^{ibk\sin\theta/2} - e^{-ibk\sin\theta/2}\right) + e^{ijak\sin\theta}\left(e^{ibk\sin\theta/2} - e^{-ibk\sin\theta/2}\right)\right.$$

$$\sum I = \frac{b}{2i\beta}\left\{2i\sin\beta + \sum_j (e^{i\beta} - e^{-i\beta})(e^{ijak\sin\theta} + e^{-ijak\sin\theta})\right\}$$

$$\sum I = \frac{b}{2i\beta}\left\{2i\sin\beta + 2i\sin\beta \sum_{j=1}^{(N-1)/2} 2\cos(2j\alpha)\right\}$$

$$\sum I = \frac{b\sin\beta}{\beta}\left\{1 + 2\,\mathrm{Re}\sum e^{i2j\alpha}\right\} = \frac{b\sin\beta}{\beta}\left\{1 + 2\,\mathrm{Re}\left[e^{i2\alpha} + e^{i4\alpha} + \ldots + e^{i(N-1)\alpha}\right.\right.$$

$$\sum I = \frac{b\sin\beta}{\beta}\left\{1 + 2\,\mathrm{Re}\; e^{i2\alpha}\left[\frac{(e^{i2\alpha})^{\frac{N-1}{2}} - 1}{(e^{i2\alpha}) - 1}\right]\right\}$$

$$\sum I = b\frac{\sin\beta}{\beta}\left\{1 + 2\,\mathrm{Re}\left[\frac{e^{iN\alpha} - e^{-i\alpha}}{e^{i\alpha} - e^{-i\alpha}}\right]\right\}$$

Write $\dfrac{e^{iN\alpha} - e^{i\alpha}}{e^{i\alpha} - e^{-i\alpha}} = \dfrac{(\cos N\alpha - \cos\alpha) + i(\sin N\alpha - \sin\alpha)}{2i\sin\alpha}$

$$= \frac{-(\sin N\alpha - \sin\alpha) + i(\cos N\alpha - \cos\alpha)}{-2\sin\alpha}$$

$$\sum I = \frac{b\sin\beta}{\beta}\left\{1 + 2\,\frac{\sin N\alpha - \sin\alpha}{2\sin\alpha}\right\} = b\,\frac{\sin\beta}{\beta}\,\frac{\sin N\alpha}{\sin\alpha}$$

16-19. (cont'd.)

Thus, $E_R = \frac{E_L b}{r_0} \frac{\sin\beta}{\beta} \frac{\sin N\alpha}{\sin\alpha}$

$$I = I_0 \left(\frac{\sin\beta}{\beta}\right)^2 \left(\frac{\sin N\alpha}{\sin\alpha}\right) \quad \text{Q.E.D.}$$

16-20.

(a) $I = I_0 \left(\frac{\sin\alpha}{\alpha}\right)^2 \left(\frac{\sin\beta}{\beta}\right)^2$ $\quad \alpha = \frac{K}{2} a\sin\theta \cong \frac{\pi a}{\lambda}\frac{y}{f}$

$\beta = \frac{K}{2} b\sin\theta = \frac{\pi b}{\lambda}\frac{x}{f}$

$$\alpha = \frac{\pi(0.2)y}{(546\times10^{-6})(10^3)} = 1.151y \text{ (mm)}$$

$$\beta = \frac{\pi(0.1)x}{(546\times10^{-6})(10^3)} = 0.575x \text{ (mm)}$$

$$I = I_0\left[\frac{\sin(1.151y)}{1.151y}\right]^2\left[\frac{\sin(0.575x)}{0.575x}\right]^2 = I_0\frac{\sin^2(1.151y)\sin^2(0.575x)}{0.438x^2y^2}$$

(b) Minima occur first at $m=1$ in $y = \frac{m\lambda f}{a}$ and $n=1$ in $x = \frac{n\lambda f}{b}$. Thus $y = \frac{(546\times10^{-6})(10^3)}{0.2} = 2.73\text{mm}$

$$x = \frac{(546\times10^{-6})(10^3)}{0.1} = 5.46\text{mm}$$

(c) As $x \to 0$, $\left(\frac{\sin\beta}{\beta}\right)^2 \to 1$ and, as $y \to 0$, $\left(\frac{\sin\alpha}{\alpha}\right)^2 \to 1$.

At $(x=0, y=1)$ mm, $I = I_0\frac{\sin^2(1.151)}{(1.151)^2} = 0.629 I_0$

At $(x=1, y=0)$ mm, $I = I_0\frac{\sin^2(0.575)}{(0.575)^2} = 0.895 I_0$

(d) At $(x=2, y=3)$ mm, $I = I_0\frac{\sin^2[3(1.151)]}{[3(1.151)]^2} = 0.005 I_0$

16-21. $m\lambda = a\sin\theta$

For $m=1$, $\sin\theta_{1/2} = \frac{\lambda}{a}$

(a) $\sin\theta_{1/2} = \frac{\lambda}{\lambda} = 1$ ; $\theta_{1/2} = 90°$

(b) $\sin\theta_{1/2} = \frac{\lambda}{5\lambda} = 0.2$ ; $\theta_{1/2} = 11.5°$

(c) $\sin\theta_{1/2} = \frac{\lambda}{10\lambda} = 0.1$ ; $\theta_{1/2} = 5.7°$

16-22.

$$I = I_0\left(\frac{J_1(\gamma)}{\gamma}\right)^2 \xrightarrow[\text{large } \gamma]{} \frac{I_0}{\gamma^2}\left[\frac{\sin\gamma - \cos\gamma}{\gamma\sqrt{\pi\gamma}}\right]^2 = I_0\frac{(\sin\gamma - \cos\gamma)^2}{\pi\gamma^3}$$

Minima occur at $I=0$ or $\sin\gamma = \cos\gamma$, or $\tan\gamma = 1$. Thus minima correspond to $\gamma = \pi/4, 5\pi/4, 9\pi/4, \ldots = (4m-3)\pi/4$. For $m = 1,2,3\ldots$

$$\gamma = \frac{K}{2}D\sin\theta = \frac{\pi D}{\lambda}\sin\theta = (4m-3)\pi/4$$

16-22. (cont'd.)

$$\sin\theta = (4m-3)\frac{\lambda}{4D}$$

the angular separation between consecutive orders ($\Delta m = 1$) of minima is

$$\cos\theta\,\Delta\theta = 4\Delta m\frac{\lambda}{4D} = \frac{\lambda}{D}\Delta m$$

$$\Delta\theta = \frac{\lambda}{D}\frac{1}{\cos\theta}$$

16-23. $I = I_0\left(\frac{\sin\beta}{\beta}\right)^2$. At secondary maxima, $\beta_1 = 1.43\pi$, $\beta_2 = 2.46\pi$, $\beta_3 = 3.47\pi$. Approximately, $\beta \cong 1.5\pi, 2.5\pi, \ldots \cong (m+1/2)\pi$, so that $\sin\beta \cong \pm 1$

(a) Then $I = I_0\left(\frac{\pm 1}{\beta}\right)^2 = \frac{I_0}{[(m+\frac{1}{2})\pi]^2}$

(b) Approximate:

$$I_1 \cong \frac{I_0}{(1.5\pi)^2} = 0.0450\,I_0$$

$$I_2 \cong \frac{I_0}{(2.5\pi)^2} = 0.0162\,I_0$$

$$I_3 \cong \frac{I_0}{(3.5\pi)^2} = 0.00827\,I_0$$

More Accurate:

$$I_1 = \left(\frac{\sin 1.43\pi}{1.43\pi}\right)^2 I_0 = 0.0472\,I_0$$

$$I_2 = \left(\frac{\sin 2.46\pi}{2.46\pi}\right)^2 I_0 = 0.0165\,I_0$$

$$I_3 = \left(\frac{\sin 3.47\pi}{3.47\pi}\right)^2 I_0 = 0.00834\,I_0$$

The % errors are therefore 4.7%, 1.8% and 0.84% for $m = 1, 2, 3$, resp.

16-24.

The principal maxima satisfy $m\lambda = a\sin\theta$, so that

$$m_{max} = \frac{a}{\lambda} = \frac{2/3}{1} = \frac{2}{3}.$$

Thus $m = 1$ is not allowed and only the central maximum ($m=0$) appears. The beam width is confined by the first minimum, given by $m\lambda = a\sin\theta$, with

$$m = \frac{p}{N} = \frac{\pm 1}{N} = \pm\frac{1}{3}. \text{ Then}$$

$$\sin\theta = \pm\frac{\lambda}{3}\cdot\frac{3}{2} = \pm\frac{1}{2} \quad \text{or } \theta = \pm 30°$$

The angular half-width of the beam is 30°.

16-25. (a) For three equal slits, the amplitude phasors must be equal and form a closed polygon. Thus the phase difference must be $\phi = 2\pi/3 = 120°$

16-25 (cont'd.)

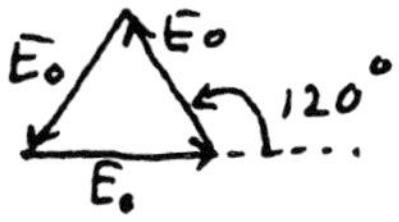


Alternatively, using Eq. (16-33), $I = 0$ when $\alpha = p\pi/N$ and $p = \pm 1, \pm 2, \ldots$ Then

$\alpha = \pm \frac{\pi}{3}, \pm \frac{2\pi}{3}, \ldots$ and, since $\phi = 2\alpha$,

$\phi = \pm \frac{2\pi}{3}, \pm \frac{4\pi}{3}, \ldots = \pm 120°, \pm 240°, \ldots$

the additional values of $\phi$ also produce equilateral triangles (notice that for $b \cong 0$, $\beta \cong 0$ and $\sin\beta/\beta \cong 1$.)

(b) If $\phi = \pi$, the phasors

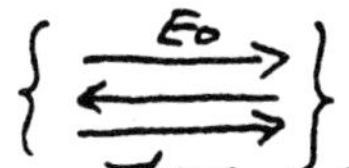


are such that two cancel, leaving one contributing. Thus, at P, $I_p \propto E_0^2$

while at the center

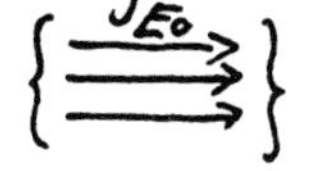


, $I_{max} \propto (3E_0)^2 = 9E_0^2$.

Thus $I_p = 1/9\ I_{max}$.

Alternatively, $I_p = I_0 \left[\frac{\sin 3(\pi/2)}{\sin(\pi/2)}\right]^2 = I_0$ since $\phi = 2\alpha$

and so $\alpha = \pi/2$. Compared with $I_{max} = 9 I_0$, again,

$$I_p = \frac{1}{9} I_0$$

(c) At a principal maximum, $p = 0, \pm N, \pm 2N, \ldots$

So $\alpha = \frac{p\pi}{N} = 0, \pm\pi, \pm 2\pi$ ; $\frac{\sin N\alpha}{\sin\alpha} = \pm N$

Then $I_p = N^2 I_0 = I_{max}$ and $I_p/I_{max} = 1$

(d) $I_{av} = I$ on the screen when it is uniformly illuminated with the energy from the 3 slits. Thus $I_{av} = 3I_0$, as in the case of coheren light. On the other hand, $I_p = 9I_0$ in the case of coherence. Thus $I_p = 3I_{av}$.

16-26 Principal maxima and zeros of a 4-slit aperture in terms of phasor diagrams:

P.MAX : $\alpha = 0, \pi, 2\pi, \ldots$ OR $\phi = 2\alpha = 0, 2\pi, 4\pi, \ldots$

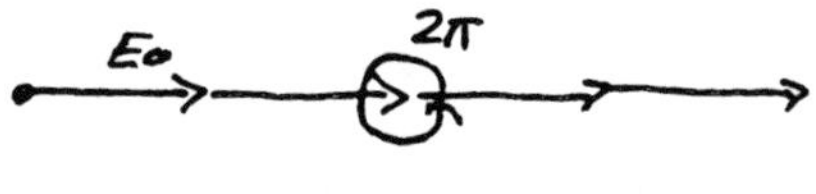


Zeros : $\alpha = p\frac{\pi}{N} = \pm\frac{\pi}{4}, \pm\frac{2\pi}{4}, \pm\frac{3\pi}{4}, \ldots$ ; $p = \pm 1, \pm 2, \ldots$

$p \neq \pm 4, \pm 8, \ldots$

$\phi = 2\alpha = \pm\frac{\pi}{2}, \pm\pi, \pm\frac{3\pi}{2},$

$\phi = 90°$

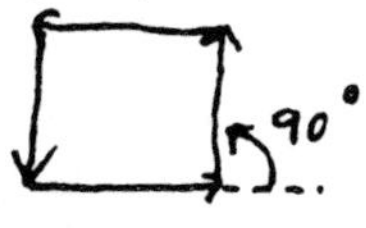


$\phi = 180°$

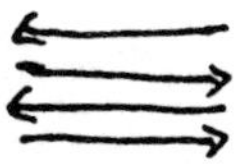

$\phi = 270°$

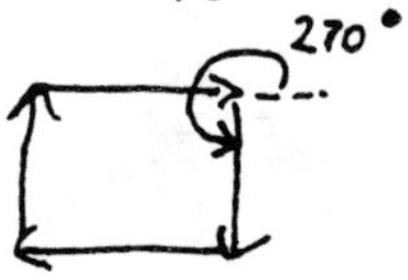

# Chapter 17 - The Diffraction Grating

17-1. $m\lambda = a\sin\theta$ $\qquad \lambda_1 = 400\,nm \qquad \lambda_2 = 600\,nm$

$m = 2$

$a = 1/5000$ cm

$$\theta_1 = \sin^{-1}\left(\frac{m\lambda_1}{a}\right) = \sin^{-1}\left(\frac{2\,(400\times10^{-7})\,cm}{1/5000\ cm}\right) = 23.58^\circ$$

$$\theta_2 = \sin^{-1}\left(\frac{m\lambda_2}{a}\right) = \sin^{-1}\left(\frac{2\times600\times10^{-7}\,cm}{1/5000\ cm}\right) = 36.87^\circ$$

$$\Delta\theta = \theta_2 - \theta_1 = 13.292^\circ = 13^\circ 18'$$

17-2. $m\lambda = a\sin\theta$

$$\mathcal{D} \equiv \frac{d\theta}{d\lambda} = \frac{m}{a\cos\theta} = \frac{m}{a\cos(\sin^{-1} m\lambda/a)}$$

$$\mathcal{D} = \frac{3}{\left(\frac{1}{3500}\right)\cos\left(\sin^{-1}\frac{3\times650\times10^{-7}}{1/3500}\right)} = 14366\ rad/cm.$$

$$\mathcal{D} = 14366\ \frac{rad}{cm}\times\frac{180}{\pi}\frac{deg}{rad}\times10^{-7}\frac{cm}{nm} = 0.0823\ deg/nm$$

$$\frac{dl}{d\lambda} = f\frac{d\theta}{d\lambda} = f\mathcal{D} = 1500\,mm\left(14366\times10^{-7}\frac{rad}{nm}\right) = 2.1549\ mm/nm$$

$$\frac{d\lambda}{dl} = 0.464\ nm/mm$$

17-3. (a) Principal maxima: $m\lambda = a\sin\theta$

$$\theta_1 = \sin^{-1}\left(\frac{m\lambda}{a}\right) = \sin^{-1}\left(\frac{2\times600\times10^{-7}}{10^{-3}}\right) = 6.8921^\circ$$

Minima: $(m \pm \frac{1}{N})\lambda = a\sin\theta$

$$\theta_2 = \sin^{-1}\frac{(m\pm\frac{1}{N})\lambda}{a} = \sin^{-1}\frac{(2+\frac{1}{24})(600\times10^{-7})}{10^{-3}} = 7.0364^\circ$$

$$\Delta\theta = \theta_2 - \theta_1 = 0.1443^\circ = 8.7''$$

For $(m-\frac{1}{N})$, we get $\sin\theta = 0.1175$, $\theta = 6.7478^\circ$ and $\Delta\theta = 8.7'$ again.

(b) At the minimum, we found $\theta = 7.0364^\circ$ or $\sin\theta = 0.1225$.

Thus $\lambda = \frac{a\sin\theta}{m} = \frac{(10^{-3}cm)(0.1225)}{2} = 6.125\times10^{-5}cm = 612.5\,nm$

If we had taken $(m-\frac{1}{N}) = (2 - 1/24)$ instead, $\sin\theta = 0.1175$

and $\lambda = \frac{a\sin\theta}{m} = \frac{(10^{-3}cm)(0.1175)}{2} = 5.875\times10^{-5}cm = 587.5\,nm$

(c)

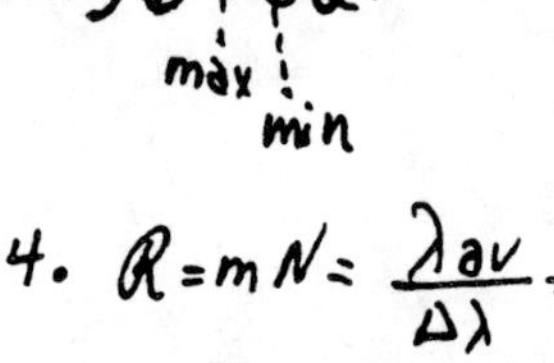


$(\Delta\lambda)_{min} = 612.5\,nm - 600\,nm = 12.5\,nm$

$$\mathcal{R}_{m=2} = \frac{\lambda}{\Delta\lambda} = \frac{600}{12.5} = 48$$

From theory, $\mathcal{R} = mN = (2)(24) = 48$

17-4. $\mathcal{R} = mN = \frac{\lambda_{av}}{\Delta\lambda} = \frac{589.2935}{0.597} = 987$ ; $N = \frac{\mathcal{R}}{m}$

$m = 1$: $N = 987$

$m = 2$: $N = 494$

17-5. $FSR = \lambda_2 - \lambda_1 = \frac{\lambda_1}{m}$  $\lambda_1 = 350$ nm, crown ; $\lambda_1 = 180$ nm, quartz

(a) $\lambda_2 = \lambda_1 + \frac{\lambda_1}{m} = 350 + \frac{350}{1} = 700$ nm, crown

$\lambda_2 = 180 + \frac{180}{1} = 360$ nm, quartz

(b) $a = 1/1200$ mm

$\theta = \sin^{-1}(m\lambda/a) = \sin^{-1}\left[\frac{(1)(700 \times 10^{-6})}{1/1200}\right] = 57.14°$, crown

$\theta = \sin^{-1}(m\lambda/a) = \sin^{-1}\left[\frac{(1)(360 \times 10^{-6})}{1/1200}\right] = 25.59°$, quartz

(c) $FSR = \lambda_1/m$

m=1 : FSR = 350/1 = 350nm, crown

FSR = 180/1 = 180nm, quartz

m=2 : FSR = 350/2 = 175nm, crown

FSR = 180/2 = 90nm, quartz

17-6. $\mathcal{R}(m=3) = mN = (3)(16{,}000 \times 2.5) = 120{,}000$

$\mathcal{R}(m=2) = mN = (2)(16{,}000 \times 2.5) = 80{,}000$

$\Delta\lambda = \lambda/\mathcal{R} = 550\text{nm}/80{,}000 = 0.006875 \text{ nm} = 0.069$ Å

17-7. (a) $\mathcal{R} \equiv \frac{\lambda}{\Delta\lambda} = \frac{5893}{6} = 982.16 \Rightarrow 983$

$m = \mathcal{R}/N = 983/400 = 2.46$ ; Order = 3

(b) Any width smaller than the light beam

17-8. (a) $m\lambda = a\sin\theta \cong \frac{a\,y_m}{f}$ OR $y_m = \frac{m\lambda f}{a}$

m=0 : $y_0 = 0$

m=1 : $y_1 = \frac{(1)(546 \times 10^{-6})(2000)}{0.005} = 218.4$ mm

Thus $\Delta y = y_1 - y_0 = 21.84$ cm, independent of N

(b) the first missing order occurs at $M = a/b = 5$. Thus, the number of maxima under the central peak $= 2(M-1)+1$ or $2M-1 = 9$. This is true for all 3 cases.

(c) Minima : $(m + \frac{1}{N})\lambda = a\sin\theta$.

Using zero order (m=0), $\sin\theta \cong \theta = \lambda/aN$

Peak width $= 2\theta = 2\lambda/aN$ ; $\Delta y = f\Delta\theta = 2f\lambda/aN$

(1) N=2 : $\Delta y = \frac{2(200)(546 \times 10^{-7})}{(0.0005)(2)} = 21.84$ cm

(2) N=10 : $\Delta y = 4.368$ cm

(3) N=15,000 : $\Delta y = 0.0029$ cm

17-9. (a) $\mathcal{R} = \lambda/\Delta\lambda = 3500\,\text{Å}/0.02\,\text{Å} = 175,000$

$\mathcal{R} = mN = 175,000$ so for $m = 2$, $N = 87,500$ grooves

Then $\dfrac{87500\text{ gr}}{10\text{cm}} = 8750\text{ gr/cm}$

(b) Normal incidence: $\theta_B = \frac{1}{2}\sin^{-1}\left(\frac{m\lambda}{a}\right) = \frac{1}{2}\sin^{-1}\left(\frac{2 \times 350 \times 10^{-7}\text{cm}}{1/8750\text{ cm}}\right)$

$\theta_B = 18.89°$

(c)

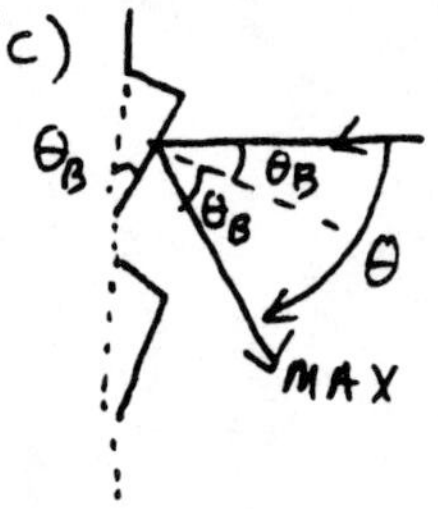


$\theta = 2\theta_B = 37.77°$

(d) $\mathcal{D} = \dfrac{m}{a\cos\theta} = \dfrac{2}{\left(\frac{1}{8750}\right)\cos 37.77} = 22139\ \dfrac{\text{rad}}{\text{cm}}$

$= 22139\ \dfrac{\text{rad}}{\text{cm}} \times \dfrac{180}{\pi}\dfrac{\text{deg}}{\text{rad}} \times 10^{-7}\dfrac{\text{cm}}{\text{nm}}$

$= 0.1268\ \text{deg/nm}$

$\dfrac{d\lambda}{d\theta} = \dfrac{1}{\mathcal{D}} = \dfrac{1}{0.1268} = 7.88\ \text{nm/deg}$

17-10. (a) $\mathcal{R} = \dfrac{\lambda}{\Delta\lambda}$. Taking worst case, or $\lambda = 700$ nm

$\mathcal{R} = \dfrac{7000\,\text{Å}}{1\,\text{Å}} = 7000 = mN = (1)N$ OR $N = 7000$

Then $a = 2\text{cm}/7000\text{ gr}$

(b) $m\lambda \cong a\theta = \dfrac{ay}{f}$ and $m\,d\lambda = \dfrac{a\,dy}{f}$

$dy = \dfrac{mf\,d\lambda}{a} = \dfrac{(1)(50\text{cm})(1 \times 10^{-8}\text{cm})}{(2/7000)\text{ cm}} = 0.00175\text{ cm}$

17-11. (a) $m\lambda = a(\sin\theta_i + \sin\theta_m)$; $\sin\theta_m = \dfrac{m\lambda}{a} - \sin\theta_i$

$\lambda = 400\text{nm}$: $\theta_m = \sin^{-1}\left[\frac{(1)(400)}{1000} - \sin 30°\right] = -5.74°$

$\lambda = 700\text{ nm}$: $\theta_m = \sin^{-1}\left[\frac{(1)(700)}{1000} - \sin 30°\right] = +11.54°$

(b) $W = 10$ cm; $\mathcal{R} = mN = (1)(10,000\text{ cm}^{-1})(10\text{cm}) = 100,000$

(c) Plate factor $\equiv d\lambda/dx = d\lambda/f\,d\theta = 1/f\mathcal{D}$

$\mathcal{D} = \tan\theta/\lambda = \dfrac{\tan(\sin^{-1} m\lambda/a)}{\lambda} = \dfrac{\tan(\sin^{-1}(550/1000))}{550\text{nm}}$

$\mathcal{D} = 0.00119737$ rad/nm

Plate factor $= \dfrac{1}{(100\text{cm})(0.00119737)\text{nm}^{-1}} = 8.3516\text{ nm/cm}$

$= 8.35\ \text{Å/mm}$

(d) $R_{circle} = \frac{1}{2}R_{grating} = \frac{1}{2}(2\text{m}) = 1\text{ m}$

17-12. P.F. $= \frac{1}{f\mathcal{D}} = \frac{d\cos\theta}{fm}$ , since $\mathcal{D} = \frac{m}{d\cos\theta}$ .

Thus $\frac{1}{d}\left(\frac{gr}{cm}\right) = \frac{\cos\theta}{mf\,(P.F.)}$ . The answer depends on $\theta$. In first order, we suppose the P.F. is valid near $\theta = 0°$, so that $\cos\theta \cong 1$. Then

$$\frac{1}{d} = \frac{1}{(1)(100\,cm)(2\,nm/mm)} = 0.005\,\frac{mm}{nm\text{-}cm} \times 10^6\,\frac{nm}{mm}$$

$\frac{1}{d} \cong 5000$ gr/cm.

17-13. (a) Littrow: $m\lambda = 2a\sin\theta_b$

$$\lambda = \frac{2a\sin\theta_b}{m} = \frac{2(1/3000)\sin 10°}{1} = 1.16\,\mu m$$

(See Prob 17-12) (b) $P.F.\,(nm/mm) = \frac{10^6 a\cos\theta}{mf} = \frac{10^6(1/3000)(\cos 20.322°)}{(1)(170\,cm)}$

P.F. = 1.84 nm/mm

(where $\sin\theta = m\lambda/a = 2\sin\theta_b = 2\sin 10°$
or $\cos\theta = \cos 20.322°$)

17-14. $\mathcal{R} = mN = m(W/a) = (1)(15/a)$

or $a = 15/\mathcal{R} = 15/300{,}000 = 5\times10^{-5}\,cm = 500\,nm$

Littrow: $\theta_b = \sin^{-1}\left(\frac{m\lambda}{2a}\right) = \sin^{-1}\left(\frac{1\times200}{2\times500}\right) = 11.5°$

Normal: $2\theta_b = \sin^{-1}\left(\frac{m\lambda}{a}\right) = \sin^{-1}\left(\frac{1\times200}{500}\right) = 23.578°$

$\theta_b = 11.8°$

17-15. $d = \frac{\lambda}{2\sin\theta} = \frac{488\times10^{-6}\,mm}{2\sin 60°} = 2.8175\times10^{-4}\,mm$

$1/d = 3550$ gr/mm.

If the emulsion is of refractive index $n$, then $\lambda_0 \rightarrow \frac{\lambda_0}{n}$ and $d = \frac{\lambda_0}{2n\sin\theta}$. As $n$ increases, grating constant increases.

17-16. (a) $\mathcal{R} \equiv \frac{\lambda}{\Delta\lambda} = \frac{6563}{1.8} = mN$ or $N = \frac{6563}{1.8(1)} = 3647$ grooves

(b) Littrow: $\theta_b = \sin^{-1}\left(\frac{m\lambda}{2a}\right)$ OR $22.2° = \sin^{-1}\left(\frac{1\times6300\,Å}{2a}\right)$

$\frac{6300\,Å}{2a} = 0.37784$ or $a = 8337\,Å = 8.337\times10^{-5}\,cm$

$\frac{1}{a} = 11995$ gr/cm $\cong 1200$ gr/mm

(c) $W_{min} = \frac{3647\,gr}{1200\,gr/mm} = 3.04\,mm$

17-17.

(a) Littrow: $m\lambda = 2a \sin\theta_b$

$$m = \frac{2a \sin\theta_b}{\lambda} = \frac{2(1/80)\sin 63}{\lambda\,(cm)} = \frac{\sin 63}{40}\,\frac{1}{\lambda(cm)}$$

$\lambda = 400 \times 10^{-7}$ cm , $m = 557$

$\lambda = 700 \times 10^{-7}$ cm , $m = 318$

(b) $N = \frac{W}{a} = (12\ cm)(80\ gr/cm) = 960$ grooves

(c) $\mathcal{R} = mN$ But at $\lambda = 550$ nm, $m = \left(\frac{\sin 63}{40}\right)\frac{1}{550 \times 10^{-7}} = 405$

then $\mathcal{R} = (405)(960) = 388{,}800$

$$(\Delta\lambda)_{min} = \frac{\lambda}{\mathcal{R}} = \frac{5500\ Å}{388{,}800} = 0.014\ Å$$

(d) $$\mathcal{D} = \frac{m}{a\cos\theta} = \frac{405}{\frac{1}{80}\cos 63°} = 71367\ \frac{rad}{cm}\left(\times \frac{180}{\pi}\frac{deg}{rad} \times 10^{-7}\frac{cm}{nm}\right)$$

$\mathcal{D} = 0.4089 \cong 0.41$ deg/nm

(e) $FSR = \frac{\lambda_{min}}{m} = \frac{350}{m}$ , where $m = \left(\frac{\sin 63}{40}\right)\frac{1}{350 \times 10^{-7}}$

$m = 636.4$

$$FSR = \frac{350\ nm}{637} = 0.55\ nm = 5.5\ Å$$

# Chapter 18 - Fresnel Diffraction

18-1. Far field: $L >> \frac{Area}{\lambda} = \frac{\pi d^2}{4\lambda} = \frac{\pi(1\times10^{-3}m)^2}{4(546\times10^{-9})} = 1.4m$

thus $L = 50$ cm : near field

$L = 1$ m : near field

$L = 5$ m : far field

18-2.

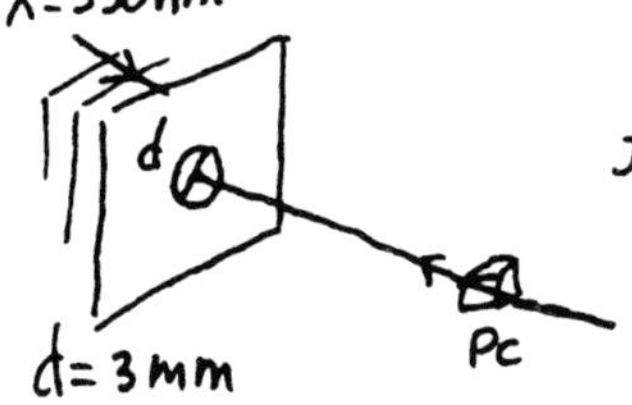


$f_N = \frac{R_1^2}{N\lambda}$, $\overbrace{N \text{ odd}}^{\text{maxima}}$ OR $f_N = \frac{f_1}{N}$

$f_1 = \frac{(0.15)^2 cm^2}{(1)(5.5\times10^{-5})cm} = 409 cm$

Max. $\left\{ f_3 = \frac{f_1}{3} = 136cm \ ; \ f_5 = \frac{f_1}{5} = 81.8cm. \right.$

Min $\left\{ \begin{array}{l} f_2 = \frac{f_1}{2} = 204.5cm \\ f_4 = \frac{f_1}{4} = 102 \text{ cm} \\ f_6 = \frac{f_1}{6} = 68.1cm \end{array} \right.$

18-3. $f_N = \frac{R_N^2}{N\lambda}$ with $f_N = r_0 = 150cm$, fixed.

$R_N^2 = N\lambda r_0$ or $\frac{D_N^2}{4} = N\lambda r_0$ and $D_N = 2\sqrt{N\lambda r_0}$

First max : $N=1$ ; $D_1 = 2[(1)(589.3\times10^{-5})(150)]^{1/2} = 0.188cm$

Second max : $N=3$ ; $D_3 = 2[(3)(589.3\times10^{-5})(150)]^{1/2} = 0.326cm$

First min : $N=2$ $D_2 = 0.266$ cm

Second min : $N=4$ $D_4 = 0.376$ cm

18-4. (a) $R_1 = \sqrt{N\lambda r_0} = \sqrt{(1)(6\times10^{-5})(20)} = 0.346$ mm

(b) $R_1 = 1$ cm ; $N = R_1^2/\lambda r_0 = (1)^2/(6\times10^{-5})(20) = 833$

(c) No minima appear now. Maxima are

$f_1 = r_0 = \frac{R_1^2}{N\lambda} = \frac{(0.0346)^2}{(1)(6\times10^{-5})} = 20$ cm

$f_3 = \frac{f_1}{3} = 6.67cm$ ; $f_5 = \frac{f_1}{5} = 4cm$

18-5.

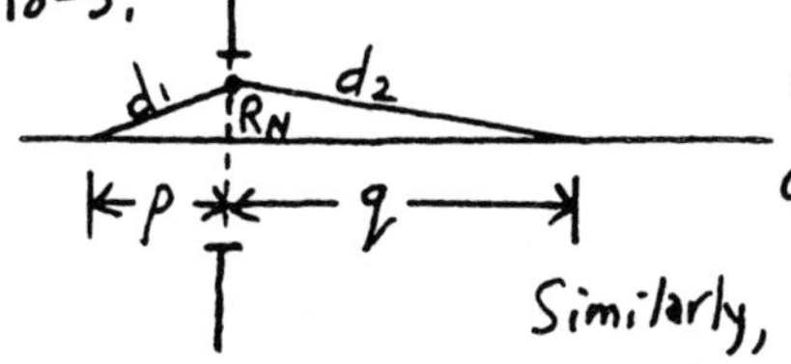


For $N^{th}$ zone, $(d_1+d_2) - (p+q) = N(\lambda/2)$

Geometry for $d_1, d_2$:

$d_1 = \sqrt{p^2+R_N^2} = p\left(1+\frac{R_N^2}{p^2}\right)^{1/2} \cong p\left(1+\frac{R_N^2}{2p^2}\right)$

Similarly, $d_2 \cong q\left(1+\frac{R_N^2}{2q^2}\right)$

$(d_1+d_2) = (p+q) + \frac{R_N^2}{2}\underbrace{\left(\frac{1}{p}+\frac{1}{q}\right)}_{\equiv \frac{1}{L}}$

$N\left(\frac{\lambda}{2}\right) = \frac{R_N^2}{2L}$

$R_N = \sqrt{NL\lambda}$ Q.E.D.

18-6. $\frac{1}{L} = \frac{1}{p} + \frac{1}{q} = \frac{1}{10} + \frac{1}{20}$ OR $L = \frac{20}{3}$ cm

(a) $R_1 = \sqrt{NL\lambda} = \sqrt{(1)\left(\frac{20}{3}\right)(6\times10^{-5})} = 0.2$ mm

(b) $N = \frac{R_1^2}{L\lambda}$ for $R_1 = 1$ cm ; $N = \frac{(1)^2}{(20/3)(6\times10^{-5})} = 2500$

18-7.

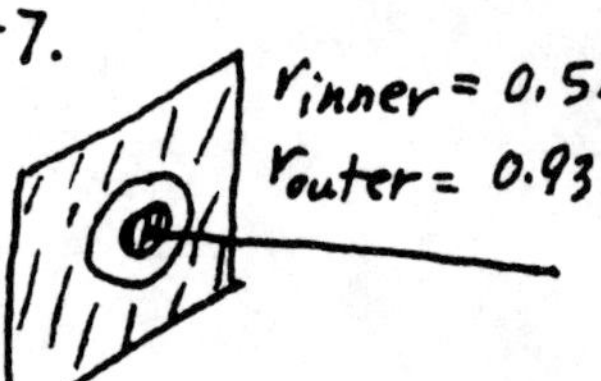


$\frac{1}{L} = \frac{1}{p} + \frac{1}{q} = \frac{1}{50} + \frac{1}{50}$ OR $L = 25$ cm

(a) How many zones contribute?

$R_N = \sqrt{NL\lambda}$ OR $N = \frac{R_N^2}{L\lambda}$

$N_{inner} = \frac{0.05^2}{25(5\times10^{-5})} = 2$ $\quad N_{outer} = \frac{0.0935^2}{25(5\times10^{-5})} = 7$

thus zones 3, 4, 5, 6 and 7 contribute. Two pairs essentially cancel, so one zone contributes:

$I_u \propto \left(\frac{a_1}{2}\right)^2$ and here $I \propto a_1^2$

assuming $a_1 \cong a_2 \cong \ldots a_7$. Thus

$$\frac{I}{I_u} = \frac{a_1^2}{a_1^2/4} = 4\times$$

(b) If $r_{outer} = 1$ mm $= 0.1$ cm, then

$$N_{outer} = \frac{0.1^2}{25(5\times10^{-5})} = 8 \text{ zones}$$

Now three pairs of zones essentially cancel, and so $I$ = very nearly zero.

(c) $7 - 2 = 5$ zones ; $8 - 2 = 6$ zones

18-8. $S_N \cong \underbrace{\left(\frac{\pi r_0' r_0^2}{r_0 + r_0'}\right)}_{\equiv A}\left[\frac{\lambda}{r_0} + (2N-1)\left(\frac{\lambda}{2r_0}\right)^2\right]$

$$\frac{S_{N1} - S_{N2}}{S_{N2}} = \frac{A\left[(2N_1-1) - (2N_2-1)\right](\lambda/2r_0)^2}{A\left[\lambda/r_0 + (2N_2-1)(\lambda/2r_0)^2\right]}$$

For $N_1 = 25$, $N_2 = 1$, $r_0 = r_0' = 50$ cm, $\lambda = 500$ nm

$$\frac{S_{25} - S_1}{S_1} = \frac{48(\lambda/2r_0)^2}{\lambda/r_0 + (\lambda/2r_0)^2} \cong 48\left(\frac{\lambda}{4r_0}\right) = 12\frac{\lambda}{r_0} = 12\,\frac{(5\times10^{-5})}{50}$$

($(\lambda/2r_0)^2$ in the denominator neglected, since $\lambda \ll r_0$)

$$\frac{S_{25} - S_1}{S_1} = 1.2\times10^{-5} \text{ OR } 0.0012\%$$

18-9. (a) $R_1 = 11.25$ cm before reduction

Must have $R_1 = \sqrt{N\lambda f_N} = (6.328\times10^{-5} \times 200)^{1/2} = 0.1125$ cm

$\therefore$ reduction factor $= 1/100$.

(b) $R_N = \sqrt{N}R_1 = \sqrt{20}\,(11.25) = 50.31$ cm

18-10. Using $R_N = \sqrt{N r_0 \lambda}$,

$D_2 = 2R_2 = 2\sqrt{2}\sqrt{r_0\lambda} = 2\sqrt{2}\,(3.708\times10^{-4}) = 1.05$ mm

$D_4 = 2R_4 = 2\sqrt{4}\sqrt{r_0\lambda} = \sqrt{2}\,D_2 = 1.48$ mm

$D_6 = 2R_6 = 2\sqrt{6}\sqrt{r_0\lambda} = \sqrt{3}\,D_2 = 1.82$ mm

18-11. The zone areas are given by Eq. (18-15), which becomes — approximately — Eq. (18-16) for $\lambda/r_0$ or $\lambda/x \ll 1$. This equation is independent of N, so areas are approximately constant. For a plane wave front, $r_0 \to \infty$. Thus

Eq. (18-16) $S_N = \left(\dfrac{r_0 r_0'}{r_0 + r_0'}\right)\pi\lambda = \dfrac{\pi\lambda}{\left(\frac{1}{r_0}+\frac{1}{r_0'}\right)} \xrightarrow[r_0\to\infty]{} \pi\lambda r_0' = \pi\lambda x$

18-12. $R_N = \sqrt{N r_0 \lambda}$

$R_4 = [(4)(2)(485\times10^{-9})]^{1/2} = 0.00197$ m $= 1.97$ mm

$A = a_1 - a_2 + a_3 - a_4$. Since $a_1 \cong a_2$ and $a_3 \cong a_4$, $A \cong 0$ and irradiance is nearly zero.

18-13. $\dfrac{1}{L} = \dfrac{1}{p} + \dfrac{1}{q}$, where $p \to \infty$, so $L = q$. Also, $\Delta z = w$.

$\Delta v = \sqrt{\dfrac{2}{L\lambda}}\,\Delta z$ or $L = \dfrac{2w^2}{(\Delta v)^2\lambda} = \dfrac{2(0.0005)^2}{(2.5)^2(540\times10^{-9})}$

$L = 0.148$ m $= 14.8$ cm

18-14.

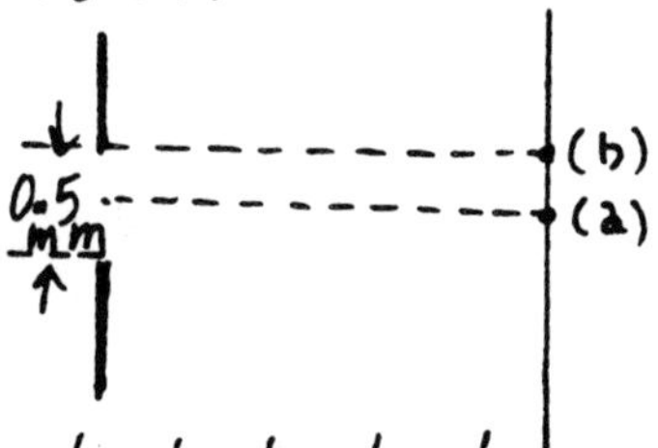


$\dfrac{1}{L} = \dfrac{1}{p} + \dfrac{1}{q} = \dfrac{1}{30} + \dfrac{1}{15}$

$L = 10$ cm

(a)

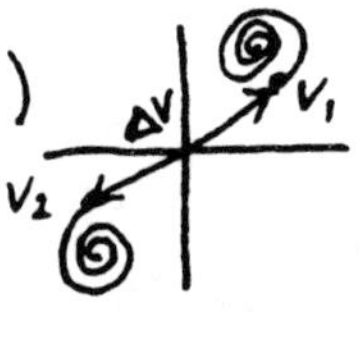


The portion of the Cornu spiral contributing to the irradiance is

$\Delta v = \sqrt{\dfrac{2}{L\lambda}}\,z = \sqrt{\dfrac{2}{(.1)(435.8\times10^{-9})}}\,(0.5\times10^{-3})$

$\Delta v = 3.3872$

For half the amplitude, from $v = 0$ to $v = \dfrac{3.3872}{2}$ we have

$C(1.6936) = 0.3265$ and $S(1.6936) = 0.5549$

Then $\dfrac{E_p}{2} = [(.5 - .3265)^2 + (.5 - .5549)^2]^{1/2} = 0.1820$

$E_p = 0.36396$ ; $E_p^2 = 0.1325$

$I_p = 0.1325\, I_o = 0.066\, I_u$

18-14. (cont'd.)

(b)

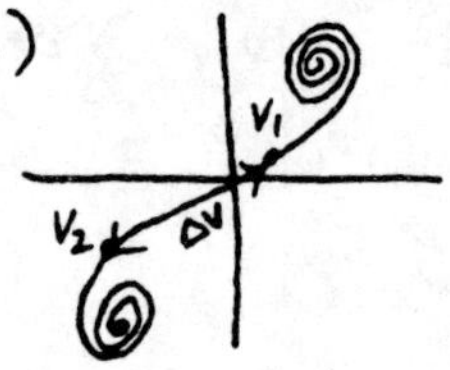


At $y = 0.25$ mm, $z = \left(\frac{p}{p+q}\right) y = \left(\frac{30}{30+15}\right)(0.25) = \frac{1}{6}$ mm

Then $v_1 = \sqrt{\frac{2}{L\lambda}}\, z = 6774.4\left(\frac{1}{6}\times 10^{-3}\right) = 1.12907$

Since $\Delta v$ remains constant for a given $\Delta z$,

$$v_2 = 1.1291 - 3.3872 = -2.2581$$

At $v_1$, $\mathcal{C}(1.1291) = 0.7497$, $\mathcal{S}(1.1291) = 0.5618$ } Quad 1

At $v_2$, $\mathcal{C}(-2.2581) = -0.6307$, $\mathcal{S}(-2.2581) = -0.5123$ } Quad 3

Then $E_p = \left[(.7497 + .6307)^2 + (.5618 + .5123)^2\right]^{1/2} = 1.74906$

$I_p = 3.059\, I_o = 1.53\, I_u$

18-15.

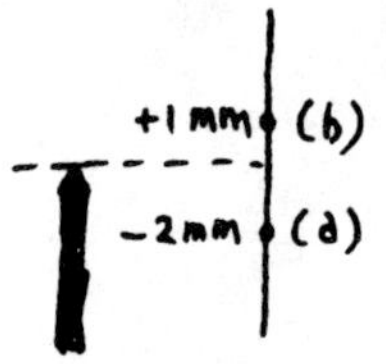


$$L = \frac{pq}{p+q} = \frac{60(120)}{60+120} = 40\text{ cm}$$

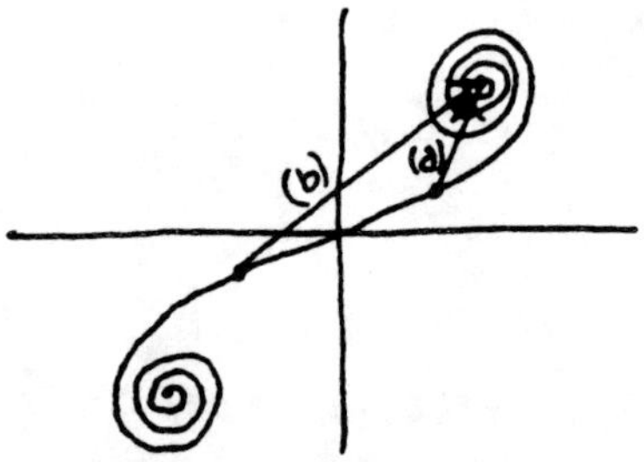


the distance z along the wavefront corresponding to the distance y on the screen is found from

$$z = \left(\frac{p}{p+q}\right) y = \left(\frac{60}{60+120}\right) y = \frac{y}{3}$$

Thus in (a): $z = -2/3$ mm

in (b): $z = +1/3$ mm

The Cornu spiral parameter V is found from

$$V = \sqrt{\frac{2}{L\lambda}}\, z = \left[\frac{2}{0.4(589.3\times 10^{-9})}\right]^{1/2} z$$

$V = 2913\, z$

Then in (a): $V = 2913(2/3) = 1.942$ in Q1

in (b): $V = 2913(1/3) = -0.9709$ in Q3

From Table 18-1, using interpolation,

(a) $\mathcal{C}(1.942) = 0.4338$     (b) $\mathcal{C}(-0.9709) = -0.7755$

$\mathcal{S}(1.942) = 0.3608$     $\mathcal{S}(-0.9709) = -0.4097$

In both cases (a) + (b), the head of the amplitude phasor is at $\mathcal{C}(\infty) = \mathcal{S}(\infty) = 0.5$

In (a), the tail of the phasor is in Q1. Then

$$E_p^2 = \left[(.5 - .4338)^2 + (.5 - .3608)^2\right] = 0.02376$$

$$I_p = 0.02376\, I_o = 0.0119\, I_u$$

In (b), the tail is in Q3:

$$E_p^2 = \left[(.5 + .7755)^2 + (.5 + .4097)^2\right] = 2.4544$$

$$I_p = 2.454\, I_o = 1.23\, I_u$$

18-16.

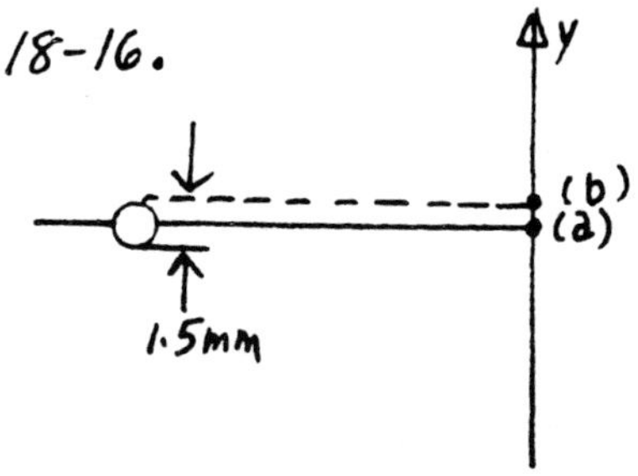


$\frac{1}{L} = \frac{1}{p} + \frac{1}{q} = \frac{1}{30} + \frac{1}{60}$ OR $L = 20$ cm

(a)

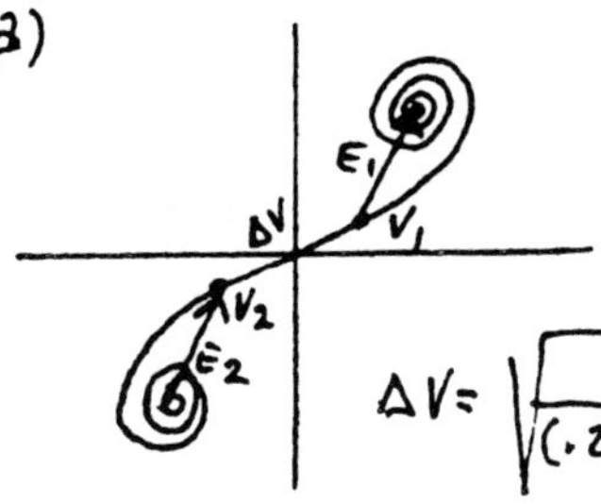


$y = 0$; $\Delta z = W = 1.5$ mm

$\Delta V = \sqrt{\frac{2}{L\lambda}}\,\Delta z$

$\Delta V = \sqrt{\frac{2}{(.2)(546.1 \times 10^{-9})}}\,(1.5 \times 10^{-3})$

$V_1 = \frac{6.4188}{2} = +3.2094$

$\Delta V = 6.4188$

$V_2 = -3.2094$

For $V_1$, $C(3.2094) = 0.4607$ and $S(3.2094) = 0.5863$

Half of the contributing amplitude is therefore

$E_1 = \left[(.5 - .4607)^2 + (.5 - .5863)^2\right]^{1/2} = 0.09486$

then $E_p = E_1 + E_2 = 2E_1 = 0.1897$

$I_p = 0.03599 = 0.018\, I_u$

(b)

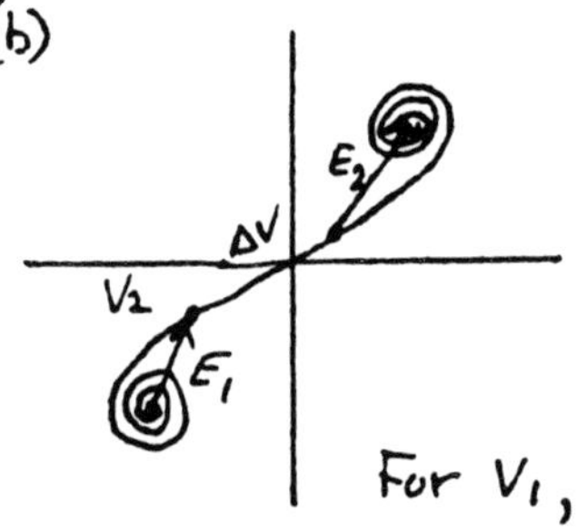


$y = \frac{1.5}{2} = 0.75$ mm so that $z = \left(\frac{p}{p+q}\right) y = \frac{30}{90} y = \frac{y}{3}$

$V_1 = \sqrt{\frac{2}{L\lambda}}\, z = +1.0698$ $\qquad z = 0.25$ mm

Since $\Delta z$ and so $\Delta V$ remain constant,

$V_2 = 1.0698 - 6.4188 = -5.3490$

For $V_1$, $C(1.0698) = 0.7687$ and $S(1.0698) = 0.5068$

For $V_2$, $C(-5.3490) = -0.5482$ and $S(-5.3490) = -0.4657$

$E_1 = \left[(.5 - .7687)^2 + (.5 - .5068)^2\right]^{1/2} = 0.2688$

$E_2 = \left[(-.5 + .5482)^2 + (-.5 + .4657)^2\right]^{1/2} = 0.05916$

$E_p = E_1 + E_2 = 0.32795$ ; $E_p^2 = 0.1075$

$I_p = 0.1075\, I_o = 0.0538\, I_u$

18-17. Max : $V = 2.3$ $\qquad$ Min ; $V = 2.75$

$C(v) = -0.6266$ $\qquad$ $C(v) = -0.4300$

$S(v) = -0.5531$ $\qquad$ $S(v) = -0.4222$

2nd max $\begin{cases} E_p = \left[(-.6266 - .5)^2 + (-.5531 - .5)^2\right]^{1/2} = 1.54216 \\ I_p = 2.37825\, I_o = 1.19\, I_u, \text{ using } 2I_o = I_u \end{cases}$

2nd min $\begin{cases} E_p = \left[(-.4300 - .5)^2 + (-.4222 - .5)^2\right]^{1/2} = 1.3097 \\ I_p = 1.71535\, I_o = 0.86\, I_u, \text{ using } 2I_o = I_u \end{cases}$

18-18.

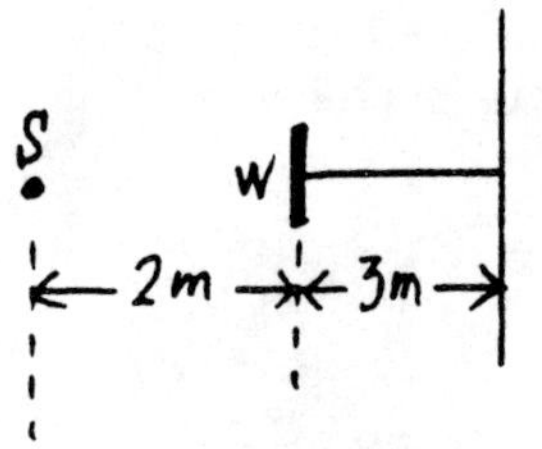


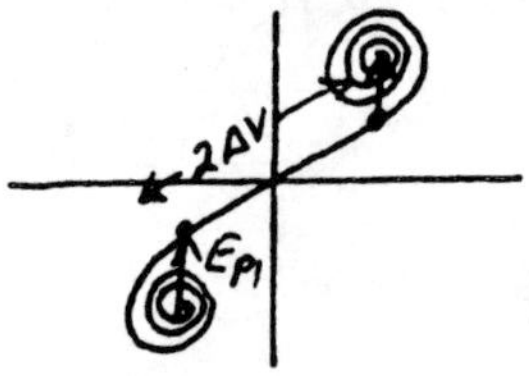


$W = 0.37$ mm  $\frac{1}{L} = \frac{1}{2} + \frac{1}{3}$ or $L = 1.2$ m

$\lambda = 630$ nm

$$2\Delta V = \sqrt{2/L\lambda}\, W = \left[\frac{2}{(120)(6.3\times10^{-5})}\right]^{1/2}(0.037) = 0.6018$$

$V = 0.3009$; $C(V) = 0.3003$; $S(V) = 0.0143$

$$E_{p1} = \left[(.5 - .3003)^2 + (.5 - .0143)^2\right]^{1/2} = 0.52515$$

$$E_p = 2E_{p1} = 1.0503$$

$$I_p = 1.103\, I_o = 0.55\, I_u$$

18-19.

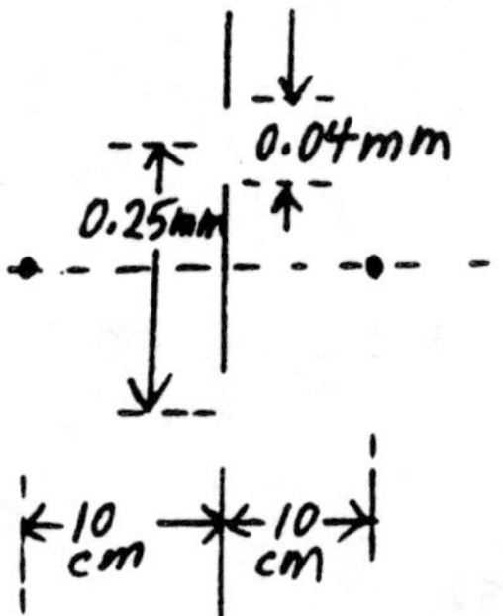


$\frac{1}{L} = \frac{1}{10} + \frac{1}{10}$ or $L = 5$cm

Top slit: $z_1$ to $z_2 = \left(\frac{.25}{2} - .02\right)$ to $\left(\frac{.25}{2} + .02\right)$ mm

$= 0.0105$ cm to $0.0145$ cm

$$V_1 = \sqrt{\frac{2}{L\lambda}}\, z_1 = \left[\frac{2}{5(5.46\times10^{-5})}\right]^{1/2}(0.0105) = 0.8987$$

$$V_2 = \sqrt{\frac{2}{L\lambda}}\, z_2 = \left[\frac{2}{5(5.46\times10^{-5})}\right]^{1/2}(0.0145) = 1.2411$$

$C(V_1) = 0.76426$  $C(V_2) = 0.68384$

$S(V_1) = 0.33862$  $S(V_2) = 0.64925$

$$E_{top} = \left[(.76426 - .68384)^2 + (.64925 - .33862)^2\right]^{1/2} = 0.32087$$

$$I_p = 2E_{top} = 0.64174$$

$$I_p = 0.41183\, I_o = 0.2059\, I_u \text{ or } 20.6\%$$

18-20.

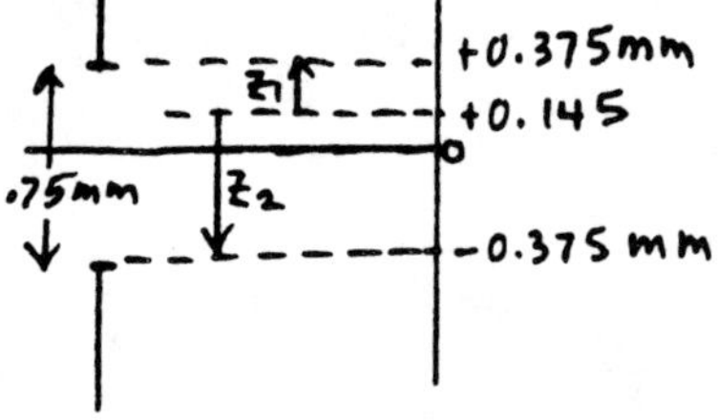


$\frac{1}{L} = \frac{1}{25} + \frac{1}{25}$ OR $L = 12.5$cm

(a) Far field: $L >> b^2/\lambda$

Here, $b^2/\lambda = (.075)^2/(4.358\times10^{-5}) = 129$cm

But $p = 25$cm $= q$

(b) Assuming far field: $m\lambda = b\sin\theta$

$\sin\theta = \frac{\lambda}{b} = \frac{4.358\times10^{-5}}{0.075}$ OR $\theta = 0.03329°$

$y = q\tan\theta = 25\tan(.03329) = 0.0145$cm

(c) $z_1 = .375 - .145 = 0.230$ mm

$z_2 = .375 + .145 = 0.520$ mm

$$V_1 = \sqrt{2/L\lambda}\, z_1 = \left[2/(12.5)(4.358\times10^{-5})\right]^{1/2}(.023) = 1.3936$$

$$V_2 = \sqrt{2/L\lambda}\, z_2 = \left[2/(12.5)(4.358\times10^{-5})\right]^{1/2}(.052) = 3.1508$$

18-20. (cont'd.)

$C(v_1) = 0.549212$ $\quad$ $C(v_2) = -0.51324$

$S(v_1) = 0.71176$ $\quad$ $S(v_2) = -0.58764$

$$E_p = \left[(.549212 + .51324)^2 + (.71176 + .58764)^2\right]^{1/2} = 1.6785$$

$$I_p = 2.8172\, I_o = 1.4\, I_u$$

18-21. By Babinet's principle, the diffraction pattern is complementary to that due to circular apertures of the same size as the particles in an otherwise opaque screen. The halo is the complement of the Airy disc. Taking $\lambda = 550$ nm,

$$1.22\lambda = a \sin\theta$$

$$a = \frac{1.22\lambda}{\sin\theta} = \frac{1.22(550 \times 10^{-9})}{\sin 2^\circ}$$

$$a \cong 19\,\mu m$$

19-1.

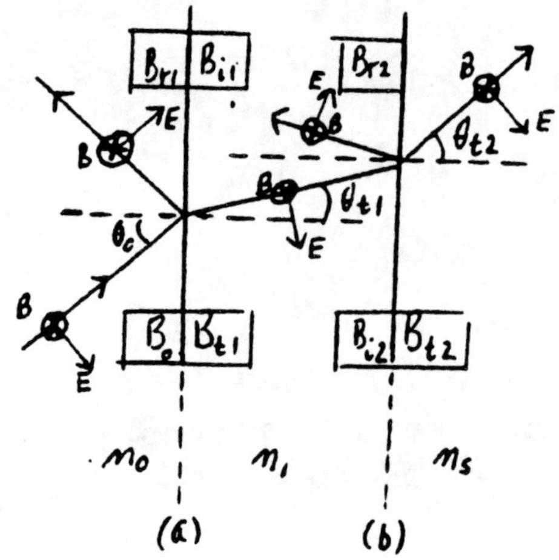


$E_1 \parallel$ plane of incidence

Boundary conditions: tangential components are continuous

$$B_a = B_0 + B_{r1} = B_{t1} + B_{i1}$$
$$B_b = B_{i2} + B_{r2} = B_{t2}$$
analogous to Eqs. 19-6, 7

and for the electric field,

$$E_a = E_0 \cos\theta_0 - E_{r1}\cos\theta_0 = E_{t1}\cos\theta_{t1} - E_{i1}\cos\theta_{t1}$$
$$E_b = E_{i2}\cos\theta_{t1} - E_{r2}\cos\theta_{t2} = E_{t2}\cos\theta_{t2}$$
analogous to Eqs. 19-8, 9

Using $B = n\sqrt{\epsilon_0\mu_0}\,E$ (Eq. 19-5), the $E$ eqs. are expressed in terms of $B$:

$$\begin{cases} E_a = \dfrac{B_0\cos\theta_0}{n_0\sqrt{\epsilon_0\mu_0}} - \dfrac{B_{r1}\cos\theta_0}{n_0\sqrt{\epsilon_0\mu_0}} = \dfrac{B_{t1}\cos\theta_{t1}}{n_1\sqrt{\epsilon_0\mu_0}} - \dfrac{B_{i1}\cos\theta_{t1}}{n_1\sqrt{\epsilon_0\mu_0}} \\ E_b = \dfrac{B_{i2}\cos\theta_{t1}}{n_1\sqrt{\epsilon_0\mu_0}} - \dfrac{B_{r2}\cos\theta_{t1}}{n_1\sqrt{\epsilon_0\mu_0}} = \dfrac{B_{t2}\cos\theta_{t2}}{n_s\sqrt{\epsilon_0\mu_0}} \end{cases}$$

Define: $\gamma_0 \equiv \dfrac{n_0\sqrt{\epsilon_0\mu_0}}{\cos\theta_0}$, $\gamma_1 \equiv \dfrac{n_1\sqrt{\epsilon_0\mu_0}}{\cos\theta_{t1}}$, $\gamma_s = \dfrac{n_s\sqrt{\epsilon_0\mu_0}}{\cos\theta_{t2}}$

So that the pair of equations becomes

$$\begin{cases} E_a = \dfrac{B_0}{\gamma_0} - \dfrac{B_{r1}}{\gamma_0} = \dfrac{B_{t1}}{\gamma_1} - \dfrac{B_{i1}}{\gamma_1} \\ E_b = \dfrac{B_{i2}}{\gamma_1} - \dfrac{B_{r2}}{\gamma_1} = \dfrac{B_{t2}}{\gamma_s} \end{cases}$$

OR

Analogous to Eqs. 19-10, 11

$$\begin{cases} E_a = \dfrac{1}{\gamma_0}(B_0 - B_{r1}) = \dfrac{1}{\gamma_1}(B_{t1} - B_{i1}) \\ E_b = \dfrac{1}{\gamma_1}(B_{i2} - B_{r2}) = \dfrac{1}{\gamma_s}B_{t2} \end{cases}$$

Now $B_{i2} = B_{t1}e^{-i\delta}$, $B_{i1} = B_{r2}e^{-i\delta}$ — analogous to Eqs. 19-16, 17

We use these eqs. to eliminate $B_{i2}$ and $B_{r2}$ in the expressions for $B_b$ and $E_b$ above, getting

$$\begin{cases} B_b = B_{t1}e^{-i\delta} + B_{i1}e^{i\delta} = B_{t2} \\ E_b = \dfrac{B_{t1}e^{-i\delta}}{\gamma_1} - \dfrac{B_{i1}e^{i\delta}}{\gamma_1} = \dfrac{B_{t2}}{\gamma_s} \end{cases}$$

Solving the last pair simultaneously for $B_{i1}$ and $B_{t1}$:

$$B_{t1} = \left(\frac{B_b + \gamma_1 E_b}{2}\right)e^{i\delta}$$

$$B_{i1} = \left(\frac{B_b - \gamma_1 E_b}{2}\right)e^{-i\delta}$$

Substituting into the eqs. for $E_a$ and $B_a$,

19-1. (cont'd.)

$$B_a = B_{t1} + B_{i1} \quad \text{or} \quad B_a = \frac{B_b + \gamma_1 E_b}{2} e^{i\delta} + \frac{B_b - \gamma_1 E_b}{2} e^{-i\delta}$$

$$E_a = \frac{B_{t1}}{\gamma_1} - \frac{B_{i1}}{\gamma_1} \quad \text{or} \quad E_a = \frac{B_b + \gamma_1 E_b}{2\gamma_1} e^{i\delta} - \frac{B_b - \gamma_1 E_b}{2\gamma_1} e^{-i\delta}$$

Simplifying, using $2\cos\delta \equiv e^{i\delta} + e^{-i\delta}$ and $2i\sin\delta \equiv e^{i\delta} - e^{-i\delta}$,

$$\begin{cases} B_a = B_b \cos\delta + E_b (i\gamma_1 \sin\delta) \\ E_a = B_b\left(\frac{i\sin\delta}{\gamma_1}\right) + E_b \cos\delta \end{cases}$$

In matrix form,

$$\begin{pmatrix} E_a \\ B_a \end{pmatrix} = \begin{pmatrix} \cos\delta & i\sin\delta/\gamma_1 \\ i\gamma_1 \sin\delta & \cos\delta \end{pmatrix} \begin{pmatrix} E_b \\ B_b \end{pmatrix} \qquad \text{Eq. (19-24)}$$

Thus, if the $\gamma$ are defined with the $\cos\theta$ factor in the denominator, — e.g.,

$$\gamma_1 = \frac{n_1 \sqrt{\epsilon_0 \mu_0}}{\cos\theta_{t1}} \qquad (E \parallel \text{ plane of incidence})$$

rather than in the numerator (see Eqs. 19-12, 13, 14), for the case when $E \parallel$ plane of incidence, the same film transfer matrix can be used.

19-2.

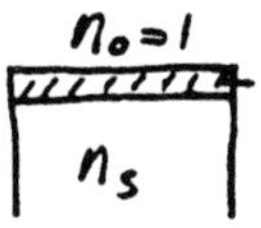


(a) $t = \frac{\lambda_F}{4} = \frac{\lambda_0}{4n_1}$ where $n_1 = \sqrt{n_0 n_s} = \sqrt{1 \times 1.5} = 1.22$

Thus $t = \frac{500\text{ nm}}{4(1.22)} = 102\text{ nm}$

(b) $\delta = K_0\Delta = \frac{2\pi}{\lambda_0}(n_1 t \cos\theta_{t1}) = \frac{2\pi}{550}\sqrt{1.5}(102)(1) = 1.428$ rad.

$\cos\delta = 0.1423 \qquad \sin\delta = 0.9898$

then

$$R = \frac{n_1^2(n_0 - n_s)^2\cos^2\delta + (n_0 n_s - n_1^2)^2 \sin^2\delta}{n_1^2(n_0 + n_s)^2 \cos^2\delta + (n_0 n_s + n_1^2)^2 \sin^2\delta} \; ; \quad n_0 n_s - n_1^2 = 0$$

$$R = \frac{1.5(1-1.5)^2(0.142315)^2 + 0}{1.5(1+1.5)^2(0.142315)^2 + (1.5+1.5)^2(0.989821)^2} = 8.432 \times 10^{-4} = 0.0843\ \%$$

19-3. From the $R$ equation (19-42), or above, Prob 19-2, with $\delta = 2\pi\left(\frac{\Delta}{\lambda}\right) = 2\pi\left(\frac{\lambda/2}{\lambda}\right) = \pi$, $\cos^2\pi = 1$, $\sin^2\pi = 0$,

$$R = \frac{n_1^2(n_0 - n_s)^2(1) + 0}{n_1^2(n_0 + n_s)^2(1) + 0} = \frac{(n_0 - n_s)^2}{(n_0 + n_s)^2} \qquad \text{Q.E.D.}$$

19-4.

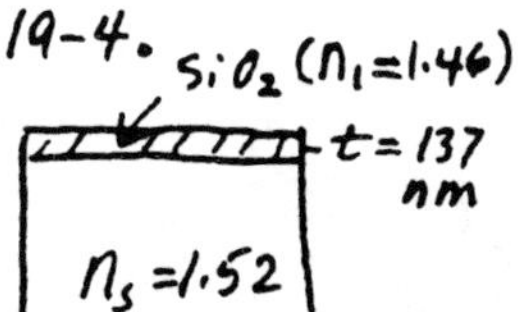


Using Eq. 19-42

$$R = \frac{1.46^2(1-1.52)^2\cos^2\delta + (1.52 - 1.46^2)^2 \sin^2\delta}{1.46^2(1+1.52)^2\cos^2\delta + (1.52 + 1.46^2)^2 \sin^2\delta}$$

(a) $\lambda = 800$ nm : $\delta = \frac{2\pi}{\lambda_0}\Delta = \frac{2\pi}{\lambda_0}(n_1 t) = \frac{2\pi}{800}(1.46 \times 137) \equiv \pi/2$

$\Delta/\lambda = \frac{200}{800} = \frac{1}{4}$ ; $\cos\delta = 0$, $\sin\delta = 1$

$R = 2.81\%$

19-4. (cont'd.)

(b) $\lambda = 600$ nm $\quad \delta = \frac{2\pi}{600}(200) = \frac{2\pi}{3}$ ; $\frac{\Delta}{\lambda} = \frac{200}{600} = \frac{1}{3}$

$\cos\delta = -0.5$ , $\sin\delta = 0.866$

$R = 3.17\%$

(c) $\lambda = 400$ nm $\quad \delta = \frac{2\pi}{400}(200) = \pi$ ; $\frac{\Delta}{\lambda} = \frac{200}{400} = \frac{1}{2}$

$\cos\delta = -1$ , $\sin\delta = 0$

$R = 4.26\%$ (same as glass of $n = 1.52$)

19-5. $\delta = \frac{2\pi}{\lambda_0} n_1 t = \frac{2\pi}{\lambda_0}(2.35)(596) = 2\pi\underbrace{\left(\frac{1400}{5600}\right)}_{\Delta = \lambda/4} = \frac{\pi}{2}$

$\cos\delta = 0$, $\sin\delta = 1$

In Eq. 19-42,

$$R = \frac{2.35^2(1-1.52)^2(0) + [(1)(1.52) - 2.35^2]^2(1)^2}{2.35^2(1+1.52)^2(0) + [(1)(1.52) + 2.35^2]^2(1)^2} = 32.3\%$$

Or, since this is a quarter-wave thickness film used at normal incidence, one can resort immediately to Eq. (19-43).

19-6. (a) $n_1 = \sqrt{n_0 n_s} = \sqrt{4} = 2$ and $t = \frac{\lambda_0}{4n_1} = \frac{2}{4(2)} = 0.25\,\mu m$

(b) $ZrO_2$ (see Table 19-1)

19-7.

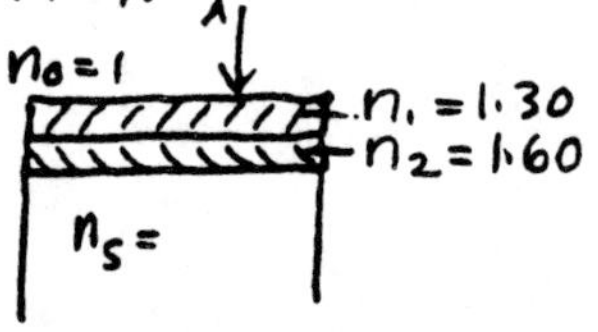


(a) Quarter wave layers for $\lambda_0 = 550$ nm

$t_1 = \frac{\lambda_F}{4} = \frac{\lambda_0}{4n_1} = \frac{550\text{ nm}}{4(1.3)} = 1058\,\mathring{A}$

$t_2 = \frac{\lambda_F}{4} = \frac{5500\,\mathring{A}}{4(1.60)} = 859.4\,\mathring{A}$

Eq. 19-45 : $R = \left[\frac{n_0 n_2^2 - n_s n_1^2}{n_0 n_2^2 + n_s n_1^2}\right]^2 = \left[\frac{1(1.6)^2 - 1.52(1.3)^2}{1(1.6)^2 + 1.52(1.3)^2}\right]^2 = 0.0003\%$

(b) Layers reversed : $R = \left[\frac{1(1.3)^2 - 1.52(1.6)^2}{1(1.3)^2 + 1.52(1.6)^2}\right]^2 = 15.55\%$

19-8

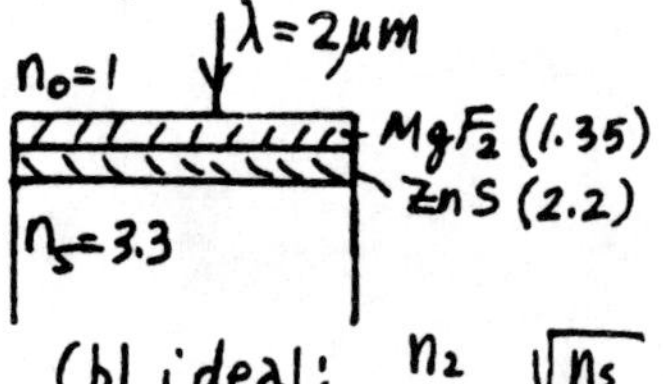


(a) Quarter wave thicknesses :

$t_1 = \lambda_0/4n_1 = 2\mu m/4(1.35) = 370$ nm

$t_2 = \lambda_0/4n_2 = 2\mu m/4(2.2) = 227$ nm

(b) ideal: $\frac{n_2}{n_1} = \sqrt{\frac{n_s}{n_0}} = \sqrt{\frac{3.3}{1}} = 1.8166$ $\qquad$ actual: $\frac{n_2}{n_1} = \frac{2.2}{1.35} = 1.6296$

$$\%\text{ difference} = \frac{1.8166 - 1.6296}{1.8166} = 10.3\%$$

19-8. (cont'd.)

$$R=\left[\frac{n_0 n_2^2 - n_s n_1^2}{n_0 n_2^2 + n_s n_1^2}\right]^2 = \left[\frac{1(2.2)^2 - 3.3(1.35)^2}{1(2.2)^2 + 3.3(1.35)^2}\right]^2 = 1.17\%$$

19-9. For $\lambda/4$ layer at $\lambda = \lambda_0$ : $\begin{cases} \cos\delta_1 = \cos(\pi/2) = 0 \\ \sin\delta_1 = \sin(\pi/2) = 1 \end{cases}$

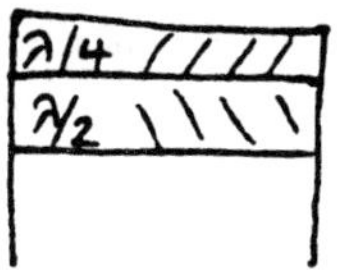


For $\lambda/2$ layer at $\lambda = \lambda_0$ : $\begin{cases} \cos\delta_1 = \cos\pi = -1 \\ \sin\delta_1 = \sin\pi = 0 \end{cases}$

The transfer matrix for a $\lambda/4$ - $\lambda/2$ double layer is, using

$$\mathcal{M} = \begin{pmatrix} \cos\delta_1 & i\sin\delta_1/\gamma_1 \\ i\gamma_1\sin\delta_1 & \cos\delta_1 \end{pmatrix}$$

$$\mathcal{M} = \underbrace{\begin{pmatrix} 0 & i/\gamma_1 \\ i\gamma_1 & 0 \end{pmatrix}}_{\lambda/4}\underbrace{\begin{pmatrix} -1 & 0 \\ 0 & -1 \end{pmatrix}}_{\lambda/2} = \begin{pmatrix} 0 & -i/\gamma_1 \\ -i\gamma_1 & 0 \end{pmatrix}$$

the matrix elements are just the negative of those for the $\lambda/4$ layer acting alone. Thus Eq. 19-36 for $r$ is just the negative, also, and $R = |r|^2$ is the same. Note this is true only at the $\lambda_0$ for which the double-layer thicknesses are determined.

19-10.

For a double layer of arbitrary thickness, (to be specified), but normal incidence, the transfer matrix is

$$\mathcal{M} = \mathcal{M}_1\mathcal{M}_2 = \begin{pmatrix} \cos\delta_1 & i\sin\delta_1/\gamma_1 \\ i\gamma_1\sin\delta_1 & \cos\delta_1 \end{pmatrix}\begin{pmatrix} \cos\delta_2 & i\sin\delta_2/\gamma_2 \\ i\gamma_2\sin\delta_2 & \cos\delta_2 \end{pmatrix}$$

$$\mathcal{M} = \begin{pmatrix} \cos\delta_1\cos\delta_2 - \frac{\gamma_2}{\gamma_1}\sin\delta_1\sin\delta_2 & i\left[\frac{\cos\delta_1\sin\delta_2}{\gamma_2} + \frac{\sin\delta_1\cos\delta_2}{\gamma_1}\right] \\ i\left[\gamma_1\sin\delta_1\cos\delta_2 + \gamma_2\cos\delta_1\sin\delta_2\right] & -\frac{\gamma_1}{\gamma_2}\sin\delta_1\sin\delta_2 + \cos\delta_1\cos\delta_2 \end{pmatrix}$$

If $\mathcal{M} = \begin{pmatrix} m_{11} & m_{12} \\ m_{21} & m_{22} \end{pmatrix}$, the transfer matrix elements are

$m_{11} = \cos\delta_1\cos\delta_2 - \frac{\gamma_2}{\gamma_1}\sin\delta_1\sin\delta_2$, etc., as read from the matrix above. The general form of the reflection coefficient is

$$r = \frac{\gamma_0 m_{11} + \gamma_0\gamma_s m_{12} - m_{21} - \gamma_s m_{22}}{\gamma_0 m_{11} + \gamma_0\gamma_s m_{12} + m_{21} + \gamma_s m_{22}}$$

Since $m_{12}$ and $m_{21}$ in our case are pure imaginary,

$$r = \frac{\gamma_0 m_{11} + i\gamma_0\gamma_s|m_{12}| - i|m_{21}| - \gamma_s m_{22}}{\gamma_0 m_{11} + i\gamma_0\gamma_s|m_{12}| + i|m_{21}| + \gamma_s m_{22}}$$

19-10 (cont'd.)

OR $$r = \frac{(\gamma_0 m_{11} - \gamma_s m_{22}) + i\,(\gamma_0\gamma_s |m_{12}| - |m_{21}|)}{(\gamma_0 m_{11} + \gamma_s m_{22}) + i\,(\gamma_0\gamma_s |m_{12}| + |m_{21}|)}$$

when substitution is made for the $\gamma$'s in the r-eq., entering both explicitly and in the m matrix elements, each term resuts with a factor of $\sqrt{\epsilon_0\mu_0}$ which then cancels out of the expression, leaving the indices of refraction.

$\gamma_0 = n_0\sqrt{\epsilon_0\mu_0} = \sqrt{\epsilon_0\mu_0}$ $\qquad \gamma_2 = n_2\sqrt{\epsilon_0\mu_0}$

$\gamma_1 = n_1\sqrt{\epsilon_0\mu_0}$ $\qquad \gamma_s = n_s\sqrt{\epsilon_0\mu_0}$

For purposes of programming, letus call $M \equiv m_{11}$, $N = |m_{12}|$, $O \equiv |m_{21}|$ and $P \equiv m_{22}$. Then

$$r = \frac{(n_0 M - n_s P) + i(n_0 n_s N - O)}{(n_0 M + n_s P) + i(n_0 n_s N + O)} \equiv \frac{A + iB}{C + iF}$$

so that $R = rr^* = \dfrac{A^2 + B^2}{C^2 + F^2}$.

To calculate M, N, O, P we need the phase differences.
For a given wavelength $\lambda$, $\delta = 2\pi\left(\frac{nt}{\lambda}\right)$ : $\lambda$ will vary
where thickness t = some fraction of the wavelength $\lambda_0$ forwhich the double layer is designed.
We write $t = Q\left(\frac{\lambda_0}{n}\right)$ where $Q = \frac{1}{4}$, for example, for a $\lambda_F/4$ layer.
Q is a variable, allowing variation of layer thicknesses. We do this for each layer.

Program variables: M, N, O, P and A, B, C, F are defined above.

$n_1 \to G$
$n_2 \to H$
$n_s \to I$
$\lambda_0 \to L$ (wavelength determining thicknesses)
$t_1 \to$ expressed as Q wavelengths $\to T$
$t_2 \to$ " " S " $\to U$
$\lambda \to W$ (running wavelength)
$\delta_1 \to D$
$\delta_2 \to E$
Reflectance $\to R$

19-10. (cont'd.) CALCULATOR PROGRAM

```
5 PRINT "2-LAYER FILM"
10 INPUT "N1= ";G,"N2= ";H,"NS= ";I,"WLO(MICRON)= ";L
15 INPUT "THICK1= ";Q,"THICK2= ";S
20 T=Q*L/G:U=S*L/H
25 FOR W=.3 TO .8 STEP .05
30 D=2*π*G*T/W:E=2*π*H*U/W
35 M=COS D*COS E-H*SIN D*SIN E/G
40 N=COS D*SIN E/H+SIN D*COS E/G
45 O=G*SIN D*COS E+H*COS D*SIN E
50 P=COS D*COS E-G*SIN D*SIN E/H
55 A=M-I*P:B=I*N-O:C=M+I*P:F=I*N+O
60 R=100*((A*A+B*B)/(C*C+F*F))
65 PRINT "WL= ";W,"REF= ";R
70 NEXT W
75 END
```

PROGRAM OUTPUT:

| $\lambda$ (μm) | R (a) | R (b) | R (c) |
|---|---|---|---|
| .3 | 7.84 % | 4.91 % | 7.96 % |
| .35 | 16.19 | 4.48 | 10.63 |
| .40 | 14.02 | 1.80 | 3.11 |
| .45 | 7.24 | 0.90 | 0.013 |
| .50 | 1.84 | 1.11 | 0.74 |
| .55 | 0.10 | 1.26 | 1.26 |
| .60 | 1.32 | 1.15 | 0.88 |
| .65 | 3.95 | 0.97 | 0.26 |
| .70 | 6.84 | 0.90 | 0.0032 |
| .75 | 9.45 | 0.98 | 0.32 |
| .80 | 11.6 | 1.22 | 1.16 |
| | $n_1$ = 1.65, $n_2$ = 2.1, Q = .25, S = .25 | $n_1$ = 1.38, $n_2$ = 1.6, Q = .25, S = .50 | $n_1$ = 1.38, $n_2$ = 1.85, Q = .25, S = .50 |

These data generate Fig. 19-4

In all cases, $n_s$ = 1.52 and $\lambda_0$ = 0.55 micron

Q = 0.25 means quarter-wave thickness
S = 0.50 means half-wave thickness

19-11. Quarter-wave matrices (as in Prob. 19-9) for normal incidence give a composite transfer matrix of

$$\mathcal{M} = \begin{pmatrix} 0 & i/\gamma_1 \\ i\gamma_1 & 0 \end{pmatrix}\begin{pmatrix} 0 & i/\gamma_2 \\ i\gamma_2 & 0 \end{pmatrix}\begin{pmatrix} 0 & i/\gamma_3 \\ i\gamma_3 & 0 \end{pmatrix} = \begin{pmatrix} 0 & -i\gamma_2/\gamma_1\gamma_3 \\ -i\gamma_1\gamma_3/\gamma_2 & 0 \end{pmatrix}$$

so that $m_{11} = m_{22} = 0$; $m_{12} = -i\gamma_2/\gamma_1\gamma_3$; $m_{21} = -i\gamma_1\gamma_3/\gamma_2$

Thus $r$ in Eq. 19-36 becomes

$$r = \frac{\gamma_0\gamma_s(-i\gamma_2/\gamma_1\gamma_3) + i\gamma_1\gamma_3/\gamma_2}{\gamma_0\gamma_s(-i\gamma_2/\gamma_1\gamma_3) - i\gamma_1\gamma_3/\gamma_2} = \frac{\left(\frac{\gamma_1\gamma_3}{2} - \frac{\gamma_0\gamma_s\gamma_2}{\gamma_1\gamma_3}\right)}{\left(-\frac{\gamma_1\gamma_3}{2} - \frac{\gamma_0\gamma_s\gamma_2}{\gamma_1\gamma_3}\right)}$$

Now $r = 0$ when $\frac{\gamma_1\gamma_3}{\gamma_2} = \frac{\gamma_0\gamma_s\gamma_2}{\gamma_1\gamma_3}$ OR $\gamma_0\gamma_s\gamma_2^2 = \gamma_1^2\gamma_3^2$

Each $\gamma = n\sqrt{\epsilon_0\mu_0}$. Substituting and cancelling all $\sqrt{\epsilon_0\mu_0}$

$$n_0 n_s n_2^2 = n_1^2 n_3^2$$

$$\frac{n_1 n_3}{n_2} = \sqrt{n_0 n_s}$$

19-12. We need, for $R=0$, $\frac{n_1 n_3}{n_2} = \sqrt{n_0 n_s} = \sqrt{1 \times 4} = 2$

From Table 19-1, we can construct a very good approximation in the following way:

| | | |
|---|---|---|
| $MgF_2$ | $n = 1.35$ | $n_3$ |
| $SiO$ | $n = 1.5$ | $n_2$ |
| $ZnS$ | $n = 2.2$ | $n_1$ |
| $n_s = 4$ | | |

This gives $\frac{n_1 n_3}{n_2} = \frac{(2.2)(1.35)}{1.5} = 1.98$

19-13. $$R = \left[\frac{\left(\frac{n_0}{n_s}\right)\left(\frac{n_L}{n_H}\right)^{2N} - 1}{\left(\frac{n_0}{n_s}\right)\left(\frac{n_L}{n_H}\right)^{2N} + 1}\right]^2 = \left[\frac{\frac{1}{1.52}\left(\frac{1.38}{2.6}\right)^{2N} - 1}{\frac{1}{1.52}\left(\frac{1.38}{2.6}\right)^{2N} + 1}\right]$$

(a) $N = 2$, $R = 81.1\%$

(b) $N = 4$, $R = 98.4\%$

(c) $N = 8$, $R = 99.99\%$

19-14. Substituting into the eq. for $R$, as in the preceding problem, one finds directly,

$$\left.\begin{array}{l} N = 4 \\ n_H = 4 \\ n_L = 1.35 \\ n_s = 1.50 \end{array}\right\} \quad R = 99.9551 \text{ or } 99.96\%$$

19-15. In Eq. 19-53, let $x = n_0/n_s$ and $z = n_L/n_H$

Then $\pm\sqrt{R} = \dfrac{xz^{2N}-1}{xz^{2N}+1}$. Since $x<1$ and $z<1$, we select the positive square root by writing

$$+\sqrt{R} = \frac{1-xz^{2N}}{1+xz^{2N}}$$

then $\sqrt{R} + xz^{2N}\sqrt{R} = 1 - xz^{2N}$

$$xz^{2N}(\sqrt{R}+1) = 1-\sqrt{R}$$

$$z^{2N} = \frac{1-\sqrt{R}}{x(1+\sqrt{R})}$$

In our case, this becomes

$$z^4 = \frac{1-\sqrt{.9}}{\frac{1}{1.5}(1+\sqrt{.9})} = 0.03950$$

$$z = 0.4458$$

and $\dfrac{n_H}{n_L} = \dfrac{1}{z} = 2.243$

19-16. $R = \left[\dfrac{xz^{2N}-1}{xz^{2N}+1}\right]$ as in Prob. 19-15, with $x = \dfrac{n_0}{n_s}$ and $z = n_L/n_H$

As $N \to \infty$, $z^{2N} \to 0$ since $z<1$.

thus $R \to \left(\frac{-1}{+1}\right)^2 = 1$ Q.E.D.

As $N \to 0$, $R \to \left(\frac{-1}{+1}\right)^2 = 1$ Q.E.D.

# Chapter 20 - Fresnel Equations

20-1. $r = \frac{E_r}{E} = \frac{n^2\cos\theta - \sqrt{n^2 - \sin^2\theta}}{n^2\cos\theta + \sqrt{n^2-\sin^2\theta}}$ Eq. (20-24)

when $r = 0$, $n^2\cos\theta = \sqrt{n^2 - \sin^2\theta}$

$n^4\cos^2\theta = n^2 - \sin^2\theta$ OR $n^4\cos^2\theta - n^2 + \sin^2\theta = 0$,

a quadratic in $n^2$. Thus

$$n^2 = \frac{1 \pm \sqrt{1 - 4\sin^2\theta\cos^2\theta}}{2\cos^2\theta}$$

with discriminant $1 - 4\sin^2\theta\cos^2\theta = 1 - 4\sin^2\theta + 4\sin^4\theta$
$= (2\sin^2\theta - 1)^2$.

Then

$$n^2 = \frac{1 \pm (2\sin^2\theta - 1)}{2\cos^2\theta} = \begin{cases} \frac{2\sin^2\theta}{2\cos^2\theta} = \tan^2\theta & \text{(using +)} \\ \frac{2\cos^2\theta}{2\cos^2\theta} = 1 & \text{(using −)} \end{cases}$$

$$n = \begin{cases} \tan\theta & \text{(Brewster's law)} \\ 1 & \text{(trivial solution)} \end{cases}$$

20-2.

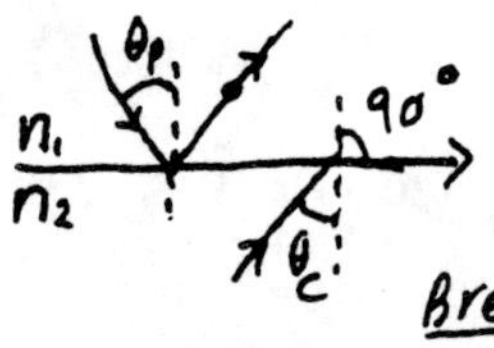


$n_2\sin\theta_c = n_1\sin 90°$

$\sin\theta_c = \frac{n_1}{n_2} = \frac{1}{n}$ OR $n = \frac{1}{\sin\theta_c} = \frac{1}{\sin 33°33'} = 1.8094$

Brewster:

$\tan\theta_p = \frac{n_2}{n_1} = n$ : External; $\theta_p = \tan^{-1}(1.8094) = 61°4'$

$\tan\theta_p' = \frac{n_1}{n_2} = \frac{1}{n}$ : Internal; $\theta_p' = \tan^{-1}\left(\frac{1}{1.8094}\right) = 28°56'$

20-3. Critical angle $\theta_c = \sin^{-1}\left(\frac{1}{n}\right) = \sin^{-1}\left(\frac{1}{1.84}\right) = 32.9°$

Polarizing angles: External: $\theta_p = \tan^{-1}(n) = \tan^{-1}(1.84) = 61.5°$

Internal: $\theta_p' = \tan^{-1}(1/n) = \tan^{-1}(1/1.84) = 28.5°$

20-4. $\sin\theta_c = \frac{1}{n}$ and $\tan\theta_p = n$

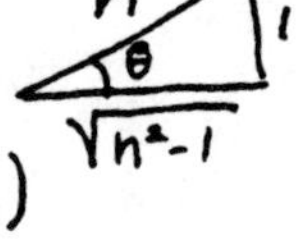


$\sin\theta = \frac{1}{n}$

when $\theta_c = \theta_p \equiv \theta$

$\tan\theta = n = \frac{1}{\sqrt{n^2 - 1}}$ (from triangle)

Thus $n^2(n^2-1) = 1$ OR $n^4 - n^2 - 1 = 0$ and $n^2 = \frac{1 \pm \sqrt{1+4}}{2} = \frac{1 \pm \sqrt{5}}{2}$

Since $n^2 > 0$, $n = 1.272 = \frac{n_2}{n_1} = n_2$

20-5. Consider them one at a time. The desired forms simply introduce $\theta_t$ in favor of $n$ through Snell's law: $n = \sin\theta/\sin\theta_t$ where $n \equiv n_2/n_1$. The rest is algebra, but somewhat tedious.

20-5. (cont'd.)

(a) $r = \dfrac{\cos\theta - \sqrt{n^2 - \sin^2\theta}}{\cos\theta + \sqrt{n^2 - \sin^2\theta}}$  (Eq 20-23)

Consider numerator $N = \cos\theta - \left[\dfrac{\sin^2\theta}{\sin^2\theta_t} - \sin^2\theta\right]^{1/2}$

$$N = \cos\theta - \frac{\sin\theta}{\sin\theta_t}\left[1 - \sin^2\theta_t\right]^{1/2}$$

$$N = \cos\theta - \frac{\sin\theta\cos\theta_t}{\sin\theta_t} = \frac{\sin\theta_t\cos\theta - \cos\theta_t\sin\theta}{\sin\theta_t} = -\frac{\sin(\theta-\theta_t)}{\sin\theta_t}$$

Similarly, the denominator $D = \dfrac{\sin\theta_t\cos\theta + \cos\theta_t\sin\theta}{\sin\theta_t} = \dfrac{\sin(\theta+\theta_t)}{\sin\theta_t}$

and $r = \dfrac{N}{D} = -\dfrac{\sin(\theta-\theta_t)}{\sin(\theta+\theta_t)}$  Q.E.D.

(b) $r = \dfrac{n^2\cos\theta - \sqrt{n^2-\sin^2\theta}}{n^2\cos\theta + \sqrt{n^2-\sin^2\theta}}$ (Eq. 20-24). As shown above, $\sqrt{n^2-\sin^2\theta} = \dfrac{\sin\theta\cos\theta_t}{\sin\theta_t}$

Thus $r = \dfrac{\left(\dfrac{\sin^2\theta}{\sin^2\theta_t}\cos\theta - \dfrac{\sin\theta\cos\theta_t}{\sin\theta_t}\right)}{\left(\dfrac{\sin^2\theta}{\sin^2\theta_t}\cos\theta + \dfrac{\sin\theta\cos\theta_t}{\sin\theta_t}\right)}$  Cancel $\sin\theta$ throughout and rationalize numerator and denominator.

$r = \dfrac{\sin\theta\cos\theta - \sin\theta_t\cos\theta_t}{\sin\theta\cos\theta + \sin\theta_t\cos\theta_t}$  Multiply each term by 1, where $1 \equiv \sin^2\theta + \cos^2\theta$

$$r = \frac{\sin\theta\cos\theta(\sin^2\theta_t + \cos^2\theta_t) - \sin\theta_t\cos\theta_t(\sin^2\theta + \cos^2\theta)}{\sin\theta\cos\theta(\sin^2\theta_t + \cos^2\theta_t) + \sin\theta_t\cos\theta_t(\sin^2\theta + \cos^2\theta)}$$

$$r = \frac{\sin\theta\cos\theta\sin^2\theta_t + \sin\theta\cos\theta\cos^2\theta_t - \sin\theta_t\cos\theta_t\sin^2\theta - \sin\theta_t\cos\theta_t\cos^2\theta}{\sin\theta\cos\theta\sin^2\theta_t + \sin\theta\cos\theta\cos^2\theta_t + \sin\theta_t\cos\theta_t\sin^2\theta + \sin\theta_t\cos\theta_t\cos^2\theta}$$

$$r = \frac{(\sin\theta\cos\theta_t - \cos\theta\sin\theta_t)(\cos\theta\cos\theta_t - \sin\theta\sin\theta_t)}{(\cos\theta\cos\theta_t + \sin\theta\sin\theta_t)(\sin\theta\cos\theta_t + \cos\theta\sin\theta_t)}$$

$r = \dfrac{\sin(\theta-\theta_t)\cos(\theta+\theta_t)}{\cos(\theta-\theta_t)\sin(\theta+\theta_t)}$  OR  $r = \dfrac{\tan(\theta-\theta_t)}{\tan(\theta+\theta_t)}$  Q.E.D.

(c) $t = \dfrac{2\cos\theta}{\cos\theta + \sqrt{n^2-\sin^2\theta}}$  (Eq. 20-25)

$$t = \frac{2\cos\theta}{\cos\theta + \dfrac{\sin\theta\cos\theta_t}{\sin\theta_t}} = \frac{2\sin\theta_t\cos\theta}{\sin\theta_t\cos\theta + \cos\theta_t\sin\theta}$$

$t = \dfrac{2\sin\theta_t\cos\theta}{\sin(\theta+\theta_t)}$  Q.E.D.

20-5. (cont'd.)

(d) $t = \dfrac{2n\cos\theta}{n^2\cos\theta + \sqrt{n^2-\sin^2\theta}}$ (Eq. 20-26)

$$t = \frac{2\left(\frac{\sin\theta}{\sin\theta_t}\right)\cos\theta}{\frac{\sin^2\theta}{\sin^2\theta_t}\cos\theta + \frac{\sin\theta\cos\theta_t}{\sin\theta_t}}$$

Multiply both numerator and denominator by $\left(\frac{\sin^2\theta_t}{\sin\theta}\right)$

$$t = \frac{2\sin\theta_t\cos\theta}{\sin\theta\cos\theta + \sin\theta_t\cos\theta_t}$$

Numerator is in desired form. To help the denominator, multiply each term by $1 \equiv \sin^2\theta + \cos^2\theta$

$$t = \frac{2\sin\theta_t\cos\theta}{\sin\theta\cos\theta(\sin^2\theta_t + \cos^2\theta_t) + \sin\theta_t\cos\theta_t(\sin^2\theta + \cos^2\theta)}$$

the denominator is then

$$D = \sin\theta\cos\theta\sin^2\theta_t + \sin\theta\cos\theta\cos^2\theta_t + \sin\theta_t\cos\theta_t\sin^2\theta + \sin\theta_t\cos\theta_t\cos^2\theta$$

$$D = (\sin\theta\cos\theta_t + \cos\theta\sin\theta_t)(\cos\theta\cos\theta_t + \sin\theta\sin\theta_t)$$

$$D = \sin(\theta+\theta_t)\cos(\theta-\theta_t)$$

$$t = \frac{2\sin\theta_t\cos\theta}{\sin(\theta+\theta_t)\cos(\theta-\theta_t)} \quad \text{Q.E.D.}$$

(No wonder nobody bothers to show the derivations!)

20-6.

TE $\begin{cases} r = \dfrac{E'}{E} = \dfrac{\cos\theta - \sqrt{n^2-\sin^2\theta}}{\cos\theta + \sqrt{n^2-\sin^2\theta}} \\ t = \dfrac{E''}{E} = \dfrac{2\cos\theta}{\cos\theta + \sqrt{n^2-\sin^2\theta}} \end{cases}$

TM $\begin{cases} r = \dfrac{E'}{E} = \dfrac{n^2\cos\theta - \sqrt{n^2-\sin^2\theta}}{n^2\cos\theta + \sqrt{n^2-\sin^2\theta}} \\ t = \dfrac{E''}{E} = \dfrac{2n\cos\theta}{n^2\cos\theta + \sqrt{n^2-\sin^2\theta}} \end{cases}$

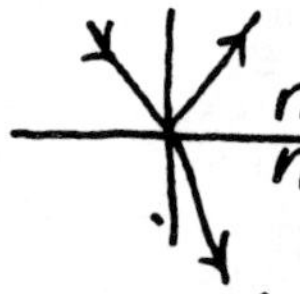


$n = n_2/n_1$

Refl. $\begin{cases} \text{External: } n > 1 \\ \text{Internal: } n < 1 \end{cases}$

Variables in computer Program:

$N = n_2/n_1$ $\quad E = \frac{E'}{E}$ or $\frac{E''}{E}$ (TE)

$T = \theta$

$S = \sqrt{n^2 - \sin^2\theta}$ $\quad M = \frac{E'}{E}$ or $\frac{E''}{E}$ (TM)

The program (following page) does all the external reflection (and transmission) calculations first — then, at step 95, goes back with a new $N$ to repeat the sequence for internal reflection and transmission.

When $n=1.5$ (external) and $n = 1/1.5$ (internal) plots of Fig 20-3 and 20-5 are generated. When $n=2.42$, sample data are given, next page.

20-6. (cont'd.)

CALCULATOR PROGRAM:

```
5 PRINT "FRESNEL EQUATIONS"
10 INPUT "EXT REF: N= ",N
15 I=0
20 FOR T=0 TO 90 STEP 5
25 PRINT "THETA = ";T
30 S=SQR(N^2-(SIN T)^2)
35 REM REFLECTION COEFFICIENT:
40 E=(COS T-S)/(COS T+S)
45 M=(-S+N^2*COS T)/(S+N^2*COS T)
50 PRINT E
55 PRINT M
60 REM TRANSMISSION COEFFICIENT:
65 E=2*COS T/(COS T+S)
70 M=2*N*COS T/(N^2*COS T+S)
75 PRINT E
80 PRINT M
85 NEXT T
90 IF I=1 THEN 110
95 INPUT "INT REF: N= ",N
100 I=1
105 GOTO 20
110 END
```

SAMPLE PROGRAM RESULTS

When $n_2 = 2.42$, $\theta_c = 24.41°$, $\theta_p = 67.55°$, $\theta_p' = 22.45°$

External Reflection

$n = n_2/n_1$

$n = 2.42$

| $\theta$ | $r = E'/E$ (TE) | $t = E''/E$ (TE) | $r = E'/E$ (TM) | $r = E''/E$ (TM) |
|---|---|---|---|---|
| 0 | −0.415 | 0.585 | 0.415 | 0.585 |
| 10 | −0.4205 | 0.580 | 0.4099 | 0.583 |
| 20 | −0.4365 | 0.563 | 0.393 | 0.576 |
| 30 | −0.464 | 0.536 | 0.363 | 0.563 |
| 40 | −0.506 | 0.494 | 0.316 | 0.544 |
| 50 | −0.562 | 0.4375 | 0.242 | 0.513 |
| 60 | −0.638 | 0.362 | 0.129 | 0.466 |
| 70 | −0.734 | 0.266 | −0.0536 | 0.39105 |
| 80 | −0.854 | 0.146 | −0.370 | 0.2604 |
| 90 | −1 | 0 | −1 | 0 |

Internal Reflection

$n = n_1/n_2$

$n = 1/2.42$

| $\theta$ | $r$ (TE) | $r$ (TM) |
|---|---|---|
| 0 | 0.4152 | −0.4152 |
| 5 | 0.423 | −0.407 |
| 10 | 0.448 | −0.381 |
| 15 | 0.500 | −0.323 |
| 20 | 0.604 | −0.182 |
| 25 | — | |
| 22 | 0.683 | −0.0484 |
| 24 | 0.852 | +0.363 |

Only $r$ values are reported since we are constructing a curve like that of Fig. 20-5.

Note: $\theta_c = 24.41°$

(22 and 24:) } calculated apart from program.

20-7. Plot $R = r^2$ and $T = 1 - R$, using the program and results given in Prob. 20-6.

20-8. Phase shift Program

TE : $\tan(\varphi/2) = \sqrt{\sin^2\theta - n^2} / \cos\theta$ $\qquad n = n_2/n_1$

TM : $\tan(\varphi/2) = \sqrt{\sin^2\theta - n^2} / n^2\cos\theta$

$$\delta = \varphi_{TM} - \varphi_{TE}$$

Program variables: $P = \varphi_{TE}$, $Q = \varphi_{TM}$, $D = \delta$, $R = \sqrt{\sin^2\theta - n^2}$, $T = \theta$
$N = n$

CALCULATOR PROGRAM

```
5 PRINT "PHASE SHIFT"
10 INPUT "N(<1)= ",N
15 FOR T=45 TO 90 STEP 5
20 R=SQR(SIN T^2-N^2)
25 P=2*ATN(R/COS T)
30 Q=2*ATN(R/N^2*COS T)
35 D=Q-P
40 PRINT "THETA= ";T,"PHI-TE= ";P,"PHI-TM= ";Q
45 PRINT "PHI-DIFF= ";D
50 NEXT T
55 END
```

SAMPLE OUTPUT: N = 1/1.50

| $\theta$ | $\phi_{TE}$ | $\phi_{TM}$ | $\phi_{TM} - \phi_{TE}$ |
|---|---|---|---|
| 45 | 36.87 | 73.74 | 36.87 |
| 50 | 60.83 | 105.74 | 44.91 |
| 55 | 79.38 | 123.66 | 44.28 |
| 60 | 95.74 | 136.20 | 40.46 |
| 65 | 110.92 | 145.98 | 35.06 |
| 70 | 125.37 | 154.15 | 28.77 |
| 75 | 139.36 | 161.31 | 21.95 |
| 80 | 153.06 | 167.84 | 14.79 |
| 85 | 166.57 | 174.01 | 7.44 |
| 90 | ERROR: COS T = 0 (DIVISION BY ZERO) | | |
| 89.99 | 179.97 | 179.99 | 0.01 |

This data generates curves of Fig 20-6.

20-9. $R = \left(\frac{1-n}{1+n}\right)^2$

(a) air → film : $n = \frac{1.38}{1}$ ; $R = \left(\frac{1-1.38}{1+1.38}\right)^2 = 2.55\%$

(b) film–glass : $n = 1.52/1.38$ ; $R = 0.233\%$

(c) air–glass : $n = \frac{1.52}{1}$ ; $R = 4.26\%$

(d) Eq 19-43 :

$$R = \left(\frac{n_0 n_s - n_1^2}{n_0 n_s + n_1^2}\right)^2 = \left(\frac{1.52 - 1.38^2}{1.52 + 1.38^2}\right)^2 = 1.26\%$$

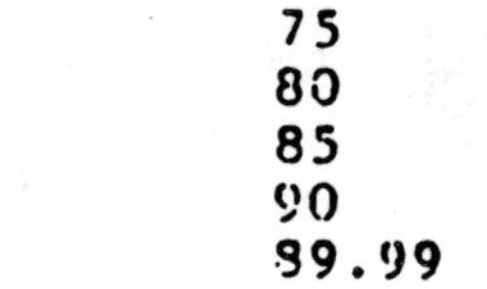


$n = n_2/n_1 = 1.52/1.38$

20-10. $r_{TE} = \dfrac{\cos\theta - \sqrt{n^2 - \sin^2\theta}}{\cos\theta + \sqrt{n^2 - \sin^2\theta}}$ $\qquad r_{TM} = \dfrac{n^2\cos\theta - \sqrt{n^2 - \sin^2\theta}}{n^2\cos\theta + \sqrt{n^2 - \sin^2\theta}}$

| $\theta$ | $r_{TE}$ | $R_{TE} = r_{TE}^2$ | $r_{TM}$ | $R_{TM} = r_{TM}^2$ |
|---|---|---|---|---|
| $0°$ | $-0.1416$ | $2.01\%$ | $0.1416$ | $2.01\%$ |
| $10°$ | $-0.1449$ | $2.10\%$ | $0.1383$ | $1.91\%$ |
| $45°$ | $-0.2287$ | $5.23\%$ | $0.5231$ | $0.274\%$ |
| $90°$ | $-1$ | $100\%$ | $-1$ | $100\%$ |

20-11. $n = 2.42$

(a) External: TM $\quad \theta_p = \tan^{-1} n = \tan^{-1} 2.42 = 67.548° = 67°33'$

$\theta_c$ – none

External: TE $\quad \theta_p, \theta_c$ none

(b) Internal: TM $\quad \theta_p' = \tan^{-1}(1/n) = \tan^{-1}(1/2.42) = 22°27'$

$\theta_c = \sin^{-1}(1/n) = \sin^{-1}(1/2.42) = 24°24'$

Internal: TE $\quad \theta_p' = \text{none}; \; \theta_c = \sin^{-1}(1/n) = 24°24'$

20-12.

(a)

$r_{TE} = \dfrac{\cos\theta - \sqrt{n^2 - \sin^2\theta}}{\cos\theta + \sqrt{n^2 - \sin^2\theta}}$

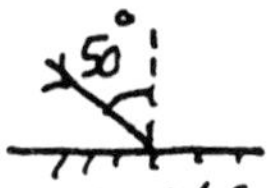


n=1.60

$\theta = 50°, \; n = 1.60$

$r_{TE} = -0.3721$

$R_{TE} = r_{TE}^2 = 13.85\%$

$T_{TE} = 1 - R_{TE} = 86.15\%$

(b)

$r_{TM} = \dfrac{n^2\cos\theta - \sqrt{n^2 - \sin^2\theta}}{n^2\cos\theta + \sqrt{n^2 - \sin^2\theta}}$

$\theta = 50°, \; n = 1.60$

$r_{TM} = 0.07896$

$R_{TM} = r_{TM}^2 = 0.623\%$

$T_{TM} = 1 - R_{TM} = 99.38\%$

Note: One can also, with more labor, calculate in each case,

$$t = r + 1$$

$$T = n\left(\frac{\cos\theta_t}{\cos\theta}\right) t^2, \text{ where } \theta_t = \sin^{-1}\left(\frac{\sin 50°}{1.60}\right)$$

20-13. Begin with

TE $\begin{cases} E + E_r = E_t & (20\text{-}16) \\ n_1 E\cos\theta - n_1 E_r \cos\theta = n_2 E_t \cos\theta_t & (20\text{-}17) \end{cases}$

TM $\begin{cases} n_1 E + n_1 E_r = n_2 E_t & (20\text{-}18) \\ -E\cos\theta + E_r\cos\theta = -E_t\cos\theta_t & (20\text{-}19) \end{cases}$

Take TE first. Eliminate $E_r$ using $E_r = E_t - E$ in second eq:

$n_1 E\cos\theta - n_1(E_t - E)\cos\theta = n_2 E_t \cos\theta_t$ (multiply by $\frac{1}{n_1 E}$)

Also, use $\left.\begin{array}{l} n = n_2/n_1 \\ t = E_t/E \end{array}\right\}$ $\quad \cos\theta - (t-1)\cos\theta = n t \cos\theta_t$

$t(n\cos\theta_t + \cos\theta) = 2\cos\theta$

$$t = \frac{2\cos\theta}{\cos\theta + n\cos\theta_t} \quad \text{OR} \quad t = \frac{2\cos\theta}{\cos\theta + \sqrt{n^2 - \sin^2\theta}} \quad \text{Eq (20-25)}$$

20-13. (cont'd.) using $n\cos\theta_t \equiv n\sqrt{1-\sin^2\theta_t} \equiv \sqrt{n^2-\sin^2\theta}$

Consider next TM: $E_r = \frac{n_2 E_t - n_1 E}{n_1} = nE_t - E$

Substitute into 2nd eq.:

$$-E\cos\theta + (nE_t - E)\cos\theta = -E_t\cos\theta_t \quad \text{Multiply by } \frac{1}{E}$$

$$-\cos\theta + (nt-1)\cos\theta = -t\cos\theta_t$$

$$t(n\cos\theta + \cos\theta_t) = 2\cos\theta$$

$$t = \frac{2\cos\theta}{n\cos\theta + \cos\theta_t} = \frac{2n\cos\theta}{n^2\cos\theta + n\cos\theta_t} \quad \text{OR} \quad t = \frac{2n\cos\theta}{n^2\cos\theta + \sqrt{n^2-\sin^2\theta}} \quad \text{Eq. (20-26)}$$

(b) Taking the first of the TE and TM equations, and dividing by E,

TE: $t = r+1$ TM: $nt = r+1$

Use r from Eq. (20-23) and (20-24), in turn:

TE: $t = r_{TE} + 1 = \frac{\cos\theta - \sqrt{n^2-\sin^2\theta}}{\cos\theta + \sqrt{n^2-\sin^2\theta}} + 1$

$$t = \frac{2\cos\theta}{\cos\theta + \sqrt{n^2-\sin^2\theta}} \quad \text{(Eq. 20-25)}$$

TM: $t = \frac{t_{TM}+1}{n} = \frac{1}{n}\left[\frac{n^2\cos\theta - \sqrt{n^2-\sin^2\theta}}{n^2\cos\theta + \sqrt{n^2-\sin^2\theta}} + 1\right]$

$$t = \frac{1}{n}\left[\frac{2n^2\cos\theta}{n^2\cos\theta + \sqrt{n^2-\sin^2\theta}}\right] = \frac{2n\cos\theta}{n^2\cos\theta + \sqrt{n^2-\sin^2\theta}} \quad \text{Eq. (20-26)}$$

20-14 (a) $\theta_c = \sin^{-1}\left(\frac{1}{n}\right) = \sin^{-1}\left(\frac{1}{1.458}\right) = 43.30°$

$\theta_p = \tan^{-1}(n) = \tan^{-1}(1.458) = 55.55°$

$\theta_p' = \tan^{-1}\left(\frac{1}{n}\right) = \tan^{-1}(1/1.458) = 34.45°$

(b) $r_{TE} = \frac{\cos\theta - \sqrt{n^2-\sin^2\theta}}{\cos\theta + \sqrt{n^2-\sin^2\theta}}$

$\theta = 0°$: $r_{TE} = -0.18633$

$R_{TE} = r_{TE}^2 = 3.47\%$

$\theta = 45°$: $r_{TE} = -0.2865$

$R_{TE} = r_{TE}^2 = 8.21\%$

(c) $r_{TM} = \frac{n^2\cos\theta - \sqrt{n^2-\sin^2\theta}}{n^2\cos\theta + \sqrt{n^2-\sin^2\theta}}$

$\theta = 0°$ $r_{TM} = 0.18633$

$R_{TM} = r_{TM}^2 = 3.47\%$

$\theta = 45°$ $r_{TM} = 0.0821$

$R_{TM} = r_{TM}^2 = 0.674\%$

Also, at $\theta = 0°$, $T_{TE} = 1 - R_{TE} = 96.53\%$ $T_{TM} = 1 - R_{TM} = 96.53\%$ at $\theta = 0°$

at $\theta = 45°$, $T_{TE} = 91.79\%$ $T_{TM} = 1 - R_{TM} = 99.33\%$ at $\theta = 45°$

(d)

| | 0° | 20° | 40° | 50° | 70° | 90° | |
|---|---|---|---|---|---|---|---|
| $\phi_{TM}$ | 180° | 180° | 0 | 96.90° | 151.88° | 180° | From Eqs. |
| $\phi_{TE}$ | 0 | 0 | 0 | 55.92° | 123.93° | 180° | 20-34 |
| $\Delta\phi$ | 180° | 180° | 0 | 41.0° | 27.90 | 0 | 20-35 |

20-15.

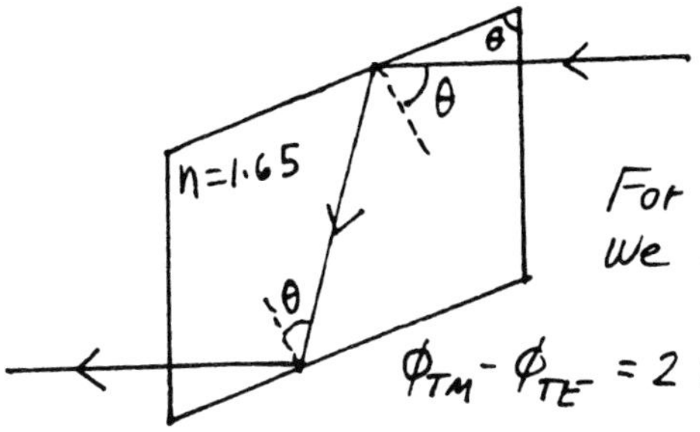


(a) Desire that $\phi_{TM} - \phi_{TE} = 90°$ after <u>two</u> internal reflections, or

$$\phi_{TM} - \phi_{TE} = 45°$$

after <u>one</u> internal reflection.

For $\theta > \theta_c = \sin^{-1}(1/n) = \sin^{-1}(1/1.65) = 37.3°$ we use Eqs. 20-34 and 20-35:

$$\phi_{TM} - \phi_{TE} = 2\tan^{-1}\left(\frac{\sqrt{\sin^2\theta - n^2}}{n^2\cos\theta}\right) - 2\tan^{-1}\left(\frac{\sqrt{\sin^2\theta - n^2}}{\cos\theta}\right) = 45°$$

Since these are internal reflections, here $n = n_2/n_1 = 1/1.65$. Then by trial and error, or aided by a calculator program, we find

| θ | Δφ |
|---|---|
| 50° | 54.3° |
| 57° | 48.3° |
| 59° | 46.0° |
| 60° | 44.8° |

59.857° → (between 59° and 60°) ← 45.000°

Thus, $\theta = 59.857°$

or $\theta = 59°51'$

(b) 5% $\theta = 0.05 \times 59.857° = 2.993°$

$\theta + 2.993° = 62.850°$ and $\Delta\phi = 41.16° \times 2 = 82.32°$

$\theta - 2.993° = 56.864°$ and $\Delta\phi = 48.50° \times 2 = 97.00°$

20-16. We calculate using Eqs. (20-61) and (20-62), not easily solved. In step-wise fashion, however, with the help of a calculator program, we can solve for reflectance at any given angle of incidence, as follows:

<u>TE case</u>:
$$\frac{E_R}{E} = \frac{\cos\theta - \sqrt{(n_R^2 - n_I^2 - \sin^2\theta) + i(2n_R n_I)}}{\cos\theta + \sqrt{(n_R^2 - n_I^2 - \sin^2\theta) + i(2n_R n_I)}}$$

Let $z = \underbrace{n_R^2 - n_I^2 - \sin^2\theta}_{A} + i\underbrace{(2n_R n_I)}_{B} = A + iB \rightarrow \sqrt{A^2+B^2}\, e^{i(\text{atn } B/A)}$

$$z^{1/2} = \underbrace{(A^2+B^2)^{1/4}}_{C} e^{i\underbrace{(\frac{1}{2}\text{atn } B/A)}_{D}} = Ce^{iD}$$

$$z^{1/2} = \underbrace{C\cos D}_{E} + i\underbrace{C\sin D}_{F} = E + iF$$

Then
$$\frac{E_R}{E} = \frac{\cos\theta - E - iF}{\underbrace{\cos\theta}_{L} + E + iF} = \frac{\overbrace{(L-E)}^{S} - iF}{\underbrace{(L+E)}_{V} + iF} = \frac{S - iF}{V + iF}$$

$$R_{TE} = \left|\frac{E_R}{E}\right|^2 = \frac{S^2 + F^2}{V^2 + F^2} \text{ gives } R_{TE}.$$

Other Program Variables:
$T = \theta$
$N = n_R$
$K = n_I$
$Z = R_{TE}, R_{TM}$

<u>TM case</u>: Using $z^{1/2}$ as calculated above,

$$\frac{E_R}{E} = \frac{(n_R^2 - n_I^2)\cos\theta + i(2n_R n_I)\cos\theta - (E + iF)}{\underbrace{(n_R^2 - n_I^2)\cos\theta}_{G} + i\underbrace{(2n_R n_I)\cos\theta}_{H} + (E + iF)}$$

20-16. (cont'd.)

$$\frac{E_R}{E} = \frac{\overbrace{(G-E)}^{J} + i\overbrace{(H-F)}^{M}}{\underbrace{(G+E)}_{P} + i\underbrace{(H+F)}_{Q}} = \frac{J+iM}{P+iQ}$$

$$R_{TM} = \left|\frac{E_R}{E}\right|^2 = \frac{J^2+M^2}{P^2+Q^2} \text{ gives } R_M.$$

The programmed steps suggested by these equations are given

CALCULATOR PROGRAM

$n_R = 2.485$

$n_I = 1.381$

```
5 PRINT "METALLIC REFLECTANCE"
10 INPUT "N= ";N,"K= ";K
15 INPUT "THETA= ";T
20 A=N^2-K^2-(SIN T)^2:B=2*N*K:L=COS T
25 C=(A^2+B^2)^.25:D=.5*ATN(B/A)
30 E=C*COS D:F=C*SIN D
35 S=L-E:V=L+E:Z=(S^2+F^2)/(V^2+F^2)
40 PRINT "RTE= ";Z
45 G=(N^2-K^2)*L:H=2*N*K*L
50 J=G-E:P=G+E:M=H-F:Q=H+F
55 Z=(J^2+M^2)/(P^2+Q^2)
60 PRINT "RTM= ";Z
65 GOTO 15
```

OUTPUT USING PROGRAM ABOVE:

| $\theta$ | $R_{TE}$ % | $R_{TM}$ % |
|---|---|---|
| 0 | 29.3 | 29.3 |
| 30 | 34.5 | 24.2 |
| 50 | 45.4 | 14.9 |
| 70 | 65.7 | 5.4 |
| 90 | 100 | 100 |

20-17. Repeat program given in Prob. 20-16.

With $n_R = 1.5$, $n_I = 5.3$, we find

| $\theta$ | (a) $R_{TE}$ | (b) $R_{TM}$ |
|---|---|---|
| 0° | 82.5% | 82.5% |
| 30° | 84.7% | 80.1% |
| 60° | 90.9% | 69.5% |

20-18. $n_I = 5.3$ at $\lambda = 589.3$ nm

(a) $\alpha = 4\pi n_I/\lambda = 4\pi(5.3)/589.3 \text{ nm} = 0.113 \text{ nm}^{-1}$

(b) $I = I_o e^{-\alpha r}$

For $I = 0.01 I_o$, $e^{-\alpha r} = 0.01$

$\ln(0.01) = -\alpha r$

$r = \frac{1}{\alpha}\ln(100) = 40.75 \text{ nm}$ or $0.069\lambda$ deep

20-19. $1 = r^2 + n\left(\dfrac{\cos\theta_t}{\cos\theta_i}\right)t^2 \quad , \quad n = \dfrac{n_2}{n_1}$ Eq. (20-43)

(a) External reflection: $n > 1$; $\theta_t < \theta_i$; $\cos\theta_t > \cos\theta_i$

Thus $1 - r^2 = n(\cos\theta_t / \cos\theta_i)t^2 > t^2$ or $t^2 < 1 - r^2$

Since $r^2 < 1$, $t^2 < 1$

Internal reflection: $n < 1$; $\theta_t > \theta_i$; $\cos\theta_t < \cos\theta_i$

Thus $1 - r^2 = n(\cos\theta_t / \cos\theta_i)t^2 < t^2$ or $t^2 > 1 - r^2$

No upper limit imposed.

(b) Snell's law: $\sin\theta_i = n\sin\theta_t$. For $n = n_2/n_1 < 1$, as $\theta_i \to \theta_c$, $\theta_t \to 90°$ and $\sin\theta_i \to n$. then in

Eq. (20-25) TE: $t' = \dfrac{2\cos\theta}{\cos\theta + \sqrt{n^2 - \sin^2\theta}} \xrightarrow[\theta \to \theta_c]{} \dfrac{2\cos\theta}{\cos\theta} = 2$

Eq. (20-26) TM: $t' = \dfrac{2n\cos\theta}{n^2\cos\theta + \sqrt{n^2 - \sin^2\theta}} \xrightarrow[\theta \to \theta_c]{} \dfrac{2n\cos\theta}{n^2\cos\theta} = \dfrac{2}{n}$

(c)

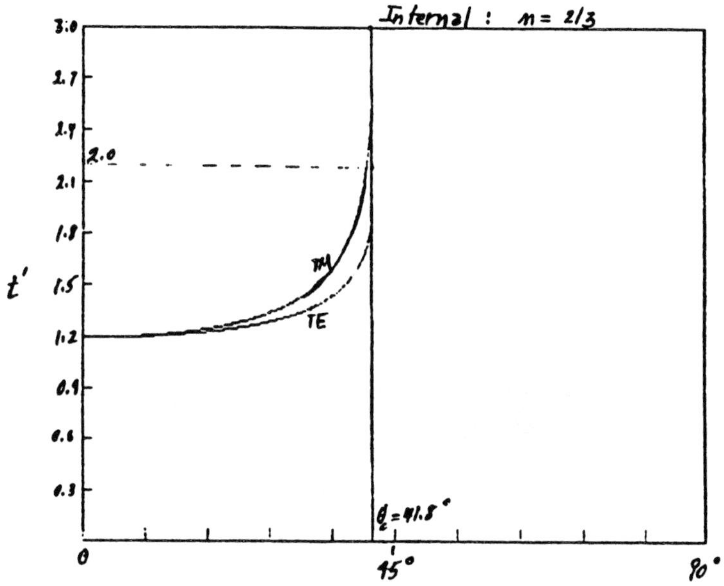


20-20. (a) $y_{1/e} \equiv \dfrac{1}{\alpha} = \dfrac{\lambda}{2\pi}\dfrac{1}{\sqrt{\dfrac{\sin^2\theta}{n^2} - 1}} = \dfrac{0.546\,\mu m}{2\pi}\dfrac{1}{\sqrt{\dfrac{\sin^2 45}{(1/1.6)^2} - 1}}$

$y_{1/e} \equiv \dfrac{1}{\alpha} = 0.164\,\mu m$

(b) $\alpha \equiv \dfrac{1}{y_{1/e}} = 6.089\,\mu m^{-1}$

$\left|\dfrac{E_t}{E_{ot}}\right|^2 = e^{-2y\alpha} = e^{-2(1)(6.089)} = 5.1 \times 10^{-6}$

# Chapter 21 - Laser Basics

**21-1.** $\frac{dN_2}{dt} = -A_{21} N_2$; collecting terms & forming integral:

$$\int_{N_{20}}^{N_2(t)} \frac{dN_2}{N_2} = \int_0^t -A_{21}\,dt, \quad \therefore \ln \frac{N_2(t)}{N_{20}} = -A_{21}t, \text{ or}$$

$$N_2(t) = N_{20}\, e^{-A_{21}t}$$

when $t = \tau = \frac{1}{A_{21}}$, solve for $N_2(\tau)$

$$N_2(\tau) = N_{20}\, e^{-A_{21}/A_{21}} = N_{20}\, e^{-1} = N_{20}/e.$$

**21-2.** For non-degenerate levels, $\frac{N_2}{N_1} = e^{-\frac{\Delta E}{KT}} = e^{-\frac{h\nu}{KT}} = e^{-\frac{hc}{\lambda KT}}$

$$\therefore \frac{N_2}{N_1} = e^{-\frac{(6.625\times10^{-34})(3\times10^{8})\ \text{J-m}}{(632.8\times10^{-9})(1.38\times10^{-23})(300^\circ)\ \text{J-m}}} = e^{-75.86}$$

$$\frac{N_2}{N_1} = e^{-75.86} \simeq 1.2\times10^{-33}$$

$\therefore N_2 \simeq 10^{-33} N_1$; excited level is relatively unpopulated.

**21-3.** From Eq 2-12, $M_\lambda = \frac{2\pi hc^2}{\lambda^5}\left[\frac{1}{e^{\frac{hc}{\lambda KT}}-1}\right]$

let $\frac{1}{[e^{\frac{hc}{\lambda KT}}-1]} = \frac{1}{[e^{\frac{h\nu}{KT}}-1]} \equiv [\ ]$ for brevity

Multiply $M_\lambda$ by $d\lambda$ and convert $\lambda \to \nu$ and $d\lambda \to d\nu$ by using $\lambda = c/\nu$ and $|d\lambda| = \frac{c\,|d\nu|}{\nu^2}$

Note that $M_\lambda$ has units $\left(\frac{\text{Power}}{\text{Area}-\Delta\lambda}\right)$ and $M_\lambda d\lambda$ units $\left(\frac{\text{Power}}{\text{Area}}\right)$

Thus:

$$M_\lambda d\lambda = \frac{2\pi hc^2}{\lambda^5}[\ ]\,d\lambda = \frac{2\pi hc^2}{c^5/\nu^5}[\ ]\,c\frac{d\nu}{\nu^2}$$

Simplifying:

$$M_\lambda d\lambda = \frac{2\pi h\nu^3}{c^2}[\ ]\,d\nu$$

Multiplying thru by $4/c$: See Klein [8] for details

$$4/c\,(M_\lambda d\lambda) = 4/c \cdot \frac{2\pi h\nu^3}{c^2}[\ ]\,d\nu$$

$$\left(\frac{4 M_\lambda d\lambda}{c\,d\nu}\right) = \frac{8\pi h\nu^3}{c^3}\left[\frac{1}{e^{\frac{h\nu}{KT}}-1}\right]$$

21-3 (cont'd.)

Investigate dimensions for left side $\left(\frac{M_\lambda d\lambda}{c\,d\nu}\right)$:

$$\frac{M_\lambda d\lambda}{c\,d\nu} \rightarrow \frac{\text{Power/Area}}{(\ell/t)(\Delta\nu)} \rightarrow \frac{(\text{Power}\cdot t)}{\ell^3}\cdot\frac{1}{\Delta\nu} = \frac{\text{Energy}}{\text{Vol}}\cdot\frac{1}{\Delta\nu}$$

Thus $\frac{M_\lambda d\lambda}{c\,d\nu}$ has the dimensions of $\frac{\text{Energy}}{\text{Vol}\cdot\Delta\nu} \Rightarrow \rho_\nu(\nu)$, the same units for spectral energy density.

Thus: $\rho_\nu(\nu) = \frac{8\pi h\nu^3}{c^3}\left[\frac{1}{e^{\frac{h\nu}{kT}}-1}\right]$ ... Eq 21-2

21-4. $$\rho(\nu) = \frac{8\pi h\nu^3}{c^3}\left[\frac{1}{e^{\frac{h\nu}{kT}}-1}\right] = \frac{8\pi h}{\lambda^3}\left[\frac{1}{e^{\frac{hc}{\lambda kT}}-1}\right]$$

Plugging in values:

$$\rho(\nu) = \frac{8\pi(6.625\times10^{-34})\,J\cdot s}{(550\times10^{-9})^3\,m^3}\left[\frac{1}{e^{\frac{19.875\times10^{-26}}{4.554\times10^{-26}}}-1}\right]$$

$$\rho(\nu) = (1.008\times10^{-13})(1.289\times10^{-2})\,\frac{J}{m^3\text{-}Hz}$$

$$\rho(\nu) = 1.3\times10^{-15}\,\frac{J}{m^3\text{-}Hz}$$

21-5. The ratio $\frac{A_{21}}{B_{21}} = \frac{8\pi h\nu^3}{c^3} = \frac{8\pi h}{\lambda^3}$. Since $\lambda^3$ is a much smaller factor at UV wavelengths than at IR wavelengths, the ratio $A_{21}/B_{21}$ is much larger at UV wavelengths. That means that $\left.\frac{A_{21}}{B_{21}}\right)_{UV} > \left.\frac{A_{21}}{B_{21}}\right)_{IR}$.

Since $A_{21}$ is related to spontaneous emission and $B_{21}$ to stimulated emission, a larger value for $A_{21}/B_{21}$ will make a population inversion at UV wavelengths more difficult to achieve. Every spontaneous emission ($\propto$ to $A_{21}$) depletes the population inversion, leading to less atoms in the upper laser level for the stimulated emission process.

21-6. $$\frac{\left(\frac{dN}{dt}\right)_{SE}}{\left(\frac{dN}{dt}\right)_{SPONT}} = \frac{B_{21}\,\rho(\nu)}{A_{21}} = \frac{\lambda^3}{8\pi h}\left(\frac{8\pi h}{\lambda^3}\cdot\frac{1}{e^{\frac{h\nu}{kT}}-1}\right)$$

So $$\frac{(dN/dt)_{SE}}{(dN/dt)_{SPONT}} = \left(\frac{1}{e^{\frac{h\nu}{kT}}-1}\right)$$

21-6 (cont'd.)

Plugging in the numbers:

$$\frac{\left(\frac{dN}{dt}\right)_{SE}}{\left(\frac{dN}{dt}\right)_{SPONT}} = \left[\frac{1}{e^{\frac{hc}{\lambda KT}} - 1}\right] = \left[\frac{1}{e^{\frac{19.875\times10^{-26}}{(5\times10^{-7})(1.38\times10^{-23})(5\times10^{3})}} - 1}\right]$$

$$\frac{\left(\frac{dN}{dt}\right)_{SE}}{\left(\frac{dN}{dt}\right)_{SPONT}} = \frac{1}{e^{5.76} - 1} = 0.00318$$

This value implies that the rate of SPONT. EMISS. is about 314 times larger than the rate of STIM. EMISS. This is to be expected since the term $\left(\frac{1}{e^{h\nu/KT} - 1}\right)$ is greater than 1 whenever $h\nu \gg KT$.

21-7.

(a) Use the relation $|\Delta\nu| = \frac{c}{\lambda_0^2}|\Delta\lambda|$ to verify entries in Table 21-1.

For example: ordinary discharge lamp $\begin{cases}\lambda_0 = 589.6\times10^{-9}\text{ m}\\ \Delta\lambda \simeq 1\text{ Å} = 10^{-10}\text{ m}\end{cases}$

Thus $\Delta\nu = \frac{c\Delta\lambda}{\lambda_0^2} = \frac{(3\times10^8)(1\times10^{-10})}{(589.6\times10^{-9})^2}$

$\Delta\nu = 8.63\times10^{10}$ Hz (Table 21-1 rounds to $9\times10^{10}$ Hz)

(b) $\frac{\Delta\nu|_{HeNe}}{\Delta\nu|_{Na\ Lamp}} \simeq \frac{7.5\times10^{3}\text{ Hz}}{9\times10^{10}\text{ Hz}} \simeq 8\times10^{-8}$, about $1\times10^{-7}$

So, the linewidth for the emission of a HeNe laser is about ONE TEN-MILLIONTH of the linewidth for the emission of a Na discharge lamp.

21-8

(a) $t_c \simeq \frac{1}{\Delta\nu_{FWHM}} = \frac{1}{7.5\times10^{3}\text{ Hz}} = 1.33\times10^{-4}\text{ s} = 0.13\text{ ms}$

(b) $l_c \simeq c\,t_c = (1.33\times10^{-4})(3\times10^{8}) \simeq 4\times10^{4}\text{ m}$; (40 Km)

21-9. Beam divergence $\phi = \frac{1.27\lambda}{D}$

$\lambda_{HeNe} = 632.8\ nm$ ; $D = 0.1\ mm = 10^{-3}\ m$

Thus, $\phi = \frac{1.27 \times 632.8 \times 10^{-9}\ m}{1 \times 10^{-3}\ m}$

$\phi = 803.6 \times 10^{-6}\ r$ or about 0.8 mrad

21-10. $\frac{\Delta N_{phot}}{\Delta t} = \frac{1}{\lambda^2} \cdot \frac{1}{e^{h\nu/kT} - 1} \cdot \Delta A \cdot \Delta \nu$, where $|\Delta\nu| = \frac{c|\Delta\lambda|}{\lambda^2}$

$\frac{\Delta N}{\Delta t} = \frac{c\Delta\lambda}{\lambda^4} \cdot \frac{\pi d^2}{4} \cdot \frac{1}{e^{h\nu/kT} - 1}$ $\quad \left\{ \begin{array}{l} \Delta\lambda = 100\ nm \\ d = 5 \times 10^{-4}\ m \\ \lambda = 633 \times 10^{-9}\ m \\ T = 10^3\ K \end{array} \right.$

$\therefore \frac{\Delta N}{\Delta t} = \frac{(3 \times 10^8)(100 \times 10^{-9})}{(633 \times 10^{-9})^4} \cdot \frac{\pi (5 \times 10^{-4})^2}{4} \cdot \frac{1}{e^{\frac{19.875 \times 10^{-26}}{(633 \times 10^{-9})(10^3)(1.38 \times 10^{-23})}}}$

$\frac{\Delta N}{\Delta t} = (1.87 \times 10^{26}) \cdot (1.96 \times 10^{-7}) \cdot (1.315 \times 10^{-10})$

$\frac{\Delta N_{phot}}{\Delta t} = 4.8 \times 10^{9}\ \frac{\text{photons}}{s}$ $\left(\sim 5 \times 10^9\ \frac{\text{photons}}{s}\right)$

21-11.

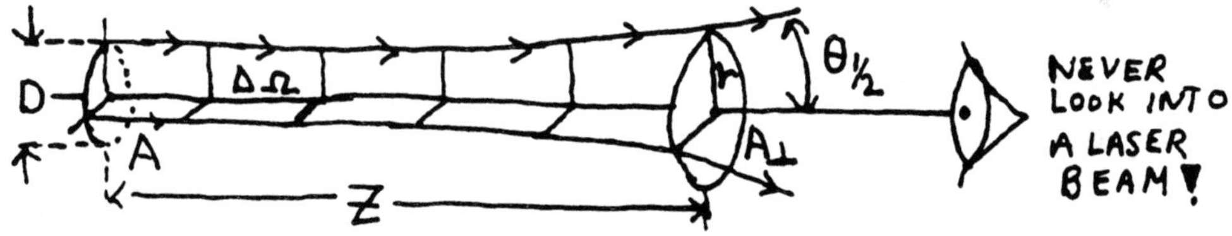


(a) Show that spectral radiance $\frac{\Delta L_e}{\Delta\nu}$ is independent of the aperture diameter D.

$\frac{\Delta L_e}{\Delta\nu} = \frac{\phi_e}{\Delta A \cdot \Delta\Omega \cdot \Delta\nu}$ ; $\phi_e$ = laser power $P_o$

$\Delta\Omega = \frac{A_\perp}{Z^2} = \frac{\pi r^2}{Z^2} = \frac{\pi (Z\theta_{1/2})^2}{Z^2} = \pi(\theta_{1/2})^2 = \pi\left(\frac{0.635\lambda}{D}\right)^2 = 1.27\frac{\lambda^2}{D^2}$

$A = \frac{\pi D^2}{4}$, so $D^2 = \frac{4A}{\pi}$

$\therefore \Delta\Omega = 1.27\frac{\lambda^2}{D^2} = \frac{1.27\lambda^2}{4A/\pi} = \frac{0.995\lambda^2}{A}$

So $\left(\frac{\Delta L_e}{\Delta\nu}\right) = \frac{P_o}{A(\Delta\Omega) \cdot \Delta\nu} = \frac{P_o}{A\left(\frac{0.995\lambda^2}{A}\right)\Delta\nu} = \frac{P_o}{(0.995\lambda^2)(\Delta\nu)}$

Ergo, $\frac{\Delta L_e}{\Delta\nu}$ does not depend on A or D.

21.11 (Cont'd:)

(b) $L_\nu = \frac{\Delta L_e}{\Delta \nu} = \frac{P_o}{0.995\,\lambda^2 \cdot \Delta\nu}$

$P_o = 10^{-3}\,W$ ; $\lambda = 633\times10^{-9}\,m$ ; $\Delta\nu = 10^4\,Hz$

$$L_\nu = \frac{10^{-3}\,W}{(0.995)(633\times10^{-9}\,m)^2(10^4\,Hz)} = 2.5\times10^5\,\frac{W}{m^2\text{-}Sr\text{-}Hz}$$

21.12.

(a) $\phi_{out} = \frac{f_1}{f_2}\phi_{in}$ ; $\phi_{out} = \frac{1}{10}\times10^{-3}\,r = 10^{-4}\,rad$

(b) $D \simeq f\,\phi_{out}$ ; for a power of 10 diopters, $f = 0.1\,m$

$\therefore D_{WAIST} = (0.1\,m)(10^{-4}\,r) = 10^{-5}\,m = 10\,\mu m$

(C) $E_e = \frac{P}{A} = \frac{10^{-3}\,W}{\pi D^2/4} = \frac{10^{-3}\,W}{(0.7854)(10^{-5}\,m)^2} = 1.27\times10^7\,W/m^2$

$E_e = 12.7\,MW/m^2$

21.13 GEOMETRY:

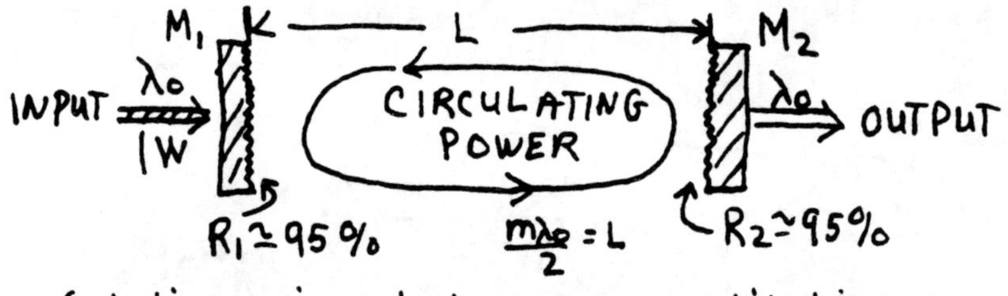


Solutions given below are qualitative; mathematics of Fabry-Perot interferometer developed in Chapter 11

(a) A resonant ($\frac{m\lambda_o}{2} = L$) F-P cavity transmits (ideally) all light energy incident on one of the mirrors. Hence, if input is 1W, output is also 1W.

(b) At mirror $M_2$, 95 % of light is reflected, 5% is transmitted. Since 1 W is transmitted, 20 W must be incident on $M_2$. Thus 20 W of power circulate back and forth between the two mirrors -- in steady state

(C) In steady state, with standing waves established, boundary conditions must be met at both mirrors. Thus, the wave that should be reflected off the left of $M_1$ (carrying 95% of 1W) interferes with the 5% of the (20-1)W wave returning from $M_2$ and cancels exactly. Thus 1 W enters, 1 W leaves, and 20 W circulate continuously.

21-14.

(a) wavelengths associated with "pump" photons:

$$\lambda = \frac{hc}{E} = \frac{(6.625\times10^{-34}\,J\cdot s)(2.998\times10^{8}\,m/s)}{E(eV)\times1.602\times10^{-19}\,\frac{J}{eV}} = \frac{1.24\times10^{-6}\,m}{E(eV)}$$

Then, $\lambda_{1.53eV} = \frac{1.24\times10^{-6}\,m}{1.53} = 8.10\times10^{-7}\,m = 0.81\,\mu m$

Using the same formula for the energies of the three other "pump" photons, one gets:

$\lambda_{1.653eV} = 0.75\,\mu m$; $\lambda_{2.119eV} = 0.585\,\mu m$; $\lambda_{2.361eV} = 0.525\,\mu m$

(b) Quantum Efficiency $= Q.E. = \frac{(hc/\lambda)_{OUT}}{(hc/\lambda)_{in}} = \frac{\lambda_{pump}}{\lambda_{laser}} = \frac{\lambda_p}{1.064\,\mu m}$

Thus, $Q.E.)_{0.81\mu m} = \frac{0.81\,\mu m}{1.064\,\mu m} = 76\,\%$

Using the same formula for the three other photons:

$Q.E.)_{0.75\mu m} = 70\%$; $Q.E.)_{0.585\mu m} = 55\,\%$; $Q.E.)_{0.525\mu m} = 49\,\%$

21-15.

(a) Taking the "component" efficiencies in order:

(2500 W × 0.8) = 2000 W into arc lamps

(2000 W × 0.3) = 600 W onto laser cavity reflectors

(600 W × 0.7) = 420 W into laser rod

(420 W × 0.15) = 63 W for pumping YAG laser levels

(63 W × 0.50) = 31.5 W in output of laser beam

(b) Wall-Plug Efficiency $\equiv \frac{\text{laser power Out}}{\text{"wall-plug" power in}}$

Wall-Plug Efficiency $= \frac{31.5\,W}{2500\,W} \simeq 1.26\,\%$

# Chapter 22 - Characteristics of Laser Beams

22-1.

(a) Eq 22-6: $r = R\left(1+\frac{x^2+y^2}{R^2}\right)^{1/2}$

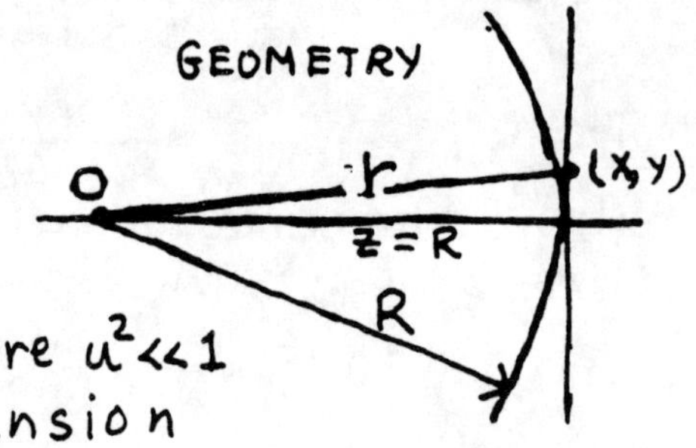


Let $u^2 = \left(\frac{x^2+y^2}{R^2}\right)$

Then $r = R(1+u^2)^{1/2}$, where $u^2 \ll 1$

Using a Binomial expansion

$$(1+u^2)^{1/2} \simeq 1 + \tfrac{1}{2}u^2 + \frac{\frac{1}{2}(-\frac{1}{2})}{2}u^4 + \cdots$$

All terms above $\frac{1}{2}u^2$ can be ignored relative to $\frac{1}{2}u^2$ and 1 since $u^2 \ll 1$. See "Geometry".

Thus $r \simeq R(1+\frac{1}{2}u^2) = R\left[1+\frac{1}{2}\left(\frac{x^2+y^2}{R^2}\right)\right] = \underline{R + \frac{x^2+y^2}{2R}}$ Q.E.D.

(b) $\tilde{E}(x,y)_{z=R} = \text{const.}\, e^{ikr}$, where $r = R + \frac{x^2+y^2}{2R}$

$$\tilde{E}(x,y)_{z=R} \simeq \text{const.}\, e^{ik\left(R+\frac{x^2+y^2}{2R}\right)} = \text{const.}\, e^{ikR}\cdot e^{ik\left(\frac{x^2+y^2}{2R}\right)}$$

22-2.

$$\nabla^2 E - \frac{n^2}{c^2}\frac{\partial^2 E}{\partial t^2} = 0 \longrightarrow \frac{\partial^2 E}{\partial x^2} + \frac{\partial^2 E}{\partial y^2} + \frac{\partial^2 E}{\partial z^2} - \frac{n^2}{c^2}\frac{\partial^2 E}{\partial t^2} = 0$$

Assume free space so that $n=1$.

Let $E = U(xyz)\, e^{i(kz-\omega t)} = Ue^{i[\,]}$ where $[\,] \equiv (kz-\omega t)$

<u>Evaluating term by term</u>:

$$\frac{\partial^2 E}{\partial x^2} = \frac{\partial}{\partial x}\left[\frac{\partial}{\partial x}\left(Ue^{i[\,]}\right)\right] = \frac{\partial}{\partial x}\left[U\frac{\partial}{\partial x}\left(e^{i[\,]}\right)^{=0} + e^{i[\,]}\frac{\partial U}{\partial x}\right] = \frac{\partial}{\partial x}\left[\frac{\partial U}{\partial x}e^{i[\,]}\right]$$

$$\frac{\partial^2 E}{\partial x^2} = \left[\frac{\partial U}{\partial x}\frac{\partial}{\partial x}\left(e^{i[\,]}\right)^{=0} + e^{i[\,]}\frac{\partial^2 U}{\partial x^2}\right] = \underline{e^{i[\,]}\frac{\partial^2 U}{\partial x^2}}$$

By symmetry, $\frac{\partial^2 E}{\partial y^2} = \underline{e^{i[\,]}\frac{\partial^2 U}{\partial y^2}}$

Now for $\frac{\partial^2 E}{\partial z^2}$, which is more complicated:

Let's do $\frac{\partial E}{\partial z}$ first:

$$\frac{\partial E}{\partial z} = \frac{\partial}{\partial z}\left(Ue^{i[\,]}\right) = U\frac{\partial}{\partial z}e^{i[\,]} + e^{i[\,]}\frac{\partial U}{\partial z} = ikUe^{i[\,]} + e^{i[\,]}\frac{\partial U}{\partial z}$$

22-2 (cont'd).

$$\frac{\partial^2 E}{\partial z^2} = \frac{\partial}{\partial z}\left(\frac{\partial E}{\partial z}\right) = \frac{\partial}{\partial z}\left(iKUe^{i[\ ]} + e^{i[\ ]}\frac{\partial U}{\partial z}\right)$$

$$\frac{\partial^2 E}{\partial z^2} = iKU\frac{\partial e^{i[\ ]}}{\partial z} + iKe^{i[\ ]}\frac{\partial U}{\partial z} + e^{i[\ ]}\frac{\partial^2 U}{\partial z^2} + \frac{\partial U}{\partial z}\frac{\partial}{\partial z}e^{i[\ ]}$$

$$\frac{\partial^2 E}{\partial z^2} = -K^2 U e^{i[\ ]} + iK\frac{\partial U}{\partial z}e^{i[\ ]} + \frac{\partial^2 U}{\partial z^2}e^{i[\ ]} + iK\frac{\partial U}{\partial z}e^{i[\ ]}$$

$$\frac{\partial^2 E}{\partial z^2} = e^{i[\ ]}\left[\frac{\partial^2 U}{\partial z^2} + 2iK\frac{\partial U}{\partial z} - K^2 U\right]$$

Finally, we need $\frac{\partial^2 E}{\partial t^2}$

$$\frac{\partial^2 E}{\partial t^2} = \frac{\partial}{\partial t}\left[\frac{\partial}{\partial t}(Ue^{i[\ ]})\right] = \frac{\partial}{\partial t}\left[U(-i\omega)e^{i[\ ]} + e^{i[\ ]}\underset{=0}{\cancel{\frac{\partial U}{\partial t}}}\right]$$

$$\frac{\partial^2 E}{\partial t^2} = \frac{\partial}{\partial t}\left[U(-i\omega)e^{i[\ ]}\right] = (-i\omega)\left[U\frac{\partial}{\partial t}e^{i[\ ]} + e^{i[\ ]}\underset{=0}{\cancel{\frac{\partial U}{\partial t}}}\right]$$

$$\frac{\partial^2 E}{\partial t^2} = (-i\omega)(-i\omega)Ue^{i[\ ]} = -\omega^2 U e^{i[\ ]}$$

collecting pieces and substituting back in Eq 22-2

$$\underbrace{\frac{\partial^2 E}{\partial x^2}}_{} + \underbrace{\frac{\partial^2 E}{\partial y^2}}_{} + \underbrace{\frac{\partial^2 E}{\partial z^2}}_{} - \underbrace{\frac{1}{c^2}\frac{\partial^2 E}{\partial t^2}}_{} = 0$$

$$e^{i[\ ]}\underbrace{\frac{\partial^2 U}{\partial x^2}}_{} + e^{i[\ ]}\underbrace{\frac{\partial^2 U}{\partial y^2}}_{} + \left(\frac{\partial^2 U}{\partial z^2} + 2iK\frac{\partial U}{\partial z} - K^2 U\right)e^{i[\ ]} - \frac{1}{c^2}\left(-\omega^2 U e^{i[\ ]}\right) = 0$$

Factoring out $e^{i[\ ]}$ and consolidating terms:

$$e^{i[\ ]}\left[\frac{\partial^2 U}{\partial x^2} + \frac{\partial^2 U}{\partial y^2} + \frac{\partial^2 U}{\partial z^2} + 2iK\frac{\partial U}{\partial z} - \left(K^2 - \frac{\omega^2}{c^2}\right)U\right] = 0$$

or

$$e^{i(Kz-\omega t)}\left[\frac{\partial^2 U}{\partial x^2} + \frac{\partial^2 U}{\partial y^2} + \frac{\partial^2 U}{\partial z^2} + 2iK\frac{\partial U}{\partial z} - \left(K^2 - \frac{\omega^2}{c^2}\right)U\right] = 0 \quad Q.E.D.$$

22-3.

(a) $\frac{1}{\tilde{q}} = \frac{1}{R} + i\frac{\lambda}{\pi w^2}$ where $R = \infty$ at waist

$$\frac{1}{\tilde{q}_0} = \cancel{\frac{1}{\infty}}^{=0} + i\frac{\lambda}{\pi w^2} \qquad \therefore \tilde{q}_0 = \frac{\pi w^2}{i\lambda} = \frac{-i\pi w^2}{\lambda}$$

$$\tilde{q}_0 = \frac{-i(3.1416)(0.5\times10^{-3}m)^2}{632.8\times10^{-9}m} = -i(1.24\,m)$$

(b) $z \overset{?}{\gg} \frac{\pi w_0^2}{\lambda}$ in the far field

from (a) $\frac{\pi w_0^2}{\lambda} = 1.24\,m$ and $z = 50\,m$

$\therefore z$ is $\gg \frac{\pi w_0^2}{\lambda}$, so transverse plane is in far field.

22-3 (cont'd).

Since transverse plane at $z = 50$ m is in the FAR FIELD, Then $R \simeq z$.

Now $\tan\theta_{1/2} = \frac{w_{50}}{50}$ so $w_{50} = 50\tan\theta_{1/2} \simeq 50(\theta_{1/2})$

$w_{50} \simeq 50\,m\,(0.4\times10^{-3}\,r) = 20\times10^{-3}$ m

First, find $\tilde{q}$ at $z = 50$ m from $\frac{1}{\tilde{q}_{50}} = \frac{1}{R} + i\frac{\lambda}{\pi w_{50}^2}$; $R \simeq z$

$$\frac{1}{\tilde{q}} = \frac{1}{50} + i\frac{632.8\times10^{-9}}{\pi(2\times10^{-2})^2} = 0.02 + i(5.036\times10^{-4})$$

Then $\tilde{q}_{50} = \frac{1}{0.02 + i(5.036\times10^{-4})} \times \frac{[0.02 - i(5.036\times10^{-4})]}{[0.02 - i(5.036\times10^{-4})]}$

$$\tilde{q}_{50} = \frac{1}{(0.02)^2 + (5.036\times10^{-4})^2}\left(0.02 - i(5.036\times10^{-4})\right)$$

$$\tilde{q}_{50} = \frac{1}{4.0025\times10^{-4}}\left\{2\times10^{-2} - i(5.036\times10^{-4})\right\}$$

$$\tilde{q}_{50} = 49.97\text{ m} - i(1.2582\text{ m})$$

$$\tilde{q}_{50} \simeq \underline{50\text{ m} - i(1.25\text{ m})} \text{ (APPROXIMATELY)}$$

Next, find $\tilde{q}$ at $z = 50$ m from $\tilde{q}_{50} = z_{50} - i\frac{\pi w_0^2}{\lambda}$

then $\tilde{q}_{50} = 50 - i\frac{(3.1416)(0.5\times10^{-3})^2}{632.8\times10^{-9}}$ ; $w_0 = 0.5$ mm, given.

$$\tilde{q}_{50} = 50\text{ m} - i(1.24\text{ m}) = \underline{50\text{ m} - i\,1.25\text{ m}} \text{ (APPROXIMATELY)}$$

22-4. $R(z) = z\left[1 + \left(\frac{\pi w_0^2}{\lambda z}\right)^2\right]$ ; $w(z)^2 = w_0^2\left[1 + \left(\frac{\lambda z}{\pi w_0^2}\right)^2\right]$

(a) $R(z) = 50\left[1 + \left(\frac{1.241}{50}\right)^2\right]$, since $\frac{\pi w_0^2}{\lambda} = 1.241$ m {See #22-3

$R(z) = \underline{50.03\text{ m}}$ (very nearly equal to $z = 50$ m)

$w(z)^2 = (0.5\times10^{-3})^2\left[1 + \left(\frac{50}{1.241}\right)^2\right]$

$w(z)^2 = 4.061\times10^{-4}$

$w(z) = 2.015\times10^{-2}\text{ m} = \underline{20.15\times10^{-3}\text{ m}}$

(b) yes, given $z = 50$, $R_{50}$ is 50.03 m so $R(z) \simeq z$ is a good approximation in the Far Field. Also, $\tan\theta \simeq \frac{w(z)}{z}$ is a good approximation since $w(z)_{50}$ equals $z\tan\theta \rightarrow 20\times10^{-3}$ m and Eq 22-24 gives $20.15\times10^{-3}$ m

22-5.

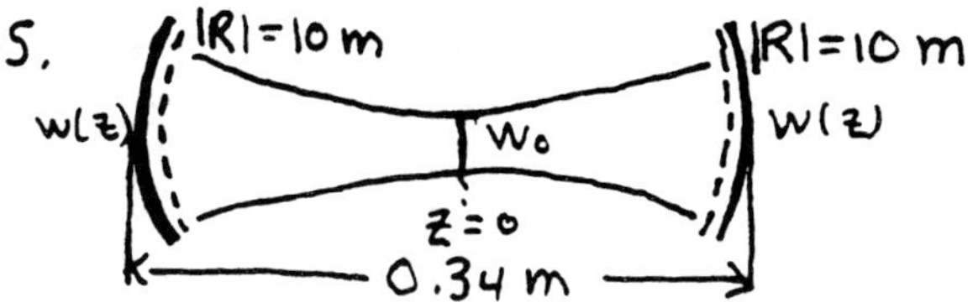


(a) From symmetry and match of wavefront/mirror curvature at mirrors, beam waist must be at center of cavity

(b) $R(z) = z\left[1 + \left(\frac{\pi W_0^2}{\lambda z}\right)^2\right]$

Solve for $W_0$ to get $W_0 = \sqrt[4]{\frac{\lambda^2 z}{\pi^2}\left(R(z) - z\right)}$

$$W_0 = \left(\frac{(632.8\times10^{-9})^2(0.17\text{ m})}{(3.1416)^2}\left[10 - 0.17\right]\right)^{1/4}$$

$W_0 = 5.10\times10^{-4}\text{ m} \simeq \underline{0.51\text{ mm}}$

(c) $w(z)^2 = W_0^2\left[1 + \left(\frac{\lambda z}{\pi W_0^2}\right)^2\right]$

$$W(z) = \left[(0.510\times10^{-3})^2\left(1 + \left\{\frac{(632.8\times10^{-9})(0.17)}{3.1416(0.51\times10^{-3})^2}\right\}^2\right)\right]^{1/2}$$

$w(z) = 5.14\times10^{-4}\text{ m} \simeq \underline{0.514\text{mm}}$

Result is essentially same as W at beam waist. This to be expected since for large radius mirrors (R=10m) and small propagation distance (z=0.17m), very little if any beam spread can occur.

(d) $\theta_{1/2} \simeq \frac{\lambda}{\pi W_0} = \frac{632.8\times10^{-9}}{\pi(5.1\times10^{-4})} = 3.95\times10^{-4}\text{ r} \simeq \underline{0.4\text{ mr}}$

(e) $z_{FF} \gg 50\left(\frac{\pi W_0^2}{\lambda}\right) = 50\left(\frac{\pi(5.1\times10^{-3})^2}{632.8\times10^{-9}}\right) = 64.6\text{ m}$

$z_{FF} \gg \underline{64.6\text{m}}$

(f) Assume a circular spot size of radius w(z) where $w(z) = 64.6(\tan\theta_{1/2})$

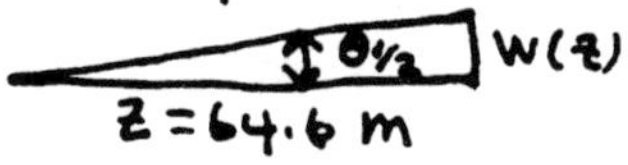


$w(z) = 64.6(3.95\times10^{-4})$

$w(z) = 0.0255\text{ m} \simeq 2.6\text{ cm}$

Now area $\simeq \pi r^2 = \pi(w(z))^2 = \pi(0.0255\text{ m})^2 = 2.043\times10^{-3}\text{ m}^2$

$(E_e)_{AV} = \frac{P_T}{A} = \frac{5\times10^{-3}\text{ W}}{2.043\times10^{-3}\text{ m}^2} = \underline{2.45\text{ W/m}^2} = 245\ \frac{\mu W}{cm^2}$

Note: Irradiance is higher near center due to Gaussian distribution; our result is an *average*.

22-6.

(a) $$\begin{bmatrix} A & B \\ C & D \end{bmatrix} = \overbrace{\begin{bmatrix} 1 & 0 \\ \frac{n-n'}{R_3 n'} & \frac{n}{n'} \end{bmatrix}}^{(REFR)_1} \overbrace{\begin{bmatrix} 1 & L \\ 0 & 1 \end{bmatrix}}^{TRANSL.} \overbrace{\begin{bmatrix} 1 & 0 \\ \frac{n-n'}{R_2 n'} & \frac{n}{n'} \end{bmatrix}}^{(REFR)_2}$$

$(Refr)_1 \begin{Bmatrix} n = 1.5 \\ n' = 1 \\ R_3 = -0.64 \end{Bmatrix}$ ; $(Refr)_2 \begin{Bmatrix} n = 1 \\ n' = 1.5 \\ R_2 = -2 \end{Bmatrix}$

$$\begin{bmatrix} A & B \\ C & D \end{bmatrix} = \begin{bmatrix} 1 & 0 \\ \frac{0.5}{-0.64} & \frac{1.5}{1} \end{bmatrix} \begin{bmatrix} 1 & 0.004 \\ 0 & 1 \end{bmatrix} \begin{bmatrix} 1 & 0 \\ \frac{-0.5}{1.5(-2)} & \frac{1}{1.5} \end{bmatrix}$$

$$\begin{bmatrix} A & B \\ C & D \end{bmatrix} = \begin{bmatrix} 1.0007 & 0.0027 \\ -0.5318 & 0.9979 \end{bmatrix}$$

(b) $$\underset{\text{THIN LENS.}}{\begin{bmatrix} A & B \\ C & D \end{bmatrix}} \simeq \begin{bmatrix} 1 & 0 \\ \frac{n-n'}{R_3 n'} & \frac{n}{n'} \end{bmatrix} \begin{bmatrix} 1 & 0 \\ 0 & 1 \end{bmatrix} \begin{bmatrix} 1 & 0 \\ \frac{n-n'}{R_2 n'} & \frac{n}{n'} \end{bmatrix}$$

$$\begin{bmatrix} A & B \\ C & D \end{bmatrix} \simeq \begin{bmatrix} 1 & 0 \\ -\frac{1}{1.28} & 1.5 \end{bmatrix} \begin{bmatrix} 1 & 0 \\ 0 & 1 \end{bmatrix} \begin{bmatrix} 1 & 0 \\ \frac{1}{6} & \frac{1}{1.5} \end{bmatrix} = \begin{bmatrix} 1 & 0 \\ -0.53125 & 1 \end{bmatrix}$$

THIN LENS

22-7.

(a) From 22-6 we showed that $\begin{bmatrix} A & B \\ C & D \end{bmatrix} = \begin{bmatrix} 1 & 0 \\ -0.53125 & 1 \end{bmatrix}$, for a thin lens.

Since the thin lens matrix is $\begin{bmatrix} A & B \\ C & D \end{bmatrix} = \begin{bmatrix} 1 & 0 \\ -1/f & 1 \end{bmatrix}$,

we see that $-\frac{1}{f} = -0.53125$,

So that $f = \frac{1}{0.53125} = \underline{1.88\ m}$

(b) Using the formula for a thin lens:

$\frac{1}{f} = \frac{n_2 - n_1}{n_1} \left( \frac{1}{R_1} - \frac{1}{R_2} \right)$, where $\begin{Bmatrix} n_1 = 1.0,\ n_2 = 1.5 \\ R_1 = -2\,m,\ R_2 = -0.64\,m \end{Bmatrix}$

$\frac{1}{f} = \frac{1.5 - 1}{1} \left( \frac{1}{-2} - \frac{1}{-0.64} \right) = 0.5 \{-0.5 + 1.5625\}$

$f = 1.88\,m$ (SAME result as in (a) above)

22-8.

Figure 22-12 is reproduced below:

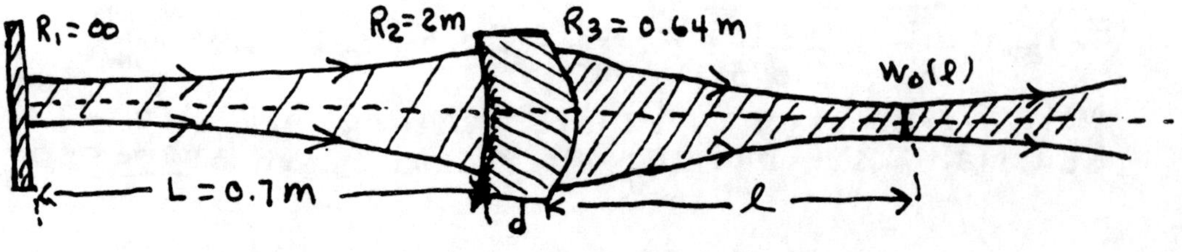

22-8 (cont'd).

Referring to the Example that accompanies Figure 22-12, the following calculations are implied:

(a) $\frac{1}{\tilde{q}_1} = \frac{1}{R_1} + \frac{i\lambda}{\pi w_1^2} = \frac{1}{\infty}\ (=0) + \frac{i\lambda}{\pi w_1^2}$ $\therefore \tilde{q}_1 = \frac{\pi w_1^2}{i\lambda} = \underline{-\frac{i\pi w_1^2}{\lambda}}$

(b) Using Eq 22-23 to relate $R_2$ to $w_1$ at the plane mirror, where the distance $z$ from $R_1$ to $R_2$ is 0.7m

$$R_2 = z_2\left[1 + \left(\frac{\pi w_1^2}{\lambda z^2}\right)^2\right] \quad \text{where} \quad \begin{cases} \lambda = 0.633 \times 10^{-9}\,\text{m} \\ z_2 = 0.7\,\text{m} \\ R_2 = 2\,\text{m} \end{cases}$$

$$2 = 0.7\left[1 + \left\{\frac{3.1416\, w_1^2}{(0.7)^2(0.633 \times 10^{-9})^2}\right\}^2\right]$$

Solve for $w_1$ to find $\underline{w_1 = 0.438\,\text{mm}}$

(c) Use this value of $w_1$ in $\tilde{q}_1 = -\frac{i\pi w_1^2}{\lambda}$ to find $\tilde{q}_1$.

$$\tilde{q}_1 = -\frac{i(3.1416)(0.438 \times 10^{-3})^2}{633 \times 10^{-9}} = \underline{-0.952\,i}$$

(d)

$$\tilde{q}_2 = \frac{A\tilde{q}_1 + B}{C\tilde{q}_1 + D} \quad \text{where} \quad \begin{cases} A = 1 - 0.53\,\ell \\ B = 0.7 + 0.63\,\ell \\ C = -0.53 \\ D = 0.63 \\ \tilde{q}_1 = -0.952\,i \end{cases}$$

Then $\frac{1}{\tilde{q}_2} = \frac{C\tilde{q}_1 + D}{A\tilde{q}_1 + B}$; rationalizing denom. by multiplying by $A\tilde{q}_1^* + B$

$$\frac{1}{\tilde{q}_2} = \left(\frac{C\tilde{q}_1 + D}{A\tilde{q}_1 + B}\right)\left(\frac{A\tilde{q}_1^* + B}{A\tilde{q}_1^* + B}\right) = \frac{AC\tilde{q}_1\tilde{q}_1^* + BC\tilde{q}_1 + AD\tilde{q}_1^* + BD}{A^2\tilde{q}_1\tilde{q}_1^* + B^2}$$

(e) Since $\frac{1}{\tilde{q}_2(\ell)} = \frac{1}{R(\ell)} + \frac{i\lambda}{\pi w^2(\ell)}$, we can equate as follows

$$\frac{AC\tilde{q}_1\tilde{q}_1^* + BC\tilde{q}_1 + AD\tilde{q}_1^* + BD}{A^2\tilde{q}_1\tilde{q}_1^* + B^2} = \frac{1}{R(\ell)}\ (=0) + \frac{i\lambda}{\pi w^2(\ell)}; \quad R(\ell) = \infty$$

Noting that $\tilde{q}_1\tilde{q}_1^*$ is real and equal to $(0.952)^2$ we equate real parts to each other and imaginary parts to each other, obtaining:

REAL: $AC\tilde{q}_1^*\tilde{q}_1 + BD = 0$

IMAGINARY: $\frac{BC\tilde{q}_1 + AD\tilde{q}_1^*}{A^2\tilde{q}_1\tilde{q}_1^* + B^2} = \frac{i\lambda}{\pi w^2(\ell)}$

22-8 (cont'd)

- Solving the real part to get $\ell$:

$$AC\tilde{q}_1\tilde{q}_1^* + BD = 0$$

and using the values for A, B, C, D and $\tilde{q}_1\tilde{q}_1^*$, we get:

$$(1-0.53\ell)(-0.53)(0.952)^2 + (0.7 + 0.63\ell)(0.63) = 0$$

$$(1-0.53\ell)(-0.48) + 0.441 + 0.397\ell = 0$$

or $0.6514\ell = 0.039$ so that $\ell = 0.0596$ m, or $\underline{\ell \simeq 6 \text{ cm}}$

- Solving the imaginary part to get $w(\ell)$:

$$\frac{BC\tilde{q}_1 + AD\tilde{q}_1^*}{A^2\tilde{q}_1\tilde{q}_1^* + B^2} = \frac{i\lambda}{\pi w^2(\ell)}$$

$$\frac{-0.952\,i\,BC + 0.952\,i\,AD}{0.906\,A^2 + B^2} = \frac{i\lambda}{\pi w^2(\ell)}$$

Recognizing that $AD - BC = \frac{n_0}{n_f}$; Eq 4-19, Chapter on Matrices, we can set $AD - BC = 1$, since $n_0 = n_f = 1$.

$$\therefore \frac{0.952}{0.906\,A^2 + B^2} = \frac{\lambda}{\pi w^2(\ell)} \quad \text{or} \quad w^2(\ell) = \frac{\lambda}{\pi}\left[\frac{0.906\,A^2 + B^2}{0.952}\right]$$

$$w(\ell)^2 = \frac{\lambda}{\pi}\left[\frac{0.906(1-0.53\ell)^2 + (0.7+0.63\ell)^2}{0.952}\right], \text{ where } \ell = 0.0596\text{m}$$

$$w(\ell)^2 = \frac{\lambda}{\pi}\left[1.464\right] = \frac{0.633\times10^{-6}}{3.1416}\left[1.464\right] = 2.95\times10^{-7}\text{ m}$$

$\therefore w(\ell) = 5.43\times10^{-4}$ m or $w(\ell) \simeq \underline{0.54\text{mm}}$

22-9.(a) Eq 22-46; $\frac{1}{W_{02}^2} = \frac{1}{W_{01}^2}\left(1-\frac{z}{f}\right)^2 + \frac{1}{f^2}\left(\frac{\pi W_{01}}{\lambda}\right)^2$; $\left\{\begin{array}{l} f = 1.88\text{m} \\ z_1 = 0.7\text{m} \\ \lambda = 0.6328\times10^{-6}\text{m} \\ W_{01} = 0.438\times10^{-3}\text{m}\end{array}\right\}$

$$\therefore \frac{1}{W_{02}^2} = \left(\frac{1}{0.438\times10^{-3}}\right)^2\left(1-\frac{0.7}{1.88}\right)^2 + \frac{1}{(1.88)^2}\left(\frac{\pi(0.438\times10^{-3})^2}{0.633\times10^{-6}}\right)^2$$

$\frac{1}{W_{02}^2} = 3.390\times10^6$, so $W_{02} = 5.43\times10^{-4}$ m, about $\underline{0.54\text{ mm}}$

good comparison!

Eq 22-47; $z_2 = f + \dfrac{f^2(z_1 - f)}{(z_1-f)^2 + \left(\frac{\pi W_{01}^2}{\lambda}\right)^2}$;

$$\therefore z_2 = 1.88 + \frac{(1.88)^2(0.7-1.88)}{(0.7-1.88)^2 + \left(\frac{\pi\times(0.438\times10^{-3})^2}{0.633\times10^{-6}}\right)^2} = 1.88 - 1.814$$

$z_2 \simeq 0.066$, about 6.6 cm (compared with 6 cm in 22-8(e)).

22-9 (cont'd).

(b) One cannot use $W_{02} \simeq \frac{f\lambda}{\pi W_{01}}$ since this approximation works only if $W_{01} >> W_{02}$. For this problem, $W_{01} \simeq 0.44$ mm and $W_{02} \simeq 0.54$ mm. Required inequality is not satisfied!

Similarly, $Z_2 \simeq f$ assumes that $\frac{\pi W_{01}^2}{\lambda} >> (Z_1 - f)^2$. Again, in this problem, $\frac{\pi W_{01}^2}{\lambda} \simeq 0.95$ m and $(Z_1 - f)^2 = 1.39$ m. Required inequality is not satisfied!

22-10.

(a) $Z_{FF} >> \frac{\pi W_{02}^2}{\lambda} = \frac{\pi (0.543 \times 10^{-3} m)}{0.6328 \times 10^{-6} m} = 1.46 m$

Since $Z = 30$ m, it is not 20 to 50 times $\frac{\pi W_{02}^2}{\lambda}$, but most practitioners would accept 30m/1.46m as a good enough ratio to use F.F. equations

(b) $\theta_{1/2} = \frac{\lambda}{\pi W_{02}} = \frac{0.6328 \times 10^{-6} m}{\pi (0.543 \times 10^{-3} m)} \simeq \underline{0.371 \text{ mrad}}$ {see drawing below.}

(c) $[W_{30}]_{in} \cong Z\theta_{1/2} = (30m)(0.371 \times 10^{-3}) = 11.31 \times 10^{-3} m = 1.113$ cm

$[W_{30}]_{out} = 10 \times [W_{30}]_{in} = 10 \times 1.113 \text{ cm} = \underline{11.13 \text{ cm}}$

(d)

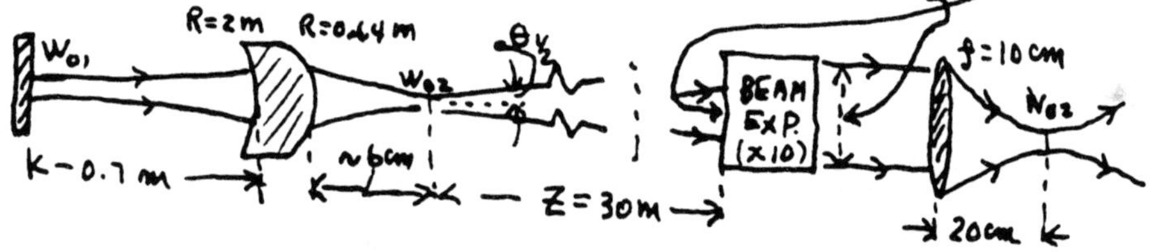


$\underline{\text{Eq 22-47}}$; $Z_2 = f + \frac{f^2(Z-f)}{(Z-f)^2 + \left(\frac{\pi W_{01}^2}{\lambda}\right)^2}$, where $\left\{ f = 0.1 m;\ Z = 0.2 m;\ W_{01} = 0.1113 m;\ \lambda = 0.6328 \times 10^{-6} m \right\}$

[Note: $W_{01}$ & $W_{02}$ now "refer to" action of 10 cm lens]

$\therefore Z_2 = 0.1 + \frac{(0.1)^2(0.2-0.1)}{(0.2-0.1)^2 + \left[\frac{\pi (0.1113 m)^2}{0.633 \times 10^{-6} m}\right]^2} \simeq 0.1 + 2.65 \times 10^{-13} \simeq 0.1$ (IGNORE)

$\underline{Z_2 \simeq 0.1 m \simeq f}$!

$\underline{\text{Eq 22-46}}$; $\frac{1}{(W_{02})^2} = \frac{1}{(W_{01})^2}\left(1 - \frac{Z_1}{f}\right)^2 + \frac{1}{f^2}\left(\frac{\pi W_{01}}{\lambda}\right)^2$; $\left\{ f = 0.1 m;\ Z = 0.2 m;\ W_{01} = 0.1113 m;\ \lambda = 0.633 \times 10^{-6} m \right\}$

$\therefore \frac{1}{(W_{02})^2} = \frac{1}{(0.1113)^2}\left(1 - \frac{0.2}{0.1}\right)^2 + \frac{1}{(0.1)^2}\left(\frac{\pi (0.1113)}{0.633 \times 10^{-6}}\right)^2$

$\left(\frac{1}{W_{02}}\right)^2 = \underbrace{80.73 (1)^2}_{\text{IGNORE}} + 100 (3.05 \times 10^{11}) \simeq 3.05 \times 10^{13} (m^{-2})$

$\therefore \underline{W_{02} \simeq 1.81 \times 10^{-7} m}$ (about 0.18 μm)

22-10 (Cont'd).

So we see that Eq 22-47 and the approximation $z_2 \simeq f$ both give values for $z_2$ of 0.1 m. But $z_2 \simeq f$ is much easier to use than Eq 22-47.

Also, The approx. formula for $w_{02} \simeq \frac{f\lambda}{\pi w_{01}} = \frac{(0.1)(0.633 \times 10^{-6} m)}{(3.1416)(0.1113 m)}$ gives $1.783 \times 10^{-7}$ m whereas Eq 22-46 gives $1.81 \times 10^{-7}$ m. Both round to $1.8 \times 10^{-7}$ m, so the approx. formula $w_{02} \simeq \frac{f\lambda}{\pi w_{01}}$ is much preferred.

These Approximations are both valid here since the conditions $w_{01} >> w_{02}$ and $\frac{\pi w_{01}^2}{\lambda} >> (z_1 - f)^2$ are both satisfied. (Look at the numbers!)

- $w_{01} = 11.13$ cm ; $w_{02} = 1.81 \times 10^{-7}$ m or $1.81 \times 10^{-5}$ cm ; $\underline{w_{01} >> w_{02}}$
- $\frac{\pi w_{01}^2}{\lambda} = 6.15 \times 10^4$ m and $(z_1 - f)^2 = 10^{-2}$ m$^2$ ; $\underline{\left(\frac{\pi w_{01}^2}{\lambda}\right)^2 >> (z-f)^2}$

22-11.

$$\frac{\Phi_{r=a}}{\Phi_{TOT}} = \frac{1}{\Phi_{TOT}} \iint |\tilde{E}(x,y,z,t)|^2 dA$$

$$\tilde{E}(x,y,z,t) = E_0(z) e^{\frac{ik(x^2+y^2)}{2R}} e^{-\frac{(x^2+y^2)}{w^2}} e^{i(kz + p(z) - \omega t)}$$

$$\text{So } |\tilde{E}|^2 = (\tilde{E})(\tilde{E})^* = E_0^2(z)\, e^{-\frac{2(x^2+y^2)}{w^2}} = E_0^2(z) e^{-\frac{2r^2}{w^2}} ; \quad dA = 2\pi r\,dr$$

$$\frac{\Phi_{r=a}}{\Phi_{TOT}} = \frac{E_0^2(z)}{\Phi_{TOT}} \int_{r=0}^{r=a} e^{-\frac{2r^2}{w^2}} \cdot (2\pi r\,dr) ;$$

change variables: let $u = \frac{2r^2}{w^2}$ ; $du = \frac{4r\,dr}{w^2}$

$r\,dr = \frac{w^2 du}{4}$ ; $r=0, u=0$ ; $r=a, u=\frac{2a^2}{w^2}$

$$\frac{\Phi_{r=a}}{\Phi_{TOT}} = \frac{E_0^2(z)}{\Phi_{TOT}} \int_{u=0}^{u=\frac{2a^2}{w^2}} e^{-u} \frac{\pi w^2 du}{2}$$

$$\frac{\Phi_{r=a}}{\Phi_{TOT}} = \frac{E_0^2(z)}{\Phi_{TOT}} \cdot \frac{\pi w^2}{2} \int_0^{\frac{2a^2}{w^2}} e^{-u} du = \left(\frac{\pi w^2 E_0^2(z)}{2\Phi_{TOT}}\right) \left[-e^{-u}\right]_0^{\frac{2a^2}{w^2}}$$

Recognizing that $\Phi_{TOT} = \left(\frac{\pi w^2}{2}\right)(E_0^2(z))$ ··· see Problem 22-12 ··· and evaluating limits, one gets

$$\frac{\Phi_{r=a}}{\Phi_{TOT}} = \left[-e^{-\frac{2a^2}{w^2}} - \underbrace{(-e^{-0})}_{-1}\right] = \underline{1 - e^{-\frac{2a^2}{w^2}}} ; \text{ Q.E.D.}$$

22-12. $$\Phi_{TOT} = \iint_A E_0^2(z)\, e^{-\frac{2(x^2+y^2)}{w^2}}\, dA = \int_{r=0}^{r=\infty} E_0^2(z)\, e^{-\frac{2r^2}{w^2}} \cdot (2\pi r\,dr)$$

As in Problem 22-11, change variables:

Let $u = \frac{2r^2}{w^2}$, $du = \frac{4r\,dr}{w^2}$, $(2\pi r\,dr) = \frac{\pi w^2 du}{2}$

and $u=0$ when $r=0$; $u=\infty$ when $r=\infty$

Thus:

$$\Phi_{TOT} = \int_{r=0}^{r=\infty} E_0^2(z)\, e^{-\frac{2r^2}{w^2}}(2\pi r\,dr) \rightarrow \int_{u=0}^{u=\infty} \frac{\pi w^2(z)}{2} E_0^2(z)\, e^{-u}\, du$$

$$\Phi_{TOT} = \frac{\pi w^2(z)}{2} \cdot E_0^2(z) \int_{u=0}^{u=\infty} e^{-u} du = E_0^2(z) \cdot \frac{\pi w^2(z)}{2}\left[-e^{-u}\right]_0^{\infty}$$

$$\Phi_{TOT} = E_0^2(z)\frac{\pi w^2(z)}{2}\left[\cancel{-e^{-\infty}}^{=0} \underbrace{-(-e^{-0})}_{+1}\right] = E_0^2(z)\frac{\pi w^2(z)}{2}(1)$$

$$\therefore \Phi_{TOT} = E_0^2(z)\frac{\pi w^2(z)}{2} \qquad \text{Q.E.D.}$$

22-13.

- Assume that $\Phi_{TOT}$ (laser output power) is known from laser specs. (If not, $\Phi_{TOT}$ can be measured with the help of a power meter set to "receive" whole beam.
- Next, center the adjustable iris at some position $z$ along the beam axis and set the iris opening to a certain value (e.g., to read ½ of full beam power) and note this reading ($r=a$). Be sure power meter is located just behind the iris.
- Use Eq 22-43, $\frac{\Phi_{r=a}}{\Phi_{TOT}} = 1 - e^{-\frac{2a^2}{w^2}}$, where values for "a" (iris setting $r=a$), $\Phi_{r=a}$ (power meter reading for iris set at $r=a$) and $\Phi_{TOT}$ (power meter reading for entire beam) are all known. Solve Eq 22-43 for remaining variable, spot size, $w(z)$. Repeat same steps at same $z$ location but for different $r=a$ settings and recalculate $w(z)$. Take average of readings for "best" $w(z)$ at that $z$.

22-14.

$2z_R$ is given as the "collimated" beam length where $2z_R = 2\left(\frac{\pi w_0^2}{\lambda}\right)$, $d = 4.5(\sqrt{2}w_0)$, so $w_0 = \frac{d}{4.5\sqrt{2}}$

Thus, $2z_R = \frac{2\pi}{\lambda}\left(\frac{d}{4.5\sqrt{2}}\right)^2 = \frac{\pi d^2}{20.25\lambda}$.

$$2z_R = \left[\frac{\pi}{20.25(1.064\times10^{-6}\,m)}\right]d^2 \quad ; \text{ d in meters}$$

$$2z_R = (1.4581\times10^{-5})\,d^2$$

$(2z_R)_{d=1cm} = (1.4581\times10^{+5})(10^{-2})^2 = \underline{14.58\,m}$

$(2z_R)_{d=2cm} = (1.4581\times10^{-5})(2\times10^{-2})^2 = \underline{58.3\,m}$

$(2z_R)_{d=3cm} = (1.4581\times10^{-5})(3\times10^{-2})^2 = \underline{131.2\,m}$

$(2z_R)_{d=5cm} = (1.4581\times10^{-5})(5\times10^{-2})^2 = \underline{364.5\,m}$

22-15.

$H_m(\xi) = (-1)^m e^{\xi^2}\frac{d^m}{d\xi^m}(e^{-\xi^2})$ ; generating function

for m=0: $H_0(\xi) = (-1)^0 e^{\xi^2}\frac{d^0}{d\xi^0}\left(e^{-\xi^2}\right) = (1)e^{\xi^2}(1)e^{-\xi^2} = e^0 = \underline{\underline{1}}$

for m=1: $H_1(\xi) = (-1)^1 e^{\xi^2}\frac{d}{d\xi}(e^{-\xi^2}) = -1e^{\xi^2}(-2\xi e^{-\xi^2}) = 2\xi$

$\therefore H_1(\xi) = 2\xi = 2\left(\frac{\sqrt{2}x}{w}\right) = \underline{\underline{\frac{2\sqrt{2}x}{w}}}$

for m=2: $H_2(\xi) = (-1)^2 e^{\xi^2}\frac{d^2}{d\xi^2}(e^{-\xi^2}) = 1e^{\xi^2}\frac{d}{d\xi}\left(\frac{d}{d\xi}(e^{-\xi^2})\right)$

$H_2(\xi) = e^{\xi^2}\frac{d}{d\xi}(-2\xi e^{-\xi^2})$

$H_2(\xi) = e^{\xi^2}\left[-2\xi(-2\xi e^{-\xi^2}) + e^{-\xi^2}(-2)\right]$

$H_2(\xi) = 4\xi^2 - 2$

$H_2(\xi) = 4\left(\frac{\sqrt{2}x}{w}\right)^2 - 2 = \underline{\underline{\frac{8x^2}{w^2} - 2}}$

22-16.

Given:

$$p(z) = \frac{i}{2} \ln\left[\frac{\lambda^2 z^2 + (\pi W_0^2)^2}{(\pi W_0^2)^2}\right] - (m+n+1)\tan^{-1}\left(\frac{\lambda z}{\pi W_0^2}\right)$$

and

Eq 22-24, $$\frac{W(z)^2}{W_0^2} = \left[1 + \left(\frac{\lambda z}{\pi W_0^2}\right)^2\right] = \frac{(\pi W_0^2)^2 + \lambda^2 z^2}{(\pi W_0^2)^2}$$

Thus, $$p(z) = \frac{i}{2} \ln\left\{\frac{W(z)^2}{W_0^2}\right\} - (m+n+1)\tan^{-1}\left(\frac{\lambda z}{\pi W_0^2}\right)$$

$$i\,p(z) = -\frac{1}{2}\ln\left\{\frac{W^2(z)}{W_0^2}\right\} - i(m+n+1)\tan^{-1}\left(\frac{\lambda z}{\pi W_0^2}\right)$$

Collecting terms

$$i p(z) + i(m+n+1)\tan^{-1}\left(\frac{\lambda z}{\pi W_0^2}\right) = -\frac{1}{2}\ln\left\{\frac{W(z)^2}{W_0^2}\right\} = \ln\left\{\frac{W(z)^2}{W_0^2}\right\}^{-\frac{1}{2}}$$

$$i p(z) + i(m+n+1)\tan^{-1}\left(\frac{\lambda z}{\pi W_0^2}\right) = \ln\left(\frac{W(z)}{W_0}\right)^{-1} = \ln\left(\frac{W_0}{W(z)}\right)$$

Making use of the properties of a logarithm, i.e., if $a = \ln x$, then $x = e^a$, we can write:

$$e^{i\{p(z) + (m+n+1)\tan^{-1}\left(\frac{\lambda z}{\pi W_0^2}\right)\}} = \frac{W_0}{W(z)}$$

$$e^{i\,p(z)} \cdot e^{i(m+n+1)\tan^{-1}\left(\frac{\lambda z}{\pi W_0^2}\right)} = \frac{W_0}{W(z)}$$

So, finally

$$e^{i p(z)} = \frac{W_0}{W(z)}\, e^{-i(m+n+1)\tan^{-1}\left(\frac{\lambda z}{\pi W_0^2}\right)} \qquad \text{Q.E.D.}$$

22-17.

For the case $m=2$, $n=0$, draw the following:

| Hermite Polynomial $H_2(x)$ | X-variation of Elect. field $H_2(x)\, e^{-x^2/2}$ | X-variation of irradiance $[H_2(x)\, e^{-\frac{x^2}{2}}]^2$ | Burn Pattern for xy plane |
|---|---|---|---|

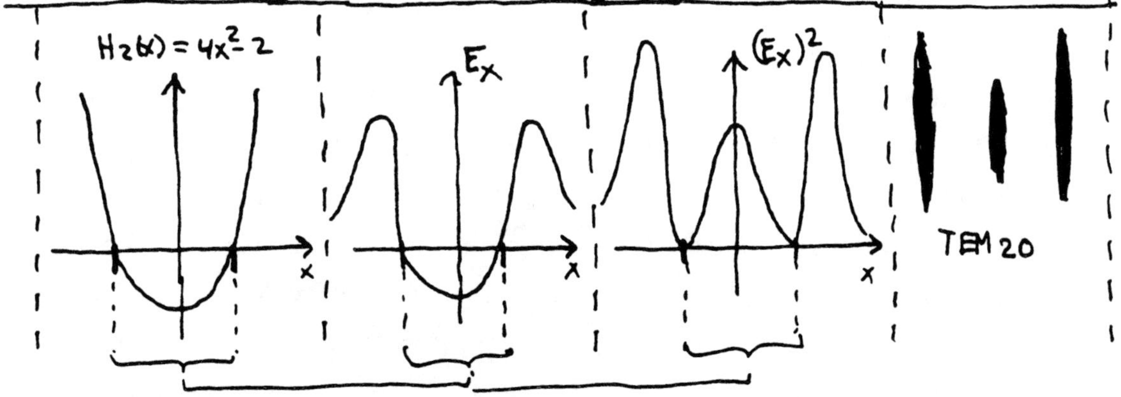

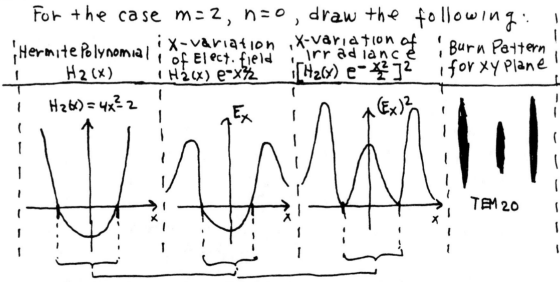

## Chapter 23 - Laser Applications

23-1. $$E_e = \frac{P_o}{A} = \frac{4P_o}{\pi D^2} = \frac{4P_o}{\pi[f\theta]^2} = \frac{4\times10^7\ W}{\pi(0.2\times1\times10^{-3})^2 m^2}$$

$$E_e = \frac{4\times10^7\ W}{4\pi\times10^{-8} m^2} = 3.18\times10^{14}\ \frac{W}{m^2} = 3.18\times10^{10}\ \frac{W}{cm^2}$$

23-2 (a) $d = \frac{2\lambda}{\pi}\sqrt{p^2-1}\left(\frac{2f}{D}\right)^2$ ; $\left\{\begin{matrix}\lambda = 10.6\,\mu m, & f = 60\,mm\\ p = 1.10 & , D = 8\,mm\end{matrix}\right\}$

$$d = \left(\frac{2\times10.6\times10^{-6}}{\pi}\right)\sqrt{(1.1)^2-1}\left(\frac{2\times60\,mm}{8\,mm}\right)^2$$

$$d = 6.96\times10^{-4} m \simeq 0.7\,mm$$

(b) $\phi = \frac{1.27\lambda}{D} = \frac{1.27\times10.6\times10^{-6}\ m}{8\times10^{-3}\ m} = 1.683\times10^{-3}\ rad$

$$D' = f\phi\,(60\times10^{-3})(1.683\times10^{-3})\,m = 1.01\times10^{-4} m$$

$D' \simeq 101\,\mu m$

Diameter at edge $= 1.1\times101\,\mu m = 111\,\mu m$

23-3 At a cutting speed of 25 mm/s, the laser in Fig 23-3 cuts a kerf about 6 mm deep in steel and 2.5 mm in aluminum. The thermal conductivity of Al is about 4-5 times that of steel, making it more difficult to localize heat energy in the "work area" for aluminum than for steel. If, in addition, the reflectivity of 10.6 μm radiation for aluminum is greater than for steel (hence less thermal energy available for absorption, the depth of cut is again less favorable for aluminum than for steel. Thus it is not unreasonable, based on such factors, that the same laser beam cuts deeper in steel than in aluminum, even though steel is more dense.

23-4.

(a) $E_e = \frac{P}{A} = \frac{(10^{-3} J/10^{-9} sec)}{(0.7854)(30 \times 10^{-6} m)^2} = \underline{1.41 \times 10^{15} \ W/m^2}$ !

(b) $E_e = \frac{\epsilon v E^2}{2}$; $v = \frac{c}{n}$; $\epsilon = 78\,\epsilon_0$; $\epsilon_0 = 8.85 \times 10^{-12}$ F/m

Solving for electric field strength E:

$$E = \sqrt{\frac{2 E_e n}{\epsilon c}} = \sqrt{\frac{2(1.41 \times 10^{15})(1.33)}{78(8.85 \times 10^{-12})(3 \times 10^8)}} = \underline{1.35 \ V/m}$$

23-5.

(a) $C = B \log\left(1 + \frac{S}{N}\right)$

$C = (4 \times 10^9 \ Hz)\left[\log_{10}(1+9)\right] = (4 \times 10^9)(1) \ Hz$

$C = \underline{4 \times 10^9 \ Hz}$; same as channel bandwidth

(b) # voice channels $= \frac{B}{\Delta f} = \frac{4 \times 10^9 \ Hz}{4 \times 10^3 \ Hz} \simeq \underline{10^6}$

Hence, this laser communication system can carry about one million telephone conversations.

23-6.

(a) Diameter $= Z\phi = (36{,}205 \times 10^3 m)(5 \times 10^{-6} r) = \underline{181 \ m}$

So, the diameter of the laser beam footprint on the Earth's surface is about 181 m.

(b) Irradiance $E_e = \frac{P}{A} = \frac{200 \times 10^6 \ W}{(0.7854)(181 \ m)^2} = \underline{7.773 \times 10^3 \ \frac{W}{m^2}}$

As in Problem 23-4,

$E = \sqrt{\frac{2 E_e n}{c \epsilon}}$ where for free space, $n = 1$ and $\epsilon = \epsilon_0$

$$E = \sqrt{\frac{(2) \times (7773) \times (1)}{(3 \times 10^8)(8.85 \times 10^{-12})}} = \underline{2.42 \times 10^3 \ V/m}$$

Thus, average electric field per pulse in the laser beam is about 2420 V/m at Earth's surface

23-7.

(a)

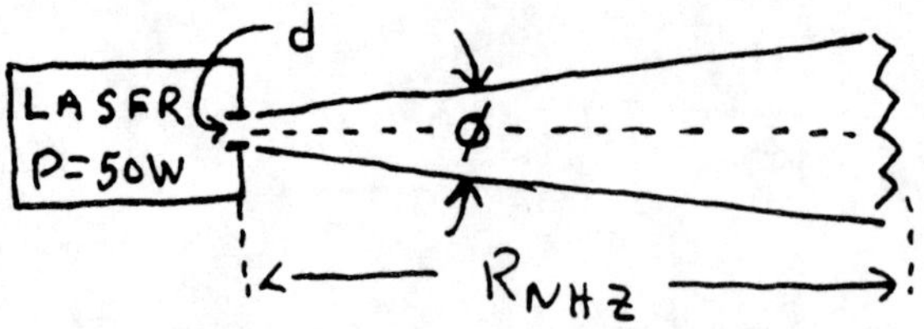


(b) $R_{NHZ} = \frac{1}{\phi}\left[\left(\frac{4P}{\pi[MPE]}\right)^{1/2} - d\right]$ where $\begin{cases} P = 50\,W \\ \phi = 3\times10^{-3}\,\text{rad} \\ d = 0.3\,\text{cm} \\ MPE = 5.1\times10^{-3}\,\frac{W}{cm^2} \end{cases}$

$$R_{NHZ} = \frac{1}{(3\times10^{-3})}\left[\left(\frac{4\times50}{\pi\times5.1\times10^{-3}}\right) - 0.3\right]$$

$R_{NHZ} = 37{,}142$ cm (about 371 m)

23-8.

(a)

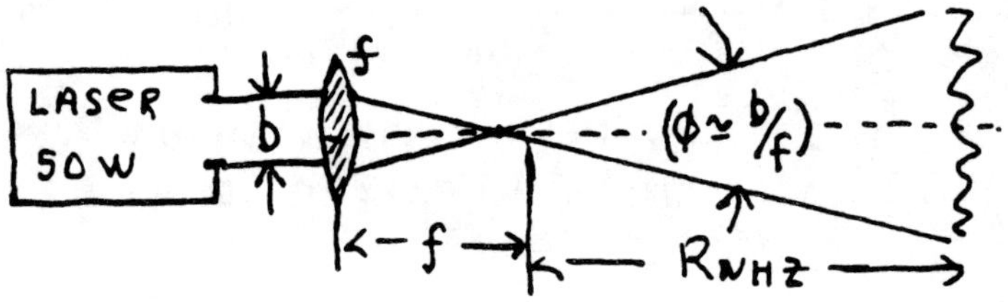


(b) $R_{NHZ} = \left(\frac{f}{b}\right)\left[\frac{4P}{\pi(MPE)}\right]^{1/2}$ $\begin{cases} f = 7.5\,\text{cm} \\ b = 0.5\,\text{cm} \\ MPE = 1.6\times10^{-3}\,W/cm^2 \\ P = 50\,W \end{cases}$

$$R_{NHZ} = \left(\frac{7.5\,\text{cm}}{0.5\,\text{cm}}\right)\left[\frac{4\times50\,W}{(3.1416)(1.6\times10^{-3}\,\frac{W}{cm^2})}\right]^{1/2}$$

$R_{NHZ} \simeq 2990$ cm (about 29.9 m)

# Chapter 24 - Fiber Optics

24-1.

Information rate = $(4\times10^3 Hz)(2 \times \text{sampling rate})(8\ \text{bits/sample})$
$= 64\ Kbps$

Number of channels $= \dfrac{44.7\ Mbps}{64\ Kbps} - 26\ (\text{assigned}) = 672$

24-2. $\nu = \dfrac{c}{\lambda} = \dfrac{3\times10^8 m/s}{1\times10^{-6} m} = 3\times10^{14} Hz$

No. of TV channels $= \dfrac{\nu}{\Delta\nu} = \dfrac{3\times10^{14} Hz}{6\times10^6 Hz} = 50$ million

24-3. (a) In general, $L_s = d\sqrt{\left(\dfrac{n_1}{\sin\theta}\right)^2 - 1}$ .

When $\theta = \theta_m$, $\sin\theta = \sin\theta_m = \sqrt{n_1^2 - n_2^2} = N.A.$

Then $L_s = d\left[\left(\dfrac{n_1}{\sqrt{n_1^2-n_2^2}}\right)^2 - 1\right]^{1/2} = \dfrac{n_2 d}{\sqrt{n_1^2-n_2^2}}$ Q.E.D.

(b) In one meter of fiber, there are $1/L_s$ reflections, so

No. of reflections $= \dfrac{\sqrt{n_1^2-n_2^2}}{n_2 d} = \dfrac{(1.46^2 - 1.457^2)^{1/2}}{1.457(50\times10^{-6} m)} = 1284\ m^{-1}$

24-4. (a) $1.52 \sin\varphi_c = 1.41$ or $\varphi_c = 68.1°$

(b) $N.A. = n_0 \sin\theta_m = n_1 \cos\varphi_c = 1.52 \cos 68.1° = 0.567$

(c) $\sin\theta_m = \dfrac{N.A.}{n_0} = \dfrac{0.567}{1} = 0.567$ ; $\theta_m = 34.5°$

24-5. (a) $N.A. = \sqrt{n_1^2 - n_2^2} = \sqrt{1.53^2 - 1.39^2} = 0.64$

(b) $n_0 \sin\theta_m = N.A.$ so $\theta_m = \sin^{-1}(0.6394) = 39.7°$

Cone angle $= 2\theta_m = 79.5°$

(c) $\dfrac{1}{L_s} = \dfrac{1}{d\sqrt{\left(\dfrac{n_1}{n_0\sin\theta}\right)^2 - 1}} = \dfrac{1}{(.0025\ in)\sqrt{\left(\dfrac{1.53}{\sin 39.75°}\right)^2 - 1}} = 184/\text{inch}$

OR 6624 reflections in 3 ft.

At half $\theta_m$, substitute $\theta = 19.87°$. Then $\dfrac{1}{L_s} = 91.14\ in^{-1}$

OR 3281 reflections in 3 ft.

24-6.

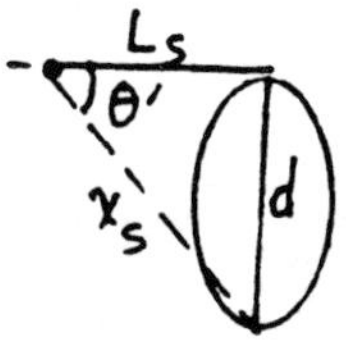


(a) $\sin\theta' = \dfrac{d}{x_s}$ and $\sin\theta = n_1 \sin\theta'$

$x_s = \dfrac{d}{\sin\theta'} = \dfrac{n_1 d}{\sin\theta}$ Q.E.D.

(b) $x_t = x_s \times$ no. of skips

$x_t = x_s\left(\dfrac{L}{L_s}\right) = \dfrac{n_1 d}{\sin\theta}\left[\dfrac{L}{d\sqrt{\left(\dfrac{n_1}{\sin\theta}\right)^2 - 1}}\right] = \dfrac{n_1 L}{(n_1^2 - \sin^2\theta)^{1/2}}$ Q.E.D.

24-6. (cont'd.)

(c) $x_s = \frac{n_1 d}{\sin\theta} = \frac{(1.5)(50\mu m)}{\sin 10^\circ} = 432\mu m$

$L_s = d\sqrt{\left(\frac{n_1}{\sin\theta}\right)^2 - 1} = 50\mu m\left[\left(\frac{1.5}{\sin 10^\circ}\right)^2 - 1\right]^{1/2} = 429\mu m$

$x_t = \frac{n_1 L}{(n_1^2 - \sin^2\theta)^{1/2}} = \frac{1.5(10m)}{[1.5^2 - \sin^2 10^\circ]^{1/2}} = 10.07m$

24-7. $m_{max} = \frac{1}{2}\left(\frac{\pi d}{\lambda}\right)^2 (N.A.)^2 = \frac{1}{2}\left(\frac{\pi d}{\lambda}\right)^2 (n_1^2 - n_2^2) = \frac{1}{2}\left(\pi \frac{40}{0.85}\right)^2 (1.461^2 - 1.456^2)$

$m_{max} = 159$

24-8 $\frac{d}{\lambda} < \frac{2.4}{\pi(N.A.)}$ ; $d < \frac{2.4\lambda}{\pi(N.A.)} = \frac{2.4(1.25\mu m)}{\pi\sqrt{1.46^2 - 1.457^2}} = 10.2\mu m$

24-9. $N = 1 + 2\left(\frac{d}{\lambda}\right)\sqrt{n_1^2 - n_2^2}$

$d/\lambda = 5$: $N = 1 + 2(5)\sqrt{3.6^2 - 3.55^2} = 6$ OR 12 for 2 polarizations

$d/\lambda = 50$: $N = 1 + 2(50)\sqrt{3.6^2 - 3.55^2} = 60$ OR 120 for 2 polarizations

24-10. $\alpha_{dB} = 10\log_{10}\frac{P_2}{P_1} = 10\log_{10}\frac{10^{-6}}{5\times10^{-6}} = -7\,dB/100\,m$

$\alpha_{dB} = -70\,dB/Km$

24-11. $\alpha_{dB} = 10\log_{10}\frac{P_2}{P_1}$ ; $P_2 = P_1 10^{\alpha/10}$

$\alpha = (3\times 5dB) + (2\times 1dB) = 17dB$ total loss

$P_2 = 4mW\ 10^{-17/10} = 0.080\ mW$

24-12. $\alpha = 10\log_{10}\frac{P_2}{P_1} = 10\log_{10}\frac{10^{-6}}{10^{-2}} = -40\,dB$

Coax cable: At $-12\,dB/Km$, $L = \frac{-40}{-12} = 3.33\,Km$

Optical fiber: At $-4\,dB/Km$, $L = -40/-4 = 10\,Km$

24-13. $\frac{\alpha_1}{\alpha_2} = \left(\frac{\lambda_2}{\lambda_1}\right)^4$ $\frac{1.2}{\alpha_2} = \left(\frac{1.55}{0.9}\right)^4$ OR $\alpha_2 = 0.136\,dB/Km$

24-14. (a) $\alpha_{dB} = 10\log_{10}\frac{P_2}{P_1}$ ; $f \equiv \frac{P_1 - P_2}{P_1}$ for 1 Km

$f = 1 - P_2/P_1$ or $P_2/P_1 = 1 - f$

Then $\alpha_{dB} = 10\log_{10}(1-f)$

(b) $f = 0.25$, $\alpha = 10\log_{10}(1 - .25) = -1.25\,dB$

$f = 0.75$, $\alpha = -6.02\,dB$; $f = 0.90$, $\alpha = -10\,dB$; $f = 0.99$, $\alpha = -20\,dB$

24-15. (a) $\frac{L_{shortest}}{L_{longest}} = \frac{n_2}{n_1} = \frac{1.45}{1.46}$

Since $L_{shortest} = L = 1\text{ Km}$, $L_{longest} = \frac{1.46}{1.45}(1) = 1.0069\text{ Km}$

(b) $t_s = \frac{L_s}{V} = \frac{n_1}{c}L_s = \frac{1.46}{3\times10^{-4}\text{ Km/ns}}(1\text{ Km}) = 4.867\,\mu s$

$t_\ell = \frac{n_1}{c}L_\ell = \frac{1.46}{3\times10^{-4}\text{ Km/ns}}(1.0069\text{ km}) = 4.900\,\mu s$

24-16. Find $n_2$: $N.A. = \sin\theta_m = \sqrt{n_1^2 - n_2^2}$ ; $n_2 = \sqrt{n_1^2 - \sin^2\theta_m}$

$n_2 = [1.446^2 - \sin^2 35]^{1/2} = 1.3274$

Then $\frac{\Delta\tau}{L} = \frac{n_1}{c}\left(\frac{n_1 - n_2}{n_2}\right) = \frac{1.446}{3\times10^{-4}\text{ Km/ns}}\left(\frac{1.446 - 1.3274}{1.3274}\right) = 431\ \frac{ns}{Km}$

For non-overlapping pulses, $\Delta\tau > T = \frac{1}{\nu}$

thus $\nu_{max} = \frac{1}{431\times10^{-9}} = 2.32\text{ MHz}$

24-17. Entrance angle $\theta = 15°$ is not given as a maximum, so Eq. (10-14) cannot be used directly. Arguing from first principles,

$\Delta\tau = \frac{\Delta L}{V} = \frac{n_1}{c}\Delta L = \frac{n_1}{c}(x_t - L)$, where $x_t$ is given in Prob. 24-6b. Then

$$\Delta\tau = \frac{n_1 L}{c}\left[\frac{n_1}{(n_1^2 - \sin^2\theta)^{1/2}} - 1\right] = \frac{1.48\ (1\text{ Km})}{3\times10^{-4}\text{ Km/ns}}\left[\frac{1.48}{(1.48^2 - \sin^2 15)^{1/2}} - 1\right]$$

$\Delta\tau = 77.2\text{ ns}$

24-18. $\Delta(\tau/L) = \frac{n_1}{c}\left(\frac{n_1 - n_2}{n_2}\right) = \frac{n_1}{c}\Delta$

$\Delta(\tau/L) = \frac{1.46}{3\times10^{-4}\text{ Km/ns}}(0.003) = 14.6\text{ ns/Km}$

24-19. N VS DISTANCE FROM CORE CENTER

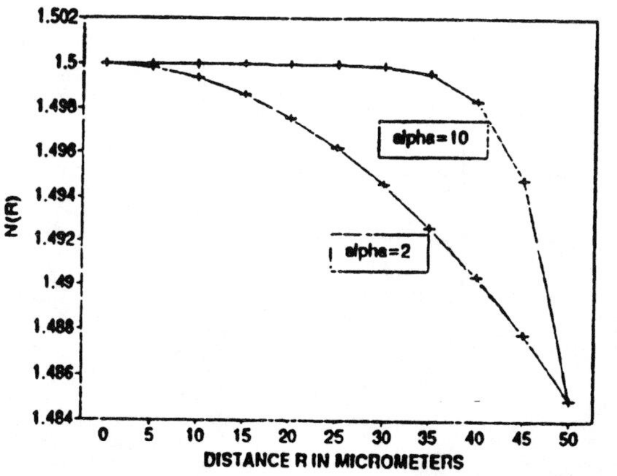


$n(r) = n_1\sqrt{1 - 2\left(\frac{r}{a}\right)^\alpha \Delta}$

$n(r) = 1.5\left[1 - .02\left(\frac{r}{50}\right)^\alpha\right]^{1/2}$

24-20. $\Delta = \frac{n_1 - n_2}{n_1} = \frac{1.46 - 1.44}{1.46} = 0.0137$

$\delta\tau = \frac{n_1 L}{2c}\Delta^2 = \frac{(1.46)(1\,Km)}{2(3\times10^{-4}\,Km/ns)}(0.0137)^2 = 457\ ps$

$(\delta\tau)_{SI} = \frac{n_1 L}{c}\Delta = \frac{2}{\Delta}\left(\frac{n_1 L}{2c}\Delta^2\right) = \frac{2}{0.0137}(457ps) = 66.7\,ns$

OR $(\delta\tau)_{SI} = 146\,(\delta\tau)_{GRIN}$

24-21. $\nu_{max} L = \frac{0.5}{\delta(\tau/L)}$

$\nu_{max} = \frac{0.5}{(1Km)(20ns/Km)} = 0.025\ ns^{-1} = 25\ MHz$

24-22. At $\lambda = 820\,nm$, Fig 24-13 gives $M \cong 100ps/nm\text{-}Km$

Then $\frac{\Delta\tau}{L} = -M\,\Delta\lambda$

LED: $\Delta\tau/1\,Km = (100)(40) = 4000\,ps = 4ns$

LD: $\Delta\tau/1Km = (100)(4) = 400\ ps = 0.4ns$

24-23. $(\Delta\tau)_{mod} = \frac{L n_1}{c}\Delta = \frac{(1\,Km)(1.46)}{3\times10^{-4}\,Km/ns}(.01) = 48.7\,ns$

$(\Delta\tau)_{mat} = M L \Delta\lambda = 100\,\frac{ps}{Km\text{-}nm}(1\,Km)(40nm) = 4ns$

$(\Delta\tau)^2 = 48.7^2 + 4^2$ OR $\Delta\tau = 48.9\ ns.$

24-24.

(d)

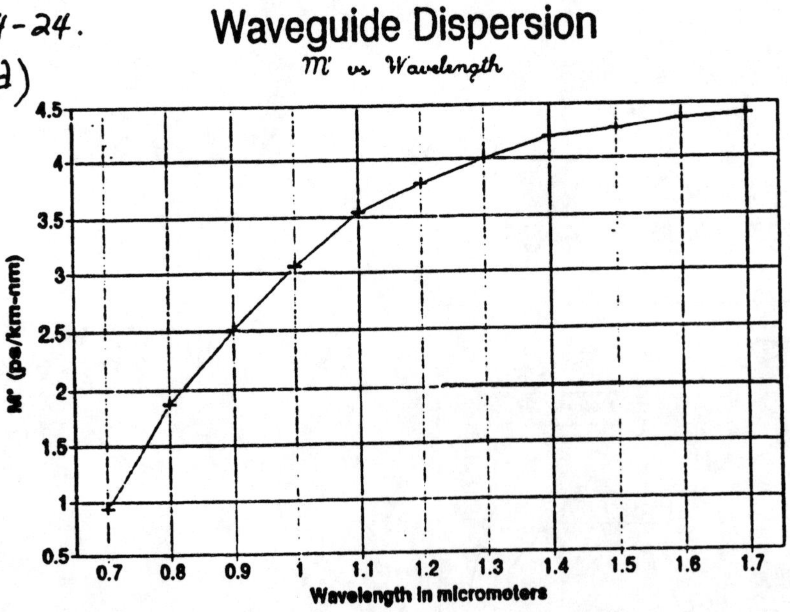


$M' = \frac{\Delta(\tau/L)}{\Delta\lambda}$

$M' = \frac{\Delta(\tau/L)}{2\,nm}$

24-24. (cont'd.)

(b) From plot, $M' \cong 3.9$ ps/Km-nm at 1.27 μm

$M' \cong 4.3$ ps/Km-nm at 1.55 μm

$\therefore \Delta(\tau/L) = (3.9)(1\,nm) = 3.9$ ps/Km at 1.27 μm

$\Delta(\tau/L) = (4.3)(1\,nm) = 4.3$ ps/Km at 1.55 μm

24-25.

(a) Modal:

$$\Delta\tau_{mod} = \frac{n_1 L}{c}\left(\frac{n_1 - n_2}{n_2}\right) = \frac{(1.47)(1)}{3\times10^{-4}}\,\frac{(1.47-1.455)}{1.455} = 50.5\ ns$$

Material:

$$\Delta\tau_{mat} = LM\Delta\lambda = (1)(43)(25) = 1.075\ ns$$

Waveguide:

$$\Delta\tau_{wg} = LM'\Delta\lambda = (1)(3)(25) = 0.075\ ns$$

(b) $(\Delta\tau)^2 = (\Delta\tau_{mod})^2 + (\Delta\tau_{mat})^2 + (\Delta\tau_{wg})^2$

$(\Delta\tau)^2 = 50.5^2 + 1.075^2 + 0.075^2$

$\Delta\tau = 50.5\ ns$

25-1. 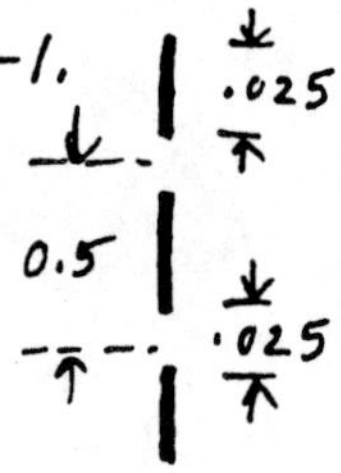


(a) $m\lambda = d\sin\theta = Y_m d/f$

or $Y_m = \frac{m\lambda f}{d} = m\left(\frac{632.8\times10^{-6}\text{ mm}\times 500\text{ mm}}{0.5\text{ mm}}\right)$

$Y_m = 0.6328\ m$ (in mm)

For $m=1$, $Y_1 = 0.633$ mm. Note that, since $d/b = 2$ for Ronchi, missing orders are those for which $m = 2, 4, 6, \ldots$

Then: $m=0$, $Y_0 = 0$ ("DC component")

$m=1$, $Y_1 = 0.633$ mm

$m=3$, $Y_3 = 1.898$ mm

$m=5$, $Y_5 = 3.164$ mm

(b) $\nu_Y = \frac{m}{d} \equiv \frac{1}{\lambda_Y}$ Fundamental frequency: $m=1$ and $\lambda_Y = \frac{d}{m} = \frac{0.5}{1} = 0.5$ mm

(c) $K_Y = \frac{kY}{f} = 2\pi\nu_Y = 2\pi\left(\frac{m}{d}\right)$

thus $K_Y = \left(\frac{2\pi}{d}\right)m = m\left(\frac{2\pi}{0.5\text{ mm}}\right)$
$m=1$, $K_Y = 12.57$ cycles/mm
$m=3$, $K_Y = 37.70$ "
$m=5$, $K_Y = 62.83$ "

(d) $f(Y) = \frac{1}{2} + \frac{2}{\pi}\left[\sin\omega Y + \frac{1}{3}\sin 3\omega Y + \frac{1}{5}\sin 5\omega Y + \ldots\right]$

fundamental amp $=1$; amp $=\frac{1}{3}$; amp $=\frac{1}{5}$

$I \propto A^2$ or $I_o = 1$; $I/I_o = \frac{1}{9}$; $I/I_o = 1/25$

25-2. (a) At any point, what is transmitted is a product.

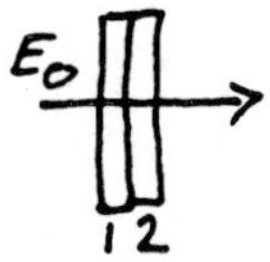


$E_1 = t_1 E_o$
$E_2 = t_2 E_1$
$E_2 = (t_1 t_2) E_o$

(b)

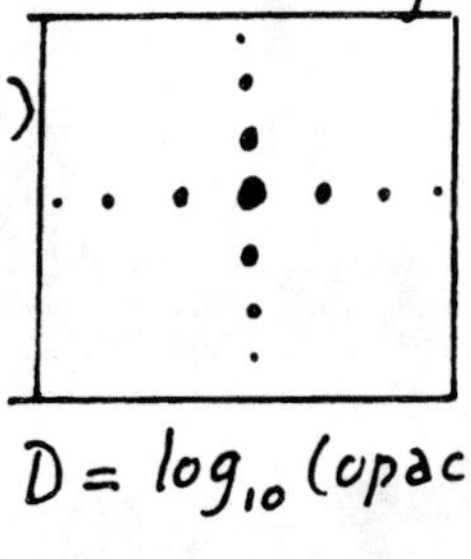

25-3. $D = \log_{10}(\text{opacity}) = \log_{10}\left(\frac{1}{T}\right)$

(a) $D = -\log_{10} T$

(b) 

$T = T_1 T_2 T_3$ ; $D = -\log_{10}(T_1 T_2 T_3)$

$D = -(\log T_1 + \log T_2 + \log T_3)$

$D = D_1 + D_2 + D_3$ Q.E.D.

25-3. (cont'd.) (c) $(\text{opacity})_i = 1.25$

$$D_i = \log_{10}(1.25) = 0.09691$$

$$D_{net} = 5 D_i = 0.48455$$

$$T_{net} = \log^{-1}(-D) = 10^{-D} = 10^{-.48455} = 0.3277$$

$$T_{net} = 32.8\%$$

25-4. $T = \frac{E_t}{E_o} = 5 \sin(ay)$ (b)

(a) Bias of 5 units locates minima at $T = 0$

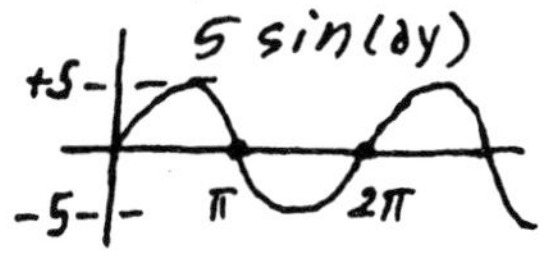


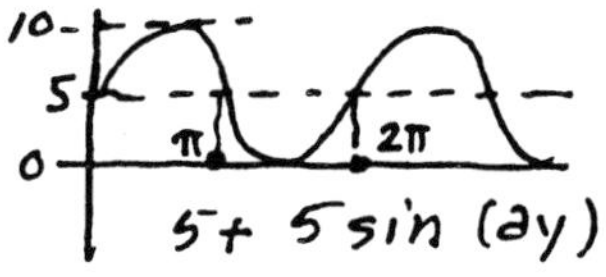


(c) $\frac{I_t}{I_o} = \left(\frac{E_t}{E_o}\right)^2 = 25(1 + \sin ay)^2$

For $I_o = 1$, $I_t = 25(1 + \sin ay)^2$

25-5. By definition of a Fourier transform,

$$\mathcal{F}[h(x)] = \int h(x) e^{ikx} dx$$

Substitute for $h(x)$ the convolution of $f$ and $g$:

$$\mathcal{F}[h(x)] = \int e^{ikx} \left[ \int f(x-x') g(x') dx' \right] dx$$

Changing the order of integration,

$$\mathcal{F}[h(x)] = \int g(x') \left[ \int e^{ikx} f(x-x') dx \right] dx'$$

then let $v \equiv x - x'$ so that $dx = dv$:

$$\mathcal{F}[h(x)] = \int g(x') \left[ \int e^{ik(v+x')} f(v) dv \right] dx'$$

$$\mathcal{F}[h(x)] = \int f(v) e^{ikv} dv \int g(x') e^{ikx'} dx'$$

or $\mathcal{F}[h(x)] = \mathcal{F}[f(x)] \times \mathcal{F}[g(x)]$ Q.E.D.

25-6.

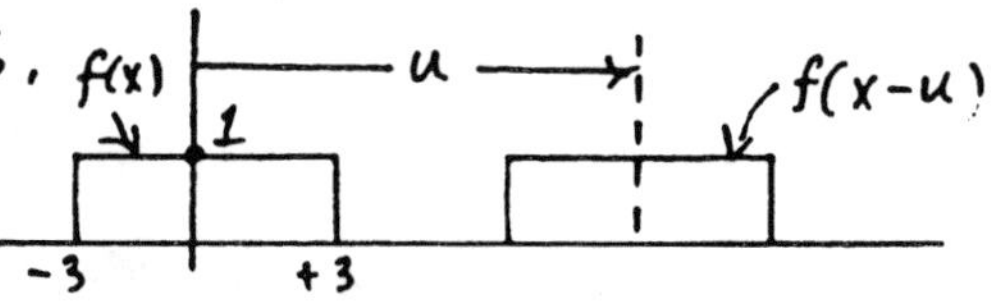


$$\rho_{11}(u) = \int f(x-u) f(x) dx$$

As $u$ varies, $\rho_{11}(u)$ measures the area of overlap of the square pulses:

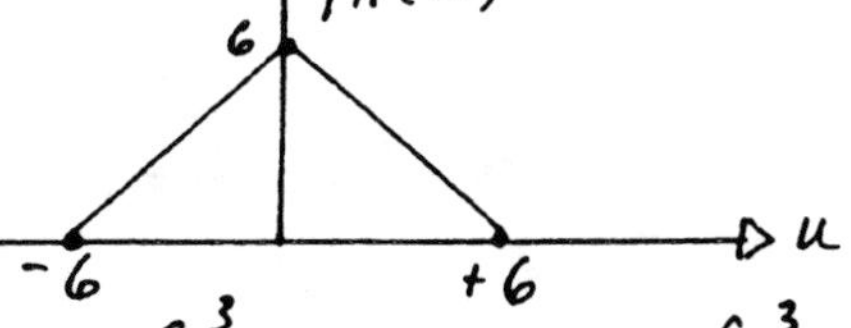


For example, $\rho_{11}(0) = \int_{-3}^{3} [f(x)]^2 dx = \int_{-3}^{3} dx = 6$

$$\rho_{11}(3) = \int_{-3}^{3} f(x) f(x-3) dx = \int_{0}^{3} dx = 3$$

25-7. $y = A\sin(\omega t + \alpha) = f(t)$. Since the fn is periodic, we integrate over one period $T$:

$$\Phi_{11}(\tau) = \int_{-T/2}^{T/2} \underbrace{A\sin\overbrace{(\omega t+\alpha)}^{\beta}}_{f(t)} \; \underbrace{A\sin[\omega(t+\tau)+\alpha]}_{f(t+\tau)}\, dt$$

$$\Phi_{11}(\tau) = A^2\int_{-T/2}^{T/2} \sin\beta\,\sin(\beta+\omega\tau)\,dt = A^2\int_{-T/2}^{T/2} \sin\beta(\sin\beta\cos\omega\tau + \cos\beta\sin\omega\tau)\,dt$$

$$\Phi_{11}(\tau) = A^2\cos\omega\tau \underbrace{\int_{-T/2}^{T/2} \sin^2\beta\,dt}_{\text{even integral}} + A^2\sin\omega\tau \underbrace{\int_{-T/2}^{T/2} \sin\beta\cos\beta\,dt}_{\text{odd integral gives zero}}$$

$$\Phi_{11}(\tau) = 2A^2\cos\omega\tau\int_0^{T/2} \sin^2\beta\,dt = 2A^2\cos\omega\tau\int_0^{T/2} \sin^2(\omega t+\alpha)\,dt$$

$$\Phi_{11}(\tau) = \frac{2A^2\cos\omega\tau}{\omega}\int_0^{T/2} \sin(\omega t+\alpha)(\omega\,dt) = \frac{2A^2\cos\omega\tau}{\omega}\left[\frac{\omega t+\alpha}{2} - \frac{\sin 2(\omega t+\alpha)}{4}\right]_0^{T/2}$$

$$\Phi_{11}(\tau) = \frac{2A^2\cos\omega\tau}{\omega}\left[\frac{\omega T}{4} - \frac{\sin 2(\omega T/2+\alpha)}{4} + \frac{\sin 2\alpha}{4}\right]$$

Since $\omega T = 2\pi f T = 2\pi$,

$$\Phi_{11}(\tau) = \frac{2A^2\cos\omega\tau}{\omega}\left[\frac{\pi}{2} - \frac{\sin 2(\pi+\alpha)}{4} + \frac{\sin 2\alpha}{4}\right]$$

$$\Phi_{11}(\tau) = \frac{2A^2\cos\omega\tau}{\omega}\left[\frac{\pi}{2} - \frac{\overbrace{\sin 2\pi}^{0}\cos 2\alpha}{4} - \frac{\overbrace{\cos 2\pi}^{1}\sin 2\alpha}{4} + \frac{\sin 2\alpha}{4}\right]$$

$$\Phi_{11}(\tau) = A^2\pi\left(\frac{\cos\omega\tau}{\omega}\right)$$

25-8. (a) A mirror movement $x\ (= x_2 - x_1)$ of $\Delta x = \lambda/2$ produces a change in $I$ from one peak to the next.

The frequency of peaks $= \dfrac{\Delta x/\Delta t}{\Delta x} = \dfrac{v}{\lambda/2} = \dfrac{2v}{\lambda}$

frequency $= \dfrac{2(5\text{ mm/s})}{546.1\times10^{-6}\text{ mm}} = 18.3\text{ KHz}$

(b) In this case (as in measuring $(\Delta\lambda)_{Na}$ using an interferometer)

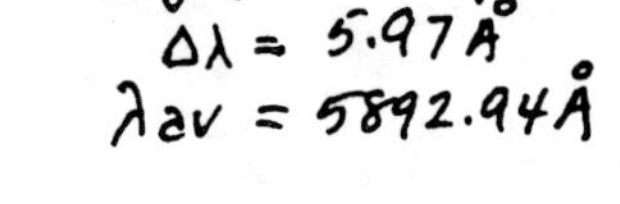

$\Delta\lambda = 5.97\text{ Å}$

$\lambda_{av} = 5892.94\text{ Å}$

Peak to peak: $\Delta x = \lambda^2/2\Delta\lambda$

frequency $= \dfrac{v}{\Delta x} = \dfrac{2v\Delta\lambda}{\lambda^2} = \dfrac{2(5)(5.97\times10^{-7})}{5892.94\times10^{-7}}$

frequency $= 17.2\text{ Hz}$

25-9. $R \equiv \frac{\lambda}{\Delta\lambda} = \frac{x_w}{\lambda}$ If the total mirror movement is 5 cm, then $x_w = 2 \times 5 = 10$ cm

$\Delta\lambda = \lambda^2/x_w$

(a) $\Delta\lambda = \frac{(6328)^2}{10 \times 10^8} = 0.040$ Å

$1\ \mu m = 10^4$ Å

(b) $\Delta\lambda = \frac{(10^4)^2}{10 \times 10^8} = 0.100$ Å

25-10. (a) During one pass, the total mirror movement is

$x = (71.5\ nm/s)(time) = 71.5\ \frac{nm}{s}\ [256\ rdg./(1.28\ rdg./s)]$

$x = 14300$ nm

$\therefore x_w = 2x = 28{,}600\ nm = 2.86 \times 10^3$ cm

(b) $\Delta\lambda_{min} = \frac{\lambda^2}{x_w} = \frac{(400 \times 10^{-7}\ cm)^2}{2.86 \times 10^{-3}\ cm} = 5.59 \times 10^{-7}\ cm = 5.59$ nm

(c) $\lambda_{min} = \frac{2x_w}{N-1} = \frac{2(2.86 \times 10^{-3})}{255} = 2.24 \times 10^{-5}\ cm = 224$ nm

(d) Peak frequency $= \frac{2v}{\lambda_{shortest}} = \frac{2(71.5\ nm/s)}{360\ nm} = 0.397$

Nyquist: Take at least 2X or 0.8 readings/s

25-11. $x_w = 2.78$ mm

$\lambda : (4400 - 400)\ cm^{-1}$

$4400\ cm^{-1} = 2.27\ \mu m$ } infrared.

$400\ cm^{-1} = 25\ \mu m$ } region

(a) We want wave number $\bar{\nu} = \frac{1}{\lambda}$. For resolution we need $\Delta\bar{\nu} = \frac{1}{\lambda^2}\Delta\lambda$, where $\Delta\lambda = \lambda^2/x_w$

Thus $\Delta\bar{\nu} = \frac{1}{\lambda^2}\left(\frac{\lambda^2}{x_w}\right) = \frac{1}{x_w}$

$\Delta\bar{\nu} = \frac{1}{0.278\ cm} = 3.597\ cm^{-1} \cong 3.6\ cm^{-1}$

(b) $N-1 = \frac{2x_w}{\lambda_{min}} = \frac{2(2.78 \times 10^{-3}\ m)}{2.27 \times 10^{-6}\ m} = 2449$ or $N = 2450$

(c) $v = \frac{2.78\ mm}{30\ s} = 0.0927$ mm/s

# Chapter 26 Nonlinear Optics and the Modulation of Light

26-1. $E = \frac{1}{2}E_0\left(e^{i\omega t} + e^{-i\omega t}\right) = E_0 \cos \omega t$

$P_3 = \epsilon_0 \chi_3 E^3$

$E^3 = \frac{E_0^3}{8}\left[e^{i3\omega t} + e^{-i3\omega t} + 3e^{i\omega t} + 3e^{-i\omega t}\right]$

$P_3 = \frac{\epsilon_0 \chi_3 E_0^3}{4}\left(\cos 3\omega t + 3\cos \omega t\right)$

Frequencies: $\omega$, $3\omega$

26-2. $E = \frac{1}{2}E_{01}\left(e^{i\omega_1 t} + e^{-i\omega_1 t}\right) + \frac{1}{2}E_{02}\left(e^{i\omega_2 t} + e^{-i\omega_2 t}\right) \equiv A + B$

$P_3 = \epsilon_0 \chi_3 E^3 = \epsilon_0 \chi_3 \left(A^3 + B^3 + 3A^2B + 3AB^2\right)$

where $A^3 = \frac{E_{01}^3}{8}\left[e^{i3\omega_1 t} + e^{-i3\omega_1 t} + 3e^{i\omega_1 t} + 3e^{-i\omega_1 t}\right] = \frac{E_{01}^3}{4}\left[\cos 3\omega_1 t + 3\cos\omega_1 t\right]$

Similarly, $B^3 = \frac{E_{02}^3}{8}\left[\cos 3\omega_2 t + 3\cos\omega_2 t\right]$

$3A^2B = \frac{3E_{01}^2 E_{02}}{8}\left[\left(e^{i2\omega_1 t} + e^{-i2\omega_1 t}\right)\left(e^{i\omega_2 t} + e^{-i\omega_2 t}\right)\right]$

$$3A^2B = \frac{3E_{01}^2 E_{02}}{8}\left[e^{i(2\omega_1+\omega_2)t} + e^{-i(2\omega_1+\omega_2)t} + e^{i(2\omega_1-\omega_2)t} + e^{-i(2\omega_1-\omega_2)t} + 2\left(e^{i\omega_2 t} + e^{-i\omega_2 t}\right)\right]$$

$3A^2B = \frac{3E_{01}^2 E_{02}}{4}\left[\cos(2\omega_1+\omega_2)t + \cos(2\omega_1-\omega_2)t + 2\cos\omega_2 t\right]$

Similarly, interchanging subscripts 1 and 2,

$3AB^2 = \frac{3E_{02}^2 E_{01}}{4}\left[\cos(2\omega_2+\omega_1)t + \cos(2\omega_2-\omega_1)t + 2\cos\omega_1 t\right]$

Frequencies appearing in all terms:

$3\omega_1$, $3\omega_2$, $2\omega_1+\omega_2$, $2\omega_1-\omega_2$, $2\omega_2+\omega_1$, $2\omega_2-\omega_1$, $\omega_1$, $\omega_2$

26-3. $E = E_{01}\cos\omega_1 t + E_{02}\cos\omega_2 t + E_{03}\cos\omega_3 t$

$E = \frac{E_{01}}{2}\left(e^{i\omega_1 t} + e^{-i\omega_1 t}\right) + \frac{E_{02}}{2}\left(e^{i\omega_2 t} + e^{-i\omega_2 t}\right) + \frac{E_{03}}{2}\left(e^{i\omega_3 t} + e^{-i\omega_3 t}\right)$

$P_2 = \epsilon_0 \chi_2 E^2$

$$P_2 = \frac{\epsilon_0\chi_2}{2}\Big\{\left(E_{01}^2 + E_{02}^2 + E_{03}^2\right) + E_{01}^2\cos 2\omega_1 t + E_{02}^2\cos 2\omega_2 t + E_{03}^2\cos 2\omega_3 t$$

$$+ 2E_{01}E_{02}\left[\cos(\omega_1+\omega_2)t + \cos(\omega_1-\omega_2)t + \cos(\omega_2+\omega_3)t\right.$$

26-3. (cont'd.)

$$+ \cos(\omega_2-\omega_3)t + \cos(\omega_1+\omega_3)t + \cos(\omega_1-\omega_3)t \Big] \Big\}$$

Frequencies include:

$$0,\ 2\omega_1,\ 2\omega_2,\ 2\omega_3,\ \omega_1 \pm \omega_2,\ \omega_1 \pm \omega_3,\ \omega_2 \pm \omega_3$$

26-4. For $+E$, $\frac{1}{n^2} = \frac{1}{n_0^2} + r(+E) + R(+E)^2$

For $-E$, $\frac{1}{n^2} = \frac{1}{n_0^2} + r(-E) + R(-E)^2$

For crystals with inversion symmetry, $1/n^2$ cannot change by reversing $E$.

Thus, to be satisfied for all $E$,

$$rE = -rE$$

$$r = 0 \qquad \text{Q.E.D.}$$

26-5. (a) $\ell_c = \frac{\lambda_0}{4\Delta n} = \frac{694\text{ nm}}{4(1.534-1.505)} = 5893\text{ nm} = 8.62\lambda_0$

(b) $\Delta n = \frac{\lambda_0}{4\ell_c} = \frac{1.06\ \mu m}{4(5.8\ \mu m)} = 0.046$

26-6. $V_{HW} = \frac{\lambda_0}{2r\,n_0^3} = \frac{546\times10^{-9}}{2(8.56\times10^{-12})(1.48)^3} = 9.84\text{ kV}$

The half-wave voltage is independent of length.

26-7. A longitudinal Pockels cell, 1 cm long:

$$\Delta n = \frac{r}{2}n_0^3 E = \frac{r}{2}n_0^3\frac{V}{L} = \frac{30.9\times10^{-12}}{2}(2.29)^3\frac{426}{.01} = 7.9\times10^{-6}$$

$$\phi = \frac{2\pi}{\lambda_0} r n_0^3 V = \frac{2\pi}{632.8\times10^{-9}}(30.9\times10^{-12})(2.29)^3(426) = 1.57 \text{ or } \frac{\pi}{2} \text{ rad.}$$

the cell behaves as a QWP.

26-8. (a) $I = I_{max}\sin^2\left(\frac{\pi}{2}\frac{V}{V_{HW}}\right)$

Combining $V_{HW} = \frac{\lambda_0}{2rn_0^3}$ and $\Phi = \frac{2\pi}{\lambda_0}rn_0^3V$, we have the ratio

$$\frac{V}{V_{HW}} = \frac{\Phi\lambda_0}{2\pi r n_0^3}\cdot\frac{2rn_0^3}{\lambda_0} = \frac{\Phi}{\pi}$$

thus $I = I_{max}\sin^2\left(\frac{\pi}{2}\frac{\Phi}{\pi}\right) = I_{max}\sin^2\left(\frac{\Phi}{2}\right)$ Q.E.D.

Now $I=0$ when the argument of $\sin^2$ is $0, \pi, 2\pi, \ldots$ The first such value above zero makes $\Phi/2 = \pi$ or $\Phi = 2\pi$ and $\frac{\pi}{2}\frac{V}{V_{HW}} = \pi$ or $V = 2V_{HW}$. At $\phi = 2\pi, 4\pi, \ldots$, $V = 2V_{HW}, 4V_{HW}, \ldots$, resp.

26-8 (cont'd.)

(b) With an initial HWP, the $\sin^2$ curve (Fig 26-6) is simply translated to the left by the angle $\pi$. Thus, at $V=0$, $I = I_{max}$, and at $V = V_{HW}$, $I = 0$.

26-9. Both effects are present in media lacking inversion symmetry. The ratio

$$\frac{\Phi_{pock}}{\Phi_{Kerr}} = \frac{2\pi r n_o^3 V}{\lambda_o} \cdot \frac{d^2}{2\pi K V^2 L} = \frac{r}{K}\,\frac{n_o^3 d^2}{\lambda_o V L}$$

$$= \frac{10}{1}\,\frac{2^3 (0.01)^2}{(550\times10^{-9})(1\times10^{4})(0.02)} = 73$$

26-10. $V_{HW} = \dfrac{d}{\sqrt{2KL}}$ or $L = \dfrac{d^2}{2K V_{HW}^2}$

$$L = \frac{(0.015)^2}{2(0.036\times10^{-12})(30\times10^3)^2} = 3.47\,m$$

The required cell is too long to be practical.

26-11. $\Delta\nu = \dfrac{2\nu u_p}{v}$, where $u_p = \pm V_s \sin\theta$ and $2\lambda_s \sin\theta = \lambda$

or, incorporating, $u_p = \pm V_s \dfrac{\lambda}{2\lambda_s} = \pm \dfrac{\nu_s \lambda}{2}$

Then

$$\Delta\nu = \frac{2\nu}{v}\left(\pm\frac{\nu_s\lambda}{2}\right) = \pm\nu\nu_s\left(\frac{\lambda}{v}\right) = \pm\nu\nu_s\left(\frac{1}{\nu}\right) = \pm\nu_s$$

$\nu' - \nu = \pm\nu_s$ or $\nu' = \nu \pm \nu_s$ or $\omega' = \omega \pm \omega_s$ Q.E.D.

26-12. Distance moved by sound wave $\equiv x = V_s t = V_s\left(\dfrac{W}{v}\right)$

$$x = V_s\left(\frac{nW}{c}\right) = 3000\left[\frac{1.5(0.01)}{3\times10^8}\right] = 150\,nm$$

The sound wave advances by $\lambda/33$ for $\lambda = 500\,nm$. The ultrasonic wave thus appears practically stationary to the light beam.

26-13

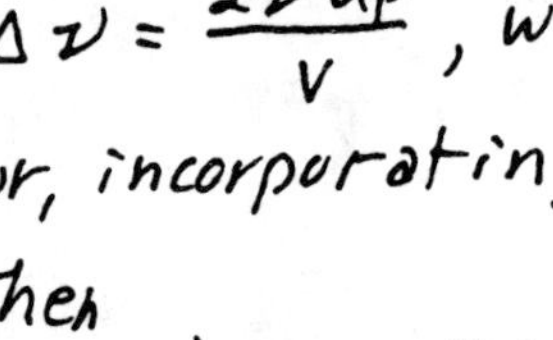


(a) From the vector diagram, for small $\Delta\theta$,

$$\Delta\theta \cong \frac{\Delta K_s}{K} \quad \text{Q.E.D.}$$

(b) $K_s = \dfrac{2\pi}{\lambda_s} = \dfrac{2\pi\nu_s}{V_s}$ so $\Delta K_s = \dfrac{2\pi\Delta\nu_s}{V_s}$

Also, $K = \dfrac{2\pi}{\lambda}$. Then $\Delta\theta = \dfrac{\Delta K_s}{K} = \dfrac{2\pi\Delta\nu_s}{V_s}\,\dfrac{\lambda}{2\pi} = \dfrac{\lambda}{V_s}\Delta\nu_s$ Q.E.D.

26-13. (cont'd.)

(c) $\frac{\Delta\theta}{\theta_D} = \frac{\lambda}{V_s}\Delta\nu_s \frac{D}{\lambda} = \left(\frac{D}{V_s}\right)\Delta\nu_s = \tau\,\Delta\nu_s$ Q.E.D.

(d) $\frac{\Delta\theta}{\theta_D} = \left(\frac{D}{V_s}\right)\Delta\nu_s = \frac{0.01}{5.95\times10^3}(120-8)10^6 = 67$

26-14. $\lambda = 2\lambda_s \sin\theta$

$\frac{\lambda_o}{n} = 2\frac{V_s}{\nu_s}\sin\theta$

$\nu_s = \frac{2n}{\lambda_o}V_s\sin\theta = \frac{2(1.6)}{632.8\times10^{-9}\,m}\left(2500\,\frac{m}{s}\right)\sin 1^\circ = 221\ MHz$

26-15.

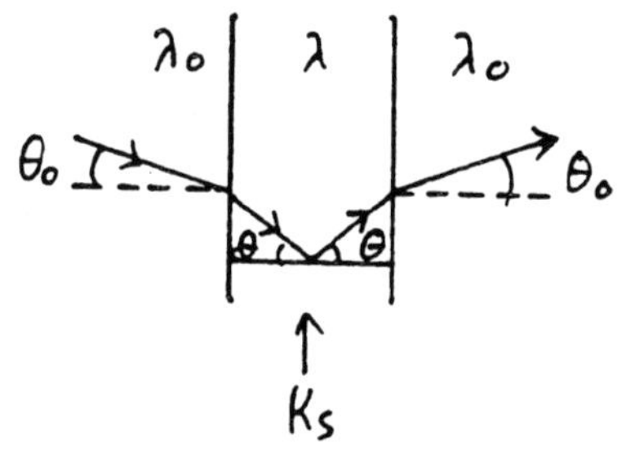

$\lambda = 2\lambda_s \sin\theta$

But $\sin\theta_o = n\sin\theta$ (Snell's law)

and $\lambda = \lambda_o/n$

$\therefore \frac{\lambda_o}{n} = 2\lambda_s \frac{\sin\theta_o}{n}$

$\lambda_o = 2\lambda_s \sin\theta_o$ Q.E.D.

26-16. $\sin\theta = \frac{\lambda}{2\lambda_s} = \left(\frac{\lambda}{2V_s}\right)\nu_s = \frac{632.8\times10^{-9}m}{2(11\times10^3\,m/s)}\nu_s = (2.876\times10^{-11}s)\nu_s$

At $\nu_s = 50$ MHz, $\sin\theta = 0.001438$; $\theta = 0.0824^\circ = 4.94'$

At $\nu_s = 80$ MHz, $\sin\theta = 0.002301$; $\theta = 0.1318^\circ = 7.91'$

$\Delta\theta = 2.97'$

26-17. $\theta = BVL$. For ZnS, $V = 0.225$ min/G-cm $= 65.45$ rad/T-m

$B = \mu_o n i$ for solenoid, where $n = \frac{N}{L} = 6000\ m^{-1}$

$\theta = \pi/4$ for optical isolator.

Design parameters are then current and length.

From $\theta = (\mu_o n i)VL$, $Li = \frac{\theta}{\mu_o n V}$

$Li = \frac{\pi/4}{(4\pi\times10^{-7})(6000)(65.45)} = 1.59$ Am

If we take $L = 5$ cm, for example, $i = \frac{1.59}{0.05} = 31.8$ A

26-18. $\beta = BVd$

(a) At 632.8 nm, $V = \frac{\beta}{Bd} = \frac{900 \text{ min}}{(5098 G)(2.73 \text{ cm})} = 0.0647 \frac{\text{min}}{\text{G-cm}}$

(b) At 543.5 nm, $V = \frac{1330 \text{ min}}{(5098 G)(2.73 \text{ cm})} = 0.0956 \frac{\text{min}}{\text{G-cm}}$

26-19. $\beta = VBd = \left(0.0423 \frac{\text{min}}{\text{G-cm}}\right)(4000 \text{ G})(5 \text{ cm}) = 846' = 14.1^\circ$

$$\frac{dn}{d\lambda} = \frac{V}{1.0083\,\lambda} = \frac{0.0423}{1.0083\,(0.589 \mu m)} = 0.0712 \ \mu m^{-1}$$

# Chapter 27 Optical Properties of Materials

27-1. $K = n^2$

(a) $K_R + iK_I = (n_R + in_I)^2 = n_R^2 - n_I^2 + 2i\,n_R n_I$

$$\left.\begin{aligned} K_I &= 2n_I n_R \\ K_R &= n_R^2 - n_I^2 \end{aligned}\right\} \text{Solve for } n_R,\ n_I$$

$$K_I = 2n_I n_R = 2n_I\sqrt{K_R^2 + n_I^2}$$

$$K_I^2 = 4n_I^2(K_R + n_I^2) = 4K_R n_I^2 + 4n_I^4$$

$$4n_I^4 + (4K_R)\,n_I^2 - K_I^2 = 0 \quad : \text{quadratic in } n_I^2$$

$$n_I^2 = \frac{-4K_R \pm \sqrt{16K_R^2 + 16K_I^2}}{8} = \frac{-K_R \pm \sqrt{K_R^2 + K_I^2}}{2}$$

To make $n_I^2 > 0$, choose the + sign. Thus

$$n_I = \left[\frac{-K_R + \sqrt{K_R^2 + K_I^2}}{2}\right]^{1/2}$$

then $n_R^2 = K_R + n_I^2 = \frac{2K_R}{2} + \frac{-K_R + \sqrt{K_R^2 + K_I^2}}{2} = \frac{K_R + \sqrt{K_R^2 + K_I^2}}{2}$

$$\text{OR} \qquad n_R = \left[\frac{K_R + \sqrt{K_R^2 + K_I^2}}{2}\right]^{1/2}$$

(b) If $K_R \cong K_I$

$$n_R = \left[\frac{K_I + \sqrt{2K_I^2}}{2}\right]^{1/2} = \sqrt{K_I}\left(\frac{1+\sqrt{2}}{2}\right)^{1/2} = 1.099\sqrt{K_I}$$

$$n_I = \left[\frac{-K_I + \sqrt{2K_I^2}}{2}\right]^{1/2} = \sqrt{K_I}\left(\frac{-1+\sqrt{2}}{2}\right)^{1/2} = 0.455\sqrt{K_I}$$

27-2 "Nearly transparent" : We assume $\omega$ is not too large and use the results of Section 27-5 :

$$\underbrace{\alpha = 2K_I}_{\text{explained in text below Eq (27-29).}} = \underbrace{2\left(\frac{\sigma\mu_0\omega}{2}\right)^{1/2}}_{\text{from Eq. (27-55)}}$$

Eliminate $\omega$ in favor of $n_R$, using Eq. (27-56),

$$n_R = \left(\frac{\sigma}{2\omega\epsilon_0}\right)^{1/2}$$

the product $K_I n_R = \left(\frac{\sigma\mu_0\omega}{2}\right)^{1/2}\left(\frac{\sigma}{2\omega\epsilon_0}\right)^{1/2} = \frac{\sigma}{2}\left(\frac{\mu_0}{\epsilon_0}\right)^{1/2}$

Thus $\alpha = 2K_I = \frac{\sigma}{n_R}\left(\frac{\mu_0}{\epsilon_0}\right)^{1/2} = 377\,\frac{\sigma}{n_R}$ Q.E.D.

27-3. $n_R^2 - n_I^2 = 1 + \frac{Ne^2}{m\epsilon_0}\left[\frac{\omega_0^2-\omega^2}{(\omega_0^2-\omega^2)^2+\gamma^2\omega^2}\right]$ Eq. 27-37

$2n_I n_R = \frac{Ne^2}{m\epsilon_0}\left[\frac{\gamma\omega}{(\omega_0^2-\omega^2)^2+\gamma^2\omega^2}\right]$ Eq. 27-38

If we set $\begin{cases} n_R^2 - n_I^2 \equiv Q \\ 2n_I n_R \equiv T \end{cases}$ then simultaneous solution gives $\begin{cases} n_R = \left[\frac{1}{2}\left(Q + \sqrt{Q^2+T^2}\right)\right]^{1/2} \\ n_I = T/2n_R \end{cases}$

In the following computer program, we use the notation

$R \equiv n_R$  $F \equiv \omega_0$  $G \equiv \gamma$  $E \equiv e$  $P \equiv \epsilon_0$

$I \equiv n_I$  $W \equiv \omega$  $N \equiv N$  $M \equiv m$

Also, $A \equiv Ne^2/m\epsilon_0$ ; $D \equiv \omega_0^2 - \omega^2$ ; $S \equiv (\omega_0^2-\omega^2)^2 + \gamma^2\omega^2$

```
5 PRINT "OPTICAL CONSTANTS -- DIELECTRIC"
10 INPUT "RES FREQ = ?"; F, "FRICT CONST = ?"; G
15 INPUT "DIPOLE DENSITY = ?"; N
20 E = 1.602E-19 : M = 9.109E-31 : P = 8.854E-12
25 A = N*E↑2/(M*P)
30 INPUT "FREQ = ?"; W
35 D = F↑2 - W↑2 : S = D↑2 + G↑2 * W↑2
40 Q = 1 + A*D/S : T = A*G*W/S
45 R = SQR(.5*(Q + SQR(Q↑2 + T↑2)))
50 I = T/(2*R)
55 PRINT R
60 PRINT I
65 GOTO 30
70 END
```

Sample Output (compare with Fig. 27-2)

| $\omega$ | $n_R$ | $n_I$ |
|---|---|---|
| $1\times10^{15}$ | 1.15 | $1.41\times10^{-4}$ |
| $5\times10^{15}$ | 1.19 | $1.185\times10^{-3}$ |
| $8\times10^{15}$ | 1.37 | $7.15\times10^{-3}$ |
| $9\times10^{15}$ | 1.63 | 0.0242 |
| $1\times10^{16}$ | 4.05 | 3.93 |
| $1.1\times10^{16}$ | 0.055 | 0.717 |
| $2\times10^{16}$ | 0.945 | $3.74\times10^{-4}$ |
| $5\times10^{16}$ | 0.993 | $1.39\times10^{-5}$ |
| $1\times10^{17}$ | 0.998 | $1.63\times10^{-6}$ |

27-4. $n = 1$ electron/atom

$\sigma_0 = 3.54 \times 10^7 / \Omega\text{-m}$

$$N = \frac{N_A \rho}{M} = \frac{(6.02 \times 10^{26})(2.70 \times 10^3)}{26.982}$$

$$N = 6.027 \times 10^{28}\ m^{-3}$$

(a) $\sigma_0 = \dfrac{Ne^2}{m\gamma}$ OR

$$\gamma = \frac{Ne^2}{m\sigma} = \frac{(6.027 \times 10^{28})(1.602 \times 10^{-19})^2}{(9.109 \times 10^{-31})(3.54 \times 10^7)} = 4.80 \times 10^{13}\ s^{-1}$$

(b) $\omega_p^2 = \dfrac{Ne^2}{m\epsilon_0} = \dfrac{(6.027 \times 10^{28})e^2}{m\epsilon_0} = 1.918 \times 10^{32}$ OR $\omega_p = 1.38 \times 10^{16}\ s^{-1}$

(c) At $\lambda = 550$ nm, $\omega = 2\pi f = 2\pi c/\lambda = 3.425 \times 10^{15}$ Hz

$$n_R^2 - n_I^2 = 1 - \left(\frac{\omega_p^2}{\omega^2 + \gamma^2}\right) \equiv A \quad \text{and} \quad 2n_R n_I = \frac{\gamma}{\omega}\left(\frac{\omega_p^2}{\omega^2 + \gamma^2}\right) \equiv B$$

$A = -15.347$ $\qquad$ $B = 0.2291$

Solving simultaneously, we get $4n_R^4 - 4A\, n_R^2 - B^2 = 0$ : quadratic

thus $n_R^2 = \dfrac{A + \sqrt{A^2 + B^2}}{2}$ and $n_R = 0.0292$

$$n_I = \frac{B}{2n_R} = 3.92$$

27-5. Before approximation, $K^2 = \dfrac{\omega^2}{c^2} + i\left(\dfrac{\sigma\omega\mu_0}{1 - i\omega/\gamma}\right)$

If $\omega \ll \gamma$ or $\frac{\omega}{\gamma} \ll 1$, we can neglect $i\omega/\gamma$ compared with the real part, 1, in the denominator : $1 - i\omega/\gamma$. Then

$$K^2 \cong \frac{\omega^2}{c^2} + i\sigma\omega\mu_0 = \frac{\omega^2}{c^2}\left(1 + \frac{i\sigma c^2 \mu_0}{\omega}\right). \quad \text{Use } c^2 \equiv \frac{1}{\epsilon_0 \mu_0}$$

$K^2 \cong \dfrac{\omega^2}{c^2}\left(1 + i\dfrac{\sigma}{\epsilon_0 \omega}\right)$. But if $\omega \ll \frac{\sigma}{\epsilon_0}$, OR $\frac{\sigma}{\epsilon_0 \omega} \gg 1$, we can neglect the real part, compared with the imaginary, so

$$K^2 \cong i\frac{\omega^2}{c^2}\frac{\sigma}{\epsilon_0 \omega} = i(\omega\epsilon_0\mu_0)\frac{\sigma}{\epsilon_0} = i\omega\sigma\mu_0$$

thus $K^2 \cong i\omega\sigma\mu_0$

This is the approximation stated at the beginning of Section 27-5 in the text. Eq. (27-58) then follows as detailed there.

27-6. $\delta = \dfrac{1}{K_I} = \sqrt{\dfrac{2}{\sigma\mu_0\omega}} = \sqrt{\dfrac{\lambda}{\sigma\mu_0 \pi c}}$, using $\omega = 2\pi c/\lambda$

then for $\sigma = 5.76 \times 10^7 / \Omega\text{-m}$ $\qquad$ ($\mu_0 = 4\pi \times 10^{-7}$) MKS.

27-6. (cont'd.)

(a) $f = 60\,Hz$, or $\omega = 2\pi(60)\ s^{-1}$

$$\delta_{cu} = \left(\frac{2}{\sigma\mu_0\omega}\right)^{1/2} = \left(\frac{2}{(5.76\times10^7)(\mu_0)(2\pi)(60)}\right)^{1/2} = 0.856\ cm$$

(b) $\lambda = 3m$

$$\delta_{cu} = \left(\frac{\lambda}{\sigma\mu_0\pi c}\right)^{1/2} = \left(\frac{3}{(5.76\times10^7)\mu_0\pi c}\right)^{1/2} = 6.63\,\mu m$$

27-7. (a) $\delta_{Al} = \left(\frac{2}{\sigma\mu_0\omega}\right)^{1/2} = \left(\frac{2}{3.54\times10^7\mu_0\times2\pi\times60{,}000}\right)^{1/2} = 0.345\,mm$

(b) $\delta_{s.w.} = \left(\frac{3.54\times10^7}{4.3}\right)\times\delta_{Al} = 0.991\,m \cong 1\,m$

27-8. $\delta_{Ag} = \left(\frac{\lambda}{\sigma\mu_0\pi c}\right)^{1/2} = \left(\frac{0.1}{3\times10^7\times\mu_0\pi c}\right)^{1/2} = 1.68\times10^{-6}\,m = 1.68\,\mu m$

27-9. (a) $I = I_0 e^{-\alpha x}$ OR $\frac{I}{I_0} = \frac{1}{4} = e^{-\alpha x} = e^{-\alpha(3.42)}$

$3.42\,\alpha = \ln 4$

$\alpha = 0.405\,m^{-1}$

(b) $\frac{I}{I_0} = \frac{1}{100} = e^{-(0.405)x}$

$0.405\,x = \ln 100$

$x = 11.37\,m$

27-10. This calculation is much like the procedure used in Prob. 27-3. For a metal, we have

$$n_R^2 - n_I^2 = 1 - \frac{\omega_p^2}{\omega^2+\gamma^2} \equiv D \qquad \text{Eq. (27-64)}$$

$$2n_R n_I = \frac{\gamma}{\omega}\left(\frac{\omega_p^2}{\omega^2+\gamma^2}\right) \equiv P \qquad \text{Eq. (27-65)}$$

Solved simultaneously, $n_R = \left[\frac{1}{2}\left(D + \sqrt{D^2+P^2}\right)\right]^{1/2}$ ; $n_I = \frac{P}{2n_R}$

To reproduce the case of Fig 27-3, take $\omega_p = 1.63\times10^{16}\,s^{-1}$ and $\gamma = 4.1\times10^{13}\,s^{-1}$.

A computer program, such as the following, in Basic, carries out the calculations:

27-10. (cont'd.)

```
10 PRINT "OPTICAL COSTANTS-- METAL"
20 INPUT "PLASMA FREQ = ? "; F, "FRICT CONST = ? "; G
30 INPUT "FREQ = ?" ; W
40 Z = F↑2/(W↑2 + G↑2) : D = 1 - Z
50 P = Z*G/W
60 N = SQR (.5 * (D + SQR (D↑2 + P↑2))) : K = P/(2*N)
70 PRINT N
80 PRINT K
90 GOTO 30
100 END
```

A sample of output values, to be compared with Fig. 27-3:

| $\omega$ | $n_R$ | $n_I$ |
|---|---|---|
| $1\times10^{14}$ | 30.3 | 153.8 |
| $1\times10^{15}$ | 0.334 | 16.26 |
| $3\times10^{15}$ | 0.0378 | 5.34 |
| $1\times10^{16}$ | 0.00423 | 1.287 |
| $1.63\times10^{16}$ | 0.0355 | 0.0354 |
| $3\times10^{16}$ | 0.8395 | $2.403\times10^{-4}$ |
| $1\times10^{17}$ | 0.9866 | $5.52\times10^{-6}$ |
| $1\times10^{18}$ | 0.9999 | $5.45\times10^{-9}$ |

27-11.

$$n^2 \cong 1 + \underbrace{\frac{Ne^2}{m\epsilon_0\omega_0^2}}_{\alpha}\left(1+\frac{\omega^2}{\omega_0^2}+\frac{\omega^4}{\omega_0^4}\right) = 1+\alpha\left(1+\frac{\omega^2}{\omega_0^2}+\frac{\omega^4}{\omega_0^4}\right)$$

$$n^2 = (1+\alpha) + \frac{\alpha\omega^2}{\omega_0^2} + \frac{\alpha\omega^4}{\omega_0^4} = (1+\alpha) + \frac{\alpha}{\omega_0^2}\frac{(2\pi c)^2}{\lambda^2} + \frac{\alpha}{\omega_0^4}\frac{(2\pi c)^4}{\lambda^4}$$

$$n^2 = A' + \frac{B'}{\lambda^2} + \frac{C'}{\lambda^4}$$ where $A' = 1+\alpha$

$B' = \alpha(2\pi c)^2/\omega_0^2$

$C' = \alpha(2\pi c)^4/\omega_0^4$

27-11 (cont'd.)

$$n = \left[A' + \frac{B'}{\lambda^2} + \frac{C'}{\lambda^4}\right]^{1/2} = A'^{1/2}\left[1 + \left(\frac{B'/A'}{\lambda^2} + \frac{C'/A'}{\lambda^4}\right)\right]^{1/2}$$

$$n \cong \sqrt{A'}\left\{1 + \frac{B'/2A'}{\lambda^2} + \frac{C'/2A'}{\lambda^4} - \frac{1}{8}\left[\left(\frac{B'/A'}{\lambda^2}\right)^2 + \cdots\right]\right\}$$ retaining only terms in $1/\lambda^4$

$$n = \sqrt{A'}\left\{1 + \frac{1}{2}\frac{B'/A'}{\lambda^2} + \frac{1}{\lambda^4}\left(\frac{C'}{2A'} - \frac{B'^2}{8A'^2}\right)\right\}$$

$$n = A + \frac{B}{\lambda^2} + \frac{C}{\lambda^4}$$ , where

$$A \equiv \sqrt{A'} = (1+\alpha)^{1/2}$$

$$B \equiv B'/2\sqrt{A'} = \frac{B'}{2A} = \frac{\alpha(2\pi c)^2}{2\omega_0^2(1+\alpha)^{1/2}}$$

$$B = 2\left(\frac{\pi c}{\omega_0}\right)^2 \frac{1}{(1+\alpha)^{1/2}}$$

and $$C \equiv \sqrt{A'}\left[\frac{C'}{2A'} - \frac{B'^2}{8A'^2}\right]$$

$$C = \frac{(2\pi c)^4\alpha}{2\omega_0^4 A'^{1/2}} - \frac{(2\pi c)^4\alpha^2}{8\omega_0^4 A'^{3/2}} = \frac{(2\pi c)^4\alpha}{2\omega_0^4 A'^{1/2}}\left[1 - \frac{\alpha}{4(1+\alpha)}\right]$$

$$C = \frac{(2\pi c)^4\alpha}{2\omega_0^4(1+\alpha)^{1/2}}\left(\frac{4+3\alpha}{4(1+\alpha)}\right)$$

$$C = 2\left(\frac{\pi c}{\omega_0}\right)^4 \frac{\alpha(4+3\alpha)}{(1+\alpha)^{3/2}}$$